THE
COMPLETE
NEXT
GENERATION
TREK
IQ BOOK

Dedicated
in loving memory
to my father,
George A. Rochussen

This one's for you, Dad!

THE
COMPLETE
NEXT
GENERATION
TREK
IQ BOOK

Alan G. Rochussen

BOXTREE

First published 1998 by Boxtree
an imprint of Macmillan Publishers Ltd
25 Eccleston Place London SW1W 9NF
and Basingstoke

Associated companies throughout the world

ISBN 0 7522 2462 X

1 3 5 7 9 8 6 4 2

A CIP catalogue record for this book is available
from the British Library.

Designed and typeset by Blackjacks
Printed by Mackays of Chatham plc, Chatham, Kent

ACKNOWLEDGEMENTS

I'd like to thank my agent, Jeannie Hanson, who had the vision and faith to represent an unknown writer. Jeannie was instrumental in polishing the proposal and helping to focus the book. She also suggested the scoring system. She's a very resourceful agent, always cheerful, an inspiration and a friend. I'm lucky to have her representing me.

Caitlin Blasdell, my editor at HarperCollins, was a joy to work with on this project. Her quiet demeanour and skilful editorial abilities provided a calming influence during the on-rush of deadlines. Always willing to listen to my suggestions, Caitlin provided clear direction throughout the project. I'd like to thank Verity Willcocks at Boxtree, for putting out a terrific UK edition. Verity and her outstanding staff helped to tie up many loose ends along the way.

A special thanks to Super Trekker Bill Mason, who unselfishly devoted many hours of his time to check facts and spellings of names and places. Bill also helped me with the Starfleet hierarchy and known Starfleet awards and commendations. He was a wealth of information. Thanks.

I thank Brad Kaenel and his company PC Help-Line for their terrific software programmes Crossword Creator 6.0 and Crossword Clipper for Windows. It was a great help in producing the crossword puzzles. Brad provided me with the latest versions of his software and assisted me with some technical questions.

As my deadline approached and I was still missing ten episodes, Bryan Langston stepped out of the shadows and lent a much needed hand, filling in the gaps in my video collection. Thanks Bryan. Also I'd like to thank Stephen Gregg who runs the Clemson Newsstand, for putting me in touch with Bryan and his much needed videos.

I thank Tom Finnegan, the freelance editor who helped to pare down the original massive manuscript to a more manageable size. I'm glad you were a dedicated *Next Generation* fan. Your insight and suggestions were extremely helpful and provided me with fresh insight.

I owe a debt of gratitude to my wife, Allison, for her patience and support. She was often instrumental in deciphering some bit of techno-babble or slurred alien words. As a result she is now quite fluent in Klingon.

I'd like to thank Brian and Kelly Rabalais, Lola Carter and Kayce Shusterman for allowing me access to their *Star Trek* videos.

Jo and Bob Carter deserve a big thanks for their support and brainstorming sessions. Thanks also to Patrick Linnane, Lisa Williams, John Wall, Jim Morgan, John Faile, Allene Gamble, Doyle Burdette and David Riley of the Pickens Area Writer's Guild for their suggestions and critiques.

I want to thank the following people who responded to my Internet puzzle preference survey and beta-tested some of the Who Am I? puzzles; Cathy J. Tuk, Holly Woodruff, Russell Sketchley, Dave Coombs, Ed Der Kinderen, and Robin Eli Richads. Thanks also to Aquiela, Tashimeg, Admiral Wombat, Brett, and Cloudshape. I only know them by their cyberspace names.

Finally, I thank God, through whom all things are possible.

TABLE OF CONTENTS

INTRODUCTION

Welcome Trek fans to *The Complete Next Generation Trek IQ Book*. It's time to see just how high your *Next Generation* IQ really is! Prepare to go where no other trivia book has gone before. Nowhere else will you find such an assortment of trivia questions, crossword puzzles, multiple choice questions, maths problems, character quotes, wordsearches, and riddles based on the series *Star Trek: The Next Generation*.

For best results, think of this book as a puzzle companion guide to the series. Watch an episode on television and then pick up your copy of *The Complete Next Generation Trek IQ Book* and complete that episode's chapter. If you've got the dialogue memorized then you probably can do each one from memory.

I hope you have as much fun with this book as I did writing it. Get together with your friends and see who can make it to the rank of admiral first! Jump onto the Internet and compare scores. Meet the *Star Trek* trivia and puzzle challenge head-on!

Alan G. Rochussen

WHAT'S YOUR RANK?

Mission Performance Rating:
Each puzzle, crossword clue, and trivia question is given a certain number of points based on the level of difficulty and the type of puzzle. The total number of points varies from episode to episode. You receive a Mission Performance Rating each time you complete an episode or special chapter. Just add up your score and find out your Mission Performance Rating at the end of the chapter.

Bonus Points:
There are three optional ways of winning bonus points to speed your promotion:

⭐ **Special Assignments:** Many chapters contain more challenging Special Assignment questions. Regular Special Assignment questions are worth 10 extra points. Those denoted by ⭐ are considered very hard and are worth 15 points. Those denoted by ⭐⭐ are considered really challenging and you are advised to review the episode first. These are also worth 15 points.

⭐ **Significant Numbers** and **Mathematically Speaking Puzzles**

⭐ **Special Chapters:** After each season there is a special chapter with more challenging material. Readers receive bonus points for all questions answered correctly. Also, anyone who scores a Superior Mission Performance Rating in any of the special chapters receives a special Starfleet award or commendation and even more bonus points.

Note: all of the above are optional ways of increasing your points as you will not be penalized for getting them wrong. It is still possible to achieve the Superior Mission Performance Rating and ultimately the highest rank of Admiral without obtaining any of the bonus points for these sections.

Your Starfleet Rank:

After each episode, you record your score at the back of the book under *Starfleet Records*. You begin as an Ensign, then as you accumulate points over time, you are promoted to higher ranks. Also, be sure to list any bonus points earned from the Special Chapters under the appropriate section. Any Starfleet awards or commendations and bonus points earned should also be listed under *Starfleet Records*.

YOUR STARFLEET RANK:

8,200 + points	**Admiral:** You can have crumpets and tea with Captain Picard!
7,300 – 8,199 points	**Vice Admiral:** Now you can tell starship captains where to go!
6,400 – 7,299 points	**Captain:** Pick any starship, except the *Enterprise* – it's taken!
5,500 – 6,399 points	**Commander:** Is that three pips on your collar or four? Be patient.
4,600 – 5,499 points	**Lieutenant Commander:** You're a role model for the junior officers.
3,700 – 4,599 points	**Lieutenant:** Now you're the same rank as Barclay!
2,800 – 3,699 points	**Lieutenant, Junior Grade:** Don't forget to feed Spot!
0 – 2,799 points	**Ensign:** You are assigned to Wesley Crusher. Report now!

ENCOUNTER AT FARPOINT - PART I

STARDATE: 41153.7

The *Enterprise* is en route to inspect the newly constructed Farpoint Station. Suddenly, a force field appears in front of the *Enterprise*. Picard and the crew encounter Q, a powerful entity who puts them on trial for the crimes of humanity. Picard argues that even though man's past has been savage, humanity is more evolved now. Q agrees to a test to see if Picard's assertions are true and allows the crew to continue their mission.

TRIVIA QUESTIONS

1. Which key officer position on the *Enterprise* is vacant at the beginning of the episode? **(3pts)**
2. What is Worf's rank on the *Enterprise*? **(3pts)**
3. How old is Admiral McCoy? **(4pts)**
4. What is the *Enterprise*'s destination? **(3pts)**
5. In which year did the new UN declare no Earth citizen could be held accountable for the past crimes of their race or ancestors? **(5pts)**
6. What does Picard order to be armed as Q's ship overtakes the *Enterprise*? **(3pts)**
7. What does Picard transfer to the battle bridge prior to saucer separation? **(3pts)**
8. Who is the battle bridge conn officer on duty when Picard and officers are returned to the *Enterprise*? **(4pts)** (Note: He is not named in this episode.)
9. What was the first item on the Administrator's desk during Riker's visit? **(4pts)**
10. What does Riker believe is of paramount importance? **(3pts)**

MULTIPLE CHOICE QUESTIONS

1. What is Data's 'special assignment'? **(2pts)**
   A. clean the latrines
   B. escort Admiral McCoy around the ship
   C. meet with the Farpoint Administrator
   D. reorganize the ship's computers

2. When Q is posing as an American soldier, what branch of service and rank is he? **(4pts)**
   A. Marine captain
   B. Navy petty officer, third class
   C. Air Force lieutenant colonel
   D. Army captain

---

3. According to Picard which mid-21st century courtroom is Q's courtroom based on? **(3pts)**
   A. preatomic horrors courtroom
   B. Los Angeles courtroom
   C. postatomic horrors courtroom
   D. Klingon courtroom

4. What does Dr Crusher buy at the Bandi marketplace? **(3pts)**
   A. Meltoid nesting fruit
   B. extremely rare pharmaceuticals
   C. bolt of cloth
   D. exotic Bandi evening gown

5. What does Picard order Riker to do in order to test his abilities? **(3pts)**
   A. fight Worf on the holodeck in a mock battle
   B. perform a manual docking of the two sections of the *Enterprise*
   C. replace the isolinear optical chips that Wesley has just removed
   D. perform a level-1 diagnostic

ANSWERS

TRIVIA ANSWERS
1. first officer
2. lieutenant, junior grade
3. 137 years old
4. Deneb IV
5. 2036
6. aft photon torpedoes
7. command
8. Miles O'Brien
9. bowl of fruit
10. Captain's safety

MULTIPLE CHOICE ANSWERS
1. B. escort Admiral McCoy around the ship
2. A. Marine captain
3. C. postatomic horrors courtroom
4. C. bolt of cloth
5. B. perform a manual docking of the two sections of the *Enterprise*

MISSION PERFORMANCE RATING:
45 – 50 points **Superior:** You're so smart you could join the Q
                 Continuum.
40 – 44 points **Above Average:** Prelaw student, huh?
30 – 39 points **Average:** You have an eye for detail.
20 – 29 points **Fair:** Even the Farpoint Administrator scored average.
 0 – 19 points **Poor:** At this rate you'll never see the bridge.

ENCOUNTER AT FARPOINT - PART II ⚓

STARDATE: 41153.8 ▬▬▬▬▬▬▬▬▬

The crew arrives at Farpoint Station but things don't seem to add up. Troi can sense emotional distress but can't pinpoint the source. The station is constructed of unknown materials and later, an unknown vessel approaches the planet and starts to fire on the inhabitants near Farpoint Station.

With Q's help, Picard figures out that the Farpoint Station is actually a shape shifting life form that was once injured. The Bandi cared for it but fed the creature only enough power to manipulate it to construct itself into Farpoint Station. The *Enterprise* beams energy to the station and it changes into a life form identical to the one orbiting the planet. The creatures leave and an unhappy Q disappears from the bridge.

TRIVIA QUESTIONS

1. What was Riker's initial reservation about working with Data? **(3pts)**
2. Who transports the away team from the alien ship to the bridge of the *Enterprise*? **(3pts)**
3. What was Troi's father? **(3pts)**
4. What type of gymnasium is on the *Enterprise*? **(3pts)**
5. What does Wesley get to do on the bridge? **(3pts)**
6. Which Starfleet class did Data graduate from? **(5pts)**
7. What rank is Q's Starfleet uniform? **(4pts)**
8. How large is the alien vessel approaching Deneb IV? **(4pts)**
9. What location on Deneb IV is under attack by hostile fire? **(4pts)**
10. Who materializes on the bridge when Picard orders phasers locked on the alien vessel? **(3pts)**

SPECIAL ASSIGNMENT (10pts)

Name the holodeck area Data is in when Riker first meets him.

MULTIPLE CHOICE QUESTIONS

1. What do the alien ship and the tunnels of Farpoint Station have in common? **(3pts)**
    A. both allow humanoid travel
    B. proximity to the *Enterprise*
    C. similar construction
    D. similar colour schemes

---

2. Which song does Data attempt to whistle in the holodeck? **(5pts)**
   A. *Dixie*
   B. *Rudolph the Red Nosed Reindeer*
   C. *Pop Goes The Weasel*
   D. *Misty*

3. What does Wesley fall into on the holodeck? **(2pts)**
   A. dung heap
   B. water
   C. sinkhole
   D. pile of rocks

4. What does Zorn state that the Bandi don't enjoy? **(2pts)**
   A. living in the Old City
   B. leaving their home world
   C. sex
   D. dealing with the Federation

5. What does Q call Captain Picard? **(3pts)**
   A. doofus
   B. submoronic twit
   C. dullard
   D. muttonhead

ANSWERS

TRIVIA ANSWERS
1. Data was a machine
2. alien vessel/life form
3. Starfleet officer
4. low gravity
5. sit in the Captain's chair
6. '78
7. captain
8. 12 times the *Enterprise*'s volume
9. Old City
10. Q

SPECIAL ASSIGNMENT SOLUTION
Holodeck Area 4J
Congratulations! Starfleet Command is proud to award you the Starfleet Medal of Honour and 10 extra points.

MULTIPLE CHOICE ANSWERS
1. C. similar construction
2. C. *Pop Goes The Weasel*
3. B. water
4. B. leaving their home world
5. C. dullard

MISSION PERFORMANCE RATING:

45 – 60 points **Superior:** You can sit in the Captain's chair like Wesley.

40 – 44 points **Above Average:** You can sit in the Captain's chair *next* time.

30 – 39 points **Average:** You're in charge of Q's wardrobe.

20 – 29 points **Fair:** Q would probably call you a pinhead.

0 – 19 points **Poor:** Go to the Old City, the aliens haven't started firing yet.

THE NAKED NOW

The *Enterprise* investigates strange happenings on a Federation research vessel studying a nearby collapsing star. The away team finds everybody dead on the vessel and evidence of some very bizarre behaviour. After the away team returns some of them begin acting strangely. Soon erratic behaviour spreads throughout the *Enterprise* as Dr Crusher tries to determine what's happening.

The cause is discovered to be a virus that mutates water molecules into an alcohol-like substance. Wesley, infected with the virus, takes over Engineering and disables the warp engines. With the star about to collapse, Riker gets into Engineering but someone has removed the control chips for the engines. Data quickly replaces the control chips even though impaired. With seconds to spare, Wesley reconfigures the ship's tractor beam to push off the other vessel giving Data time to finish. The *Enterprise* warps out of harm's way.

TRIVIA QUESTIONS

1. What does the *Enterprise* download from the science vessel? **(3pts)**
2. What do the *Enterprise* sensor scans of the science vessel reveal? **(3pts)**
3. What does Wesley hook his model tractor beam into? **(4pts)**
4. What does Geordi keep talking about wanting? **(3pts)**
5. Which science vessel does the *Enterprise* meet with? **(3pts)**
6. What does the collapse of the red supergiant star yield? **(4pts)**
7. What type of search was performed for Geordi? **(3pts)**
8. How much power does the *Enterprise* need to outrun chunks of star? **(5pts)**
9. How did Wesley isolate Engineering? **(3pts)**
10. On which ship and under which captain did a similar epidemic occur? **(4pts)**

MULTIPLE CHOICE QUESTIONS

1. What lecture did the Training Division order all officers to attend? **(3pts)**
   - A. Metaphysics
   - B. Standard Photon Torpedo Configurations
   - C. Catastrophic Emergency Procedures
   - D. Preparing For The Worst – When Your Food Replicator Won't Work

2. What does Yar tell Data after recovering from the virus? **(2pts)**
   - A. Why didn't you call?
   - B. Can't we just be friends?
   - C. It never happened.
   - D. It's been a pleasure working with you.

---

3. Where does the *Enterprise* aim the repulsor beam? **(2pts)**
   A. meteor
   B. star chunk
   C. *Tsiolkovsky*
   D. Earth

4. What does Geordi find behind sliding door number 1? **(3pts)**
   A. Monty Hall
   B. fully-clothed frozen woman
   C. deluxe antideuterium sublimator
   D. the only survivor on the vessel

5. Name the slang expression which Data doesn't understand. **(5pts)**
   A. hooch hound
   B. wiped-out
   C. snoot full
   D. drunk as a skunk

ANSWERS

TRIVIA ANSWERS

1. research data
2. no life forms
3. ship's power
4. normal vision
5. USS Tsiolkovsky
6. white dwarf
7. ship wide
8. half impulse power
9. repulsor beam
10. USS Enterprise under the command of Captain James T Kirk

MULTIPLE CHOICE ANSWERS

1. A. Metaphysics
2. C. It never happened.
3. C. Tsiolkovsky
4. B. fully-clothed frozen woman
5. C. snoot full

MISSION PERFORMANCE RATING:

45 – 50 points **Superior:** Report to Engineering, they have some chips for you.

40 – 44 points **Above Average:** You must be immune to all infectious diseases.

30 – 39 points **Average:** You have an eye for detail.

20 – 29 points **Fair:** Perhaps a touch of the virus kept you from doing better.

0 – 19 points **Poor:** The *Enterprise* must have downloaded your brain.

CODE OF HONOUR ⚓

The *Enterprise* makes a stop at Ligon II to negotiate for a rare vaccine needed to battle a plague elsewhere in the Federation. A Ligonian delegation beams aboard the *Enterprise* where they are very impressed with Federation technology. The Ligonian leader, Lutan, is especially impressed with Lieutenant Yar and kidnaps her, returning to Ligon II with his prize.

The crew determines, after studying Ligonian culture, that Lutan's act is considered brave. Picard beams down and asks for the return of Lieutenant Yar. Lutan says he wants Yar to be his wife, thus displacing his current wife who protests and challenges Yar to a deadly duel.

Yar and Lutan's wife fight with savage weapons. Yar finally strikes the fatal blow and both are immediately beamed up to the *Enterprise*. Lutan is also beamed up to the ship with Picard and the vaccine. Lutan's wife, who owns all his wealth, is saved by Dr Crusher. Since Ligonian customs state all mating arrangements dissolve at the time of death, Lutan is left penniless.

TRIVIA QUESTIONS

1. Ligonians are exceedingly what? **(3pts)**
2. Which concept does Data have trouble understanding? **(3pts)**
3. What does the Ligonian leader do to Lieutenant Yar upon leaving the *Enterprise*? **(3pts)**
4. Due to special circumstances, who leads the away team? **(3pts)**
5. What did certain American Indian tribes once do? **(5pts)**
6. To which planet is the *Enterprise* sent to get vaccine? **(3pts)**
7. What is the Ligonian term for wife? **(4pts)**
8. How long is it since a woman has challenged supersedence? **(4pts)**
9. What is dissolved at the moment of death for Ligonians? **(3pts)**
10. What does Yar wear at the fight? **(4pts)**

SPECIAL ASSIGNMENT (10pts)

How many jokes has Data told to date?

MULTIPLE CHOICE QUESTIONS

1. Name the type of holodeck programme which Lieutenant Yar calls up. **(5pts)**
   - **A.** ta'i chi chu'an
   - **B.** karate
   - **C.** aikido
   - **D.** shiatsu

2. What is an obscure language according to Data? **(3pts)**
   - **A.** French
   - **B.** Klingon
   - **C.** Latin
   - **D.** Ligionese

3. What is the duel arena surrounded by? **(2pts)**
   - **A.** people
   - **B.** an energy field
   - **C.** armed guards
   - **D.** poisonous reptiles

4. The code of honour protects one like what? **(3pts)**
   - **A.** magic cloak
   - **B.** magic wand
   - **C.** magic carpet
   - **D.** magic beans

5. Name the reason Ligonian weapons are so light. **(2pts)**
   - **A.** cheaply made
   - **B.** very old and worn
   - **C.** Ligonian men are not very athletic
   - **D.** made for women to use

ANSWERS

TRIVIA ANSWERS

1. proud
2. humour
3. he kidnaps her
4. Picard
5. counting coup
6. Ligon II
7. First One
8. over 200 years
9. Ligonian mating agreement
10. black headband

SPECIAL ASSIGNMENT SOLUTION

662 jokes

Congratulations! Starfleet Command is proud to award you the Starfleet Medal of Honour and 10 extra points.

MULTIPLE CHOICE ANSWERS

1. C. aikido
2. A. French
3. B. an energy field
4. A. magic cloak
5. D. made for women to use

MISSION PERFORMANCE RATING:

45 – 60 points **Superior:** Chief of Security position will soon be vacant, apply!

40 – 44 points **Above Average:** Been practising 'counting coups' haven't you?

30 – 39 points **Average:** You need to brush up on your Aikido.

20 – 29 points **Fair:** A little feverish are we? That would explain your score.

0 – 19 points **Poor:** You're next in the arena! (without a weapon)

HAVEN

The *Enterprise* is destined for shore leave at the beautiful planet Haven. To her surprise, Troi receives a present for her upcoming wedding. The marriage was arranged long ago according to Betazoid customs and Troi never thought anything would come of it. Her soon to be husband, Wyatt, beams aboard with his parents, followed by Mrs Troi.

While wedding plans are formulated, a Tarellian vessel approaches Haven carrying the last of their race. The Tarellians are carriers of a deadly plague, the unintended victims of their own biological weapon. Haven's leadership is alarmed and begs Picard to do something. Picard attaches a tractor beam to the Tarellian ship to prevent anyone from transporting to the planet's surface.

Wyatt discovers that the woman he has always seen in his dreams is not Troi but the Tarellian leader's daughter. He gathers some medical supplies, says good-bye to his parents and Troi and beams over to the Tarellian vessel. He realizes there is no possibility of coming back but he doesn't care. Picard releases the ship and they leave the vicinity of Haven for parts unknown.

TRIVIA QUESTIONS

1. What are Betazoid wedding presents known as? **(3pts)**
2. What does the *Enterprise* attach to the Tarellian ship? **(3pts)**
3. Who was the closest friend of Deanna's father? **(3pts)**
4. What is the leader of Haven known as? **(4pts)**
5. What is Mrs Troi the holder of? **(5pts)**
6. Mrs Troi is a daughter of what? **(4pts)**
7. To what is Mrs Troi the heir? **(4pts)**
8. What is a Betazoid tradition? **(3pts)**
9. What function will Mrs Troi's valet perform at the wedding? **(3pts)**
10. When was the last Tarellian plague ship destroyed? **(3pts)**

CHARACTER QUOTE
(4pts per word + 5pts for identifying the speaker.)

Unscramble the words below and then identify the character.

'Could you _____ _____ the "_____ _____"?
　　　　　　EEPSLA   OTNUCNEI　　　TYEPT   EKRBIGCNI
I find it most _____.'
　　　　　　NUGTNIRGII

ANSWERS

TRIVIA ANSWERS

1. bonding gifts
2. tractor beam
3. Steven Miller
4. First Electorine of Haven
5. Sacred Chalice of Rixx
6. Fifth House
7. Holy Rings of Betazed
8. genetic bonding
9. best man
10. eight years ago

CHARACTER QUOTE SOLUTION

'Could you please continue the "petty bickering"? I find it most intriguing.' – Data

---

MISSION PERFORMANCE RATING:

55 – 60 points **Superior:** You'll develop a cure for Tarellian plague some day.

50 – 54 points **Above Average:** Portrait drawer, huh?

40 – 49 points **Average:** You need some shore leave.

30 – 39 points **Fair:** May I call you Lwax for short?

0 – 29 points **Poor:** You have Tarellian plague! How *did* you get on Earth?

WHERE NO ONE HAS GONE BEFORE

STARDATE: 41263.1

Kosinski, a propulsion expert, and his assistant beam aboard the *Enterprise* to fine tune the engines. Although the crew of the *Enterprise* is sceptical of his claims, Kosinski and his assistant set up shop in Engineering and begin the first experiment. Wesley distracts his assistant for a moment and things go awry, sending the ship an incredible distance in just minutes; far too distant to return to Federation space within the crew's lifetimes.

A second experiment is attempted to recreate the same effect and return the *Enterprise* to its starting point. Kosinski's assistant, fatigued from the first experiment, ends up sending the *Enterprise* to the edge of the universe where thought becomes reality. The difference between fantasy and reality starts to blur.

Kosinski's assistant tries once more to return the *Enterprise* to Federation space. Picard instructs the crew to centre their thoughts on the assistant's well-being. Whoosh, whizz, zing – the *Enterprise* successfully makes it back again to Federation space.

CROSSWORD PUZZLE CLUES

ACROSS
1. Ensign in cargo bay. (1pt)
4. Percentage of galaxy charted in 300 years of space travel. (3pts)
6. Riker's term for Kosinski's formulas. (2pts)
7. Crew's thoughts become _____. (1pt)
9. How Picard likes his tea. (1pt)
10. Riker requests _____ to look over the visitors. (1pt)
12. Name of chief engineer who works with Kosinski. (3pts)
13. Type of expert who beams over to *Enterprise*. (2pts)
15. Number of other Starfleet vessels assisted by Kosinski. (1pt)
18. Type of course Picard orders for return trip. (3pts)
19. Picard wants Dr Crusher to do this to Traveler. (2pts)
22. Picard gives the helm to _____ before going to Engineering. (1pt)
23. Number of years for message to reach Starfleet after first jump. (3pts)
25. Important way Traveler is different from humans. (3pts)
26. In the process of forming near the *Enterprise*. (2pts)
29. *Enterprise* goes on ___ alert. (1pt)
32. Yar sees on bridge and picks it up. (1pt)
33. Worf's childhood pet. (2pts)
35. Troi senses this from Kosinski's assistant. (2pts)
36. Traveler needs this at main computer on voyage home. (2pts)
38. Picard encounters a wall of _____ in the corridor. (1pt)
39. Picard imagines stepping off the turbolift into _____. (1pt)

DOWN
2. Purpose of Traveler's journeys. (2pts)
3. Number of light years *Enterprise* has travelled after second jump. (1pt)
5. Traveler _____ at end of return trip. (1pt)
8. Kosinski's attitude. (2pts)
11. How everyone refers to Wesley. (1pt)
14. Reason Traveler's race hasn't visited mankind before. (2pts)
16. Type of adjustments made at Warp 1.5. (3pts)
17. Picard orders Data to _____ the engines to stop. (1pt)
20. Dr Crusher's diagnosis of Traveler's condition. (1pt)
21. Kosinski says the *Enterprise* crew should cast this off. (1pt)
24. *Enterprise* meet with this Starfleet vessel. (3pts)
27. Basis of all reality. (1pt)
28. Traveler can act like a lens to _____ thought. (1pt)
30. Picard meets her in corridor sitting at a table. (1pt)
31. Kosinski's assistant has six of these. (2pts)
34. Traveler is basically from another _____. (1pt)
37. Kosinski's assistant _____ in and out of our reality. (2pts)

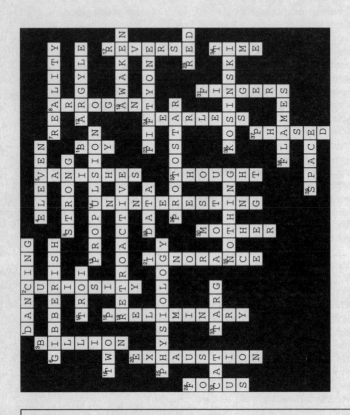

MISSION PERFORMANCE RATING:

60 – 65 points **Superior:** Prune your fingers and you'd pass for a Traveler.

54 – 59 points **Above Average:** May I call you Wesley?

43 – 53 points **Average:** You've won a delicious Klingon Targ, ready to eat!

32 – 42 points **Fair:** You can show Kosinski how warp engines really work.

0 – 31 points **Poor:** So you made lots of wonderful, incredible mistakes!

THE LAST OUTPOST

STARDATE: 41386.4 ━━━━━━━━━━━

The *Enterprise* is in pursuit of a Ferengi vessel which has stolen some Federation technology. The Federation has yet to make contact with the Ferengi. The *Enterprise* follows the Ferengi vessel into orbit around a nearby planet and experiences a powerful energy draining force field. Thinking Ferengi technology superior to the Federation's, Picard decides to surrender to them and asks for their terms. Picard realizes they are not the source of the force field when the Ferengi captain refuses to surrender.

Picard talks the Ferengi into a loose co-operative effort to send a joint away team to investigate the force field. On the surface, the *Enterprise* away team is attacked by the Ferengi landing party. An alien entity appears and tells them that he is a guardian of an ancient empire. The guardian provides Riker with a challenge to determine the worth of humanity. The *Enterprise* is released from the force field after Riker passes the challenge successfully. Riker asks the Guardian to spare the Ferengi ship. He does so and the Ferengi return the stolen items to the Federation.

TRIVIA QUESTIONS

1. What metal is used in communicators? **(3pts)**
2. Where were the two children playing? **(3pts)**
3. What is the name of one of the children Riker chases out of the room? **(3pts)**
4. What planet did the Ferengi steal the device from? **(4pts)**
5. What is the name of the entity the *Enterprise* has awakened on the planet? **(3pts)**
6. How long has the alien empire been extinct? **(3pts)**
7. How cold can it get in orbital space? **(4pts)**
8. What is the name of the solar system entered by the Ferengi vessel? **(4pts)**
9. Data doubts Ferengi look anything like whom? **(3pts)**
10. What is the acceleration delay between slow reverse impulse and top warp speed? **(5pts)**

MULTIPLE CHOICE QUESTIONS

1. Ferengi stole this from Federation. **(5pts)**
   - A. T-9 Energy Converter
   - B. M-2000 Mass Inverter
   - C. T-4 Energy Diverter
   - D. secret defence plans

---

2. Phrase Data used to describe the planet after beaming down. **(3pts)**
   - **A.** a nice place to visit but I would not want to live here
   - **B.** nothing to write home about
   - **C.** with a little work, it will make a great place
   - **D.** a desolate and lonely place

3. Purpose of crystalline tree shapes. **(2pts)**
   - **A.** energy collectors
   - **B.** life forms
   - **C.** waste collectors
   - **D.** simply rocks with no purpose

4. Data gets his fingers stuck in this device. **(2pts)**
   - **A.** antimatter containment glove
   - **B.** Jefferies tube
   - **C.** Chinese finger puzzle
   - **D.** mousetrap

5. Ferengi conduct commerce by this ancient principle. **(3pts)**
   - **A.** res ipsa loquitur
   - **B.** ex nihilo nihil fit
   - **C.** omnia vincit amor
   - **D.** caveat emptor

ANSWERS

TRIVIA ANSWERS
1. gold
2. observation lounge
3. Matthew
4. Gamma Tauri IV
5. Portal 63
6. 600,000 years
7. -200°C
8. Delphi Ardu
9. Uncle Sam
10. .300 milliseconds

MULTIPLE CHOICE ANSWERS
1. A. T-9 Energy Converter
2. B. nothing to write home about
3. A. energy collectors
4. C. Chinese finger puzzle
5. D. caveat emptor

MISSION PERFORMANCE RATING:

45 – 50 points **Superior:** Primus inter pares.

40 – 44 points **Above Average:** A student of Tkon culture?

30 – 39 points **Average:** 'In life, one is always tested.'

20 – 29 points **Fair:** Did you ever play with Chinese finger puzzles?

0 – 19 points **Poor:** Report to Deck 37. Waste Management has a job for you.

LONELY AMONG US

STARDATE: 41249.3

While carrying delegates to a diplomatic outpost the *Enterprise* encounters a fast travelling energy cloud. Investigating the phenomenon, the *Enterprise* accidentally picks up a sentient being living in the cloud and carries it off as the ship continues with its mission.

The entity seeks to communicate with the crew by jumping into various members of the crew. The entity eventually leaps into Picard who turns the ship around and heads back toward the energy cloud.

Picard/entity then beams out into the energy cloud. Riker and the crew search for Picard but with no success. Troi later senses him and using the transporter, they are able to reconstitute Picard without any significant brain damage.

TRIVIA QUESTIONS

1. How did Picard/entity beam out? **(3pts)**
2. Who is history's greatest consulting detective? **(3pts)**
3. What forms on Geordi's conn panel? **(4pts)**
4. What does Engineering have a problem with? **(3pts)**
5. The warring alien races have become deadly enemies since both achieved what? **(3pts)**
6. What term does Data make an inquiry about? **(4pts)**
7. What is the title of the dead crewman? **(5pts)**
8. What unusual object do the *Enterprise*'s sensors register? **(3pts)**
9. Yar consults with Riker concerning the Anticans' what? **(3pts)**
10. Which theory of Dr Channing's is Wesley studying? **(4pts)**

CHARACTER QUOTE
(3pts per word + 10pts for identifying the speaker.)

Unscramble the words below and then identify the character.

'A _____ is only a _____ as _____ as it _____ _____.'
   YTRYMSE   RYSMTYE GNOL   ANRMESI NTUIGESNVIEDTA

✪ SPECIAL ASSIGNMENT (15pts)

Which computer terminal does Picard tell Dr Crusher to use?

ANSWERS

TRIVIA ANSWERS

1. energy only
2. Sherlock Holmes
3. The letter 'P'
4. warp drive circuitry
5. space flight
6. private eye
7. assistant chief engineer
8. energy object
9. dietary requirements
10. dilithium crystals

CHARACTER QUOTE SOLUTION

'A mystery is only a mystery as long as it remains uninvestigated.' – Data

SPECIAL ASSIGNMENT SOLUTION

Science Station 2

Congratulations! Starfleet Command is proud to award you the Starfleet Medal of Honour and 15 extra points.

MISSION PERFORMANCE RATING:

55 – 75 points **Superior:** You get to be captain for a day (sorry energy only).

50 – 54 points **Above Average:** Engineering has an opening, go for it!

40 – 49 points **Average:** At this rate you'll make lieutenant by Season Six!

30 – 39 points **Fair:** You're in charge of keeping the Anticans and Selay apart.

0 – 29 points **Poor:** Hey the Anticans are looking for you – they're still hungry.

STARDATE: 41255.6 ▬▬▬▬▬

The *Enterprise* discovers a planet with very friendly inhabitants. Picard thinks this might be an ideal shore leave spot so he orders an away team to investigate. Picard includes Wesley in the away team so he can evaluate it from a teenage perspective.

After arriving on the planet the away team splits up. Wesley falls into a flower bed while playing with indigenous children. Edo cops appear on the scene almost immediately. It seems that the area was under surveillance and anyone caught breaking any law there is subject to the death penalty.

Aboard the *Enterprise* the crew has discovered another vessel in orbit that seems to exist in several dimensions at once. Picard is bound by Starfleet's Prime Directive not to interfere and is warned by the orbiting beings to leave the Edo alone. Picard finally decides that he must not let a crew member die for something so senseless and saves Wesley.

TRIVIA QUESTIONS

1. Until when is Wesley's execution delayed? **(3pts)**
2. What type of alert sounded when the alien globe entered the *Enterprise*? **(3pts)**
3. Data says the unknown alien object is not what? **(4pts)**
4. How do the Edo refer to the away team? **(3pts)**
5. What does Picard believe Data is undergoing with the alien object? **(4pts)**
6. What type of zone is chosen for monitoring by the Edo G-men? **(3pts)**
7. What is the method of edocution? **(3pts)**
8. Who beams down to assist the away team? **(3pts)**
9. What is the name of the Edo's planet? **(5pts)**
10. How does Picard refer to the alien object? **(4pts)**

✪✪ SPECIAL ASSIGNMENT (15pts)

How many other planets in the star cluster are suitable for colonization?

MULTIPLE CHOICE QUESTIONS

1. What is Dr Crusher's goal for the tired crew of the *Enterprise*? **(2pts)**
   A. reassignment
   B. bed rest
   C. shore leave
   D. stress reduction workshops

---

2. What is no longer justified as a deterrent within the Federation? **(2pts)**
   A. capital punishment
   B. violence
   C. life sentence without parole
   D. exile

3. Worf considers Earth females quite what? **(4pts)**
   A. hardy
   B. fragile
   C. exquisite
   D. intelligent

4. What do the aliens in orbit perceive as theirs? **(3pts)**
   A. Edo
   B. entire star cluster
   C. the *Enterprise*
   D. entire galaxy

5. What does the Edo girl want Wesley to teach her? **(4pts)**
   A. how to kiss
   B. how to play ball
   C. how to do cartwheels
   D. how to fall over backwards and play dead

ANSWERS

TRIVIA ANSWERS
1. sundown
2. intruder
3. a single entity
4. the visitors
5. information exchange
6. punishment
7. poison
8. Picard
9. Rubicun III
10. nemesis

SPECIAL ASSIGNMENT
3,004
Congratulations! Starfleet Command is proud to award you the Starfleet Medal of Honour and 15 extra points.

MULTIPLE CHOICE ANSWERS
1. C. shore leave
2. A. capital punishment
3. B. fragile
4. B. entire star cluster
5. B. how to play ball

MISSION PERFORMANCE RATING:

45 – 65 points **Superior:** You're entitled to one week of shore leave on Edo!

40 – 44 points **Above Average:** Go post bail on the rest of the crew.

30 – 39 points **Average:** Stay away from the Punishment Zones or else!

20 – 29 points **Fair:** Go play ball with Wesley, and stay out of the plants!

0 – 19 points **Poor:** You have been slated for edocution.

THE BATTLE ⌖

The *Enterprise* meets with a Ferengi ship at their request and is told to stand by. While waiting Picard develops a painful headache. Finally, the Ferengi re-establish contact and present Picard with his old ship, the *Stargazer*. Picard had to abandon the *Stargazer* after it was heavily damaged in an unprovoked attack by an unknown vessel. Picard destroyed the unknown vessel in the battle. The Ferengi identify the destroyed ship as Ferengi and dismiss it as an accident.

The captain of the Ferengi vessel, Bok, is secretly using a device that allows him to manipulate Picard's thoughts causing migraines. Meanwhile, discrepancies occur between the *Stargazer*'s logs and Picard's own personal logs. It appears that Picard fired upon the vessel under a flag of truce.

In an elaborate plan to avenge the death of his son, Bok takes control of Picard and makes him transport to the *Stargazer*. There Picard relives the battle in which Bok's son was killed. Riker is able to neutralize the *Stargazer* without hurting the Captain and convinces Picard to destroy the controlling device. Data proves the log entries were falsified and the Ferengi captain is then relieved of command by his first officer.

TRIVIA QUESTIONS

1. Who does Riker contact on the Ferengi ship? **(3pts)**
2. Riker requests what to talk to the Ferengi ship? **(4pts)**
3. What contains a different version of the Battle of Maxia? **(3pts)**
4. What did the crew of the *Stargazer* have to do after defeating the unknown vessel? **(3pts)**
5. What is the *Stargazer*'s Starfleet Registry Number? **(5pts)**
6. Low intensity transmissions from the Ferengi ship are the same as what? **(3pts)**
7. Who else is aboard the *Stargazer* besides Picard? **(4pts)**
8. What is the speed of the unknown starship coming towards the *Enterprise*? **(4pts)**
9. The unknown starship is not sending what? **(3pts)**
10. The Ferengi give Picard the starship as a gift to honour whom? **(3pts)**

SPECIAL ASSIGNMENT (10pts)

What year did the Battle of Maxia take place?

MULTIPLE CHOICE QUESTIONS

1. What will the *Enterprise*'s tractor beam do to the *Stargazer*? **(3pts)**
   A. seize it and limit its field of fire
   B. cause its warp engines to implode
   C. tow it into Shuttlebay 1
   D. prevent its weapons from firing

2. What does the Ferengi first officer identify the glowing globe as? **(3pts)**
   A. Albeni meditation crystal
   B. thought maker
   C. mind controller
   D. brain enhancer

3. Picard supposedly mistook the Ferengi ship's subspace antenna for what? **(3pts)**
   A. hyperspace antenna
   B. weapons cluster
   C. Merculite rockets
   D. Bussard collector

4. How did the *Stargazer* defeat the unknown ship? **(3pts)**
   A. Kobayashi Maru Manoeuvre
   B. Picard Manoeuvre
   C. Vigo Ferengi Manoeuvre
   D. Picard Terminal Manoeuvre

5. What does Riker tell the Ferengi about Data? **(3pts)**
   A. damaged goods
   B. batteries not included
   C. second-hand merchandise
   D. not for sale

ANSWERS

TRIVIA ANSWERS

1. Ferengi first officer
2. secure channel
3. Picard's personal log on the *Stargazer*
4. abandon ship
5. NCC-2893
6. Picard's brainwave patterns
7. DaiMon Bok
8. impulse power
9. call letters
10. hero of Maxia

SPECIAL ASSIGNMENT SOLUTION

2355

Congratulations! Starfleet Command is proud to award you the Starfleet Medal of Honour and 10 extra points.

MULTIPLE CHOICE ANSWERS

1. A. seize it and limit its field of fire
2. B. thought maker
3. B. weapons cluster
4. B. Picard Manoeuvre
5. C. second-hand merchandise

MISSION PERFORMANCE RATING:

45 – 60 points **Superior:** What's your 'Manoeuvre' called?

40 – 44 points **Above Average:** You will soon have command of the *Stargazer*.

30 – 39 points **Average:** Maybe you could be a DaiMon someday.

20 – 29 points **Fair:** Start scrubbing the decks on the *Stargazer*!

0 – 19 points **Poor:** Where did the Ferengi find you?

HIDE AND Q

The *Enterprise* is on its way to provide aid to a Federation colony when Q materializes on the Bridge. The Q Continuum is interested in humans and their capacity for growth, and grant Riker their immense powers, hoping he will join them.

Q, in the mood for games, transports some crew members to the surface of an unknown planet. Strange creatures wearing ancient Earth military uniforms attack the crew and kill several members. In a fit of rage, Riker transports the crew back to the *Enterprise* and resuscitates his dead comrades.

Fearing what unlimited power might do to Riker, Picard urges him not to use his powers again. During rescue operations at the Federation colony, Riker finds it extremely hard to curb his habit. Later, Riker gives each member of the bridge crew a gift at Q's insistence. They all refuse and Riker realizes the value of humanity. Riker tells Q he's not interested in the Continuum or its powers.

TRIVIA QUESTIONS

1. What does Worf do with the drink Q provides? **(3pts)**
2. How did Worf describe the alien soldiers? **(4pts)**
3. What does Riker give Worf as a gift? **(3pts)**
4. The alien soldiers appear to be armed with what? **(3pts)**
5. What does Picard refer to Q as? **(3pts)**
6. What does Q call Worf? **(3pts)**
7. What type of planet does the bridge crew end up on? **(3pts)**
8. Dr Crusher instructs her staff to include what with each medical kit destined for the colonists? **(4pts)**
9. How fast is the *Enterprise* travelling to the colony? **(5pts)**
10. Ball and powder muskets are accurate to how far? **(4pts)**

CHARACTER QUOTE
(3pts per word + 10pts for identifying the speaker.)

Unscramble the words below and then identify the character.

'_____ _____ is _____ _____ and _____.'
URYO   ESIPCSE   WYASLA   EFGIRNUFS   IDGYN

ANSWERS

TRIVIA ANSWERS

1. pours it out onto the ground
2. vicious animal things
3. Klingon warrior woman
4. ball and powder muskets
5. flim-flam man
6. macrohead with a microbrain
7. class-M
8. Burn Unit
9. Warp 9.1
10. 100 metres

CHARACTER QUOTE SOLUTION

'Your species is always suffering and dying.' – Q

MISSION PERFORMANCE RATING:

55 – 60 points **Superior:** Q's interested in you. He said you've got potential!

50 – 54 points **Above Average:** Macrohead with a macrobrain.

40 – 49 points **Average:** Report to the cargo bay and help with the injured.

30 – 39 points **Fair:** Macrohead with a microbrain.

0 – 29 points **Poor:** Go feed the vicious animal things, they're getting hungry.

The *Enterprise* is transporting Admiral Jameson to Mordan IV to negotiate a hostage situation at the request of Karnas, the Governor of the planet. Jameson, who has an incurable crippling disease, begins looking younger and healthier en route to the situation. Picard confronts Jameson who admits taking a rejuvenating drug obtained from another planet.

Jameson admits to Picard that in order to solve the hostage crisis, he gave weapons to Karnas. Jameson then provided Karnas's enemies with the same weapons hoping to strike a balance in power. The result was decades of civil war.

Upon arriving at the planet Jameson leads an away team down to Mordan IV in an effort to rescue the hostages. The away team is ambushed and must retreat. Karnas now demands that Picard deliver Jameson into his hands. Picard and Jameson beam down to the surface. At first Karnas doesn't believe that the young boy is actually Jameson but is eventually convinced. Jameson dies, Karnas is happy, the hostages go home.

TRIVIA QUESTIONS

1. From which planet did Jameson obtain the anti-ageing treatment? **(4pts)**
2. Jameson says Starfleet always designates him as what on special missions? **(3pts)**
3. What scar does Jameson have to prove his identity? **(3pts)**
4. Where is Jameson buried? **(3pts)**
5. The tunnel the away team beams into is located under what? **(3pts)**
6. How many hostages did Jameson secure the release of earlier in his career on Mordan IV? **(5pts)**
7. How old were the medical test results Jameson gave to Dr Crusher? **(4pts)**
8. The anti-ageing treatment is self-administered over what length of time? **(3pts)**
9. What was the last ship Jameson commanded before he was promoted to admiral? **(4pts)**
10. What is Jameson afflicted by? **(3pts)**

CHARACTER QUOTE
(3pts per word + 10pts for identifying the speaker.)

Unscramble the words below and then identify the character.

'_____ or the _____ of it, is _____ a _____ to ____.'
  ECPAE   RPAEACNEPA   TEONF LDEPERU   AWR

SPECIAL ASSIGNMENT (10pts)

At what time does Jameson first beam over to the *Enterprise*?

ANSWERS

TRIVIA ANSWERS

1. Cerebus II
2. senior mission officer
3. scar from a blood cut on forearm
4. Mordan IV
5. Governor's mansion
6. 63
7. two months old
8. two years
9. USS Gettysburg
10. Iverson's disease

CHARACTER QUOTE SOLUTION

'Peace or the appearance of it, is often a prelude to war.'
– Admiral Mark Jameson

SPECIAL ASSIGNMENT SOLUTION

15:00 hours
Congratulations! Starfleet Command is proud to award you the Starfleet Medal of Honour and 10 extra points.

MISSION PERFORMANCE RATING:
55 – 70 points **Superior:** You're Starfleet's chief hostage negotiator!
50 – 54 points **Above Average:** Going to pharmacy school?
40 – 49 points **Average:** Was that the left tunnel or the right one?
30 – 39 points **Fair:** Gunrunner from way back?
0 – 29 points **Poor:** Poor is a Galactic understatement!

THE BIG GOODBYE

STARDATE: 41997.7

The *Enterprise* is en route to meet with a race known as the Jarada to establish diplomatic relations. The Jarada insist on a flawless greeting from the captain of a starship in their own language before any talks may begin.

Picard takes a break from learning the Jaradans' language and goes to the holodeck. Data, Dr Crusher, and Whalen, a historian, accompany Picard as he configures the holodeck for a Dixon Hill mystery. The Jarada probe the *Enterprise* and inadvertently damage the holodeck with the captain in it. Picard and the others realize something is wrong when the characters start firing real bullets. Picard tries to exit the holodeck but is unable to.

Riker tries to stall the Jarada while Wesley and Geordi attempt to repair the holodeck. Wesley finally corrects the holodeck problem and the doors pop open. A couple of the holodeck-created villains walk off the holodeck and dematerialize. Picard greets the Jarada without any problems, thus paving the way for future Federation talks.

MULTIPLE CHOICE QUESTIONS

1. What happens as Picard prepares to leave Hill's office? **(3pts)**
   - **A.** Picard is shot
   - **B.** Hill's secretary appears
   - **C.** someone knocks on Hill's office door
   - **D.** Riker turns off the holodeck programme

2. Who is shot by the holodeck pistol? **(3pts)**
   - **A.** Whalen
   - **B.** Picard
   - **C.** Data
   - **D.** Wesley

3. On the holodeck, Data is supposedly from what part of Earth? **(3pts)**
   - **A.** Far East
   - **B.** South America
   - **C.** Argentina
   - **D.** Iron Curtain

4. Which city does the holodeck programme take place in? **(3pts)**
   - **A.** New York
   - **B.** Los Angeles
   - **C.** Hudson
   - **D.** San Francisco

---

5. Where is the *Enterprise* to meet with the Jaradan? **(4pts)**
   A. Torona IV
   B. Corona V
   C. Tapioca III
   D. Jordako Nebula

6. A shortstop from the _____ broke Joe DiMaggio's record for hits in consecutive games in 2026. **(4pts)**
   A. Hampshire Kings
   B. Atlanta Braves
   C. London Kings
   D. Melbourne Knights

7. Data says cars were a source of what? **(3pts)**
   A. satisfaction
   B. status and virility
   C. aggravation
   D. pollution

8. A policeman asks Dr Crusher if she likes which musician? **(3pts)**
   A. Tommy Dorsey
   B. Glenn Miller
   C. Mick Jagger
   D. Frank Sinatra

9. What pulp magazine did a Dixon Hill story first appear in? **(4pts)**
   A. *Manhunt*
   B. *Ellery Queen*
   C. *Amazing Detective Stories*
   D. *Out Of This World Adventures*

10. What was the name of the Dixon Hill novel that was published in 1936? **(5pts)**
    A. *The Short Bright Chunnel*
    B. *The Long Dark Tunnel*
    C. *The Parrot's Claw*
    D. *The Parrot's Beak*

CHARACTER QUOTE
(3pts per word + 10pts for identifying the speaker.)

Unscramble the words below and then identify the character.

'_____ _____, _____, are _____ a _____ of time.'
OGDO NRANMSE MDMAA   ENRVE   TASWE

SPECIAL ASSIGNMENT (10pts)

What is Dixon Hill's phone number?

ANSWERS

MULTIPLE CHOICE ANSWERS

1. C. someone knocks on Hill's office door
2. A. Whalen
3. B. South America
4. D. San Francisco
5. A. Torona IV
6. C. London Kings
7. B. status and virility
8. A. Tommy Dorsey
9. C. Amazing Detective Stories
10. B. The Long Dark Tunnel

CHARACTER QUOTE SOLUTION

'Good manners, madam, are never a waste of time.' – Cyrus Redblock

SPECIAL ASSIGNMENT SOLUTION

Prospect 4631

Congratulations! Starfleet Command is proud to award you the Starfleet Medal of Honour and 10 extra points.

MISSION PERFORMANCE RATING:

55 – 70 points **Superior:** You're tutoring Picard in the Jaradan language?

50 – 54 points **Above Average:** Holodeck Technician? Good work!

40 – 49 points **Average:** You just caused a 40 year rift with the Jaradan!

30 – 39 points **Fair:** You work with Leech a lot, don't you? It shows.

0 – 29 points **Poor:** Bottom of the heap. Leech is your boss.

The *Enterprise* arrives at the failed Federation colony where Data was discovered and decides to stop. An away team beams down with Data and unearths a laboratory in a hillside. Inside they find android parts that resemble Data. The parts are taken back to the ship and reassembled into Lore, Data's brother. Although Lore looks just like Data, he is capable of emotions and understands humour. Lore states that a crystalline entity attacked the colony and killed off all life.

Lore deactivates Data and assumes his identity. Lore then contacts the crystalline entity and gives it the ship's location. Soon the alien entity arrives and attacks the ship. Wesley suspects 'Data' is not who he appears to be and persuades his mother to check out his story. Dr Crusher goes to Data's quarters and activates the real Data. Together, they find Lore in a cargo bay ready to betray the ship to the alien entity. Data and Lore fight and Wesley beams Lore out into space.

TRIVIA QUESTIONS

1. What is the name of the chief engineer who supervised Lore's reconstruction? **(4pts)**
2. What is Dr Soong's first name? **(3pts)**
3. What was Dr Crusher's 'small payment' for Wesley's misdeeds? **(3pts)**
4. In what star system was Data discovered? **(4pts)**
5. What phrase did Picard use that Lore did not understand? **(3pts)**
6. What material does Lore ask for that is used in the android's construction? **(5pts)**
7. What does the alien entity feed on? **(2pts)**
8. What nickname does Lore call Dr Soong? **(3pts)**
9. What do Data and a flashlight have in common? **(4pts)**
10. Who was first to propose the concept of a positronic brain? **(4pts)**

WHO AM I? (25pts)

The head spoke as always but I knew not what it said. I laugh for what I show is only part of what I know. One is not two and two isn't one.

SPECIAL ASSIGNMENT (10pts)

Where is the large transporter located?

ANSWERS

TRIVIA ANSWERS

1. Argyle; 2. Noonien; 3. phaser blast; 4. Omicron Theta; 5. Make it so; 6. fine-ground quadritanium 7. life force; 8. Good ole often-wrong Soong; 9. on/off switch; 10. Asimov

WHO AM I? SOLUTION

Lore

EXPLANATION:

The head spoke as always – Picard (the head of the ship) always says, 'Make it so'.

but I knew not what it said. – Lore did not understand this expression.

I laugh – Lore is capable of emotions.

for what I show is only part of what I know. – Lore knows a lot more than he lets on.

One is not two – This is based on Lore saying Data was created first. Data (one) can't use contractions (is not) and is different from Lore who was created second (two).

and two isn't one. – Lore (two) can use contractions (isn't) and is different from Data (one).

NOTE: Yes, Data occasionally blurts out a contraction (including the end of this episode) but these are due to production blunders. Data's inability to use contractions is reinforced throughout this episode and others.

SPECIAL ASSIGNMENT SOLUTION

Cargo Room 3

Congratulations! Starfleet Command is proud to award you the Starfleet Medal of Honour and 10 extra points.

MISSION PERFORMANCE RATING:

55 – 70 points **Superior:** You could assemble Lore without looking at Data!

50 – 54 points **Above Average:** You're part of Dr Soong's group aren't you?

40 – 49 points **Average:** Get rid of that twitch, you remind me of someone.

30 – 39 points **Fair:** Even Wesley could tell which android Data was.

0 – 29 points **Poor:** Where's that crystalline entity when you need it?

ANGEL ONE ⬡

The *Enterprise* searches for survivors from a disabled vessel and tracks them to the planet known as Angel One. The leader of Angel One allows the *Enterprise* to search for the survivors but only if they take the survivors with them. As the search begins, an unknown virus is spreading throughout the ship, incapacitating much of the crew. Dr Crusher struggles to find a cure for the virus.

The *Enterprise* locates the survivors and beams an away team there. However, the survivors don't want to leave Angel One. The planet's leader, who sees the survivors as a threat to their way of life, schedules the survivors for termination. After Riker makes an impassioned plea for the lives of the survivors, the leader of Angel One decides not to kill the survivors but instead exiles them and their supporters to a remote part of the planet. Dr Crusher finds a cure and the *Enterprise* heads to the Neutral Zone in search of Romulans.

TRIVIA QUESTIONS

1. How was the ship *Odin* disabled? **(3pts)**
2. Who is the leader of the *Odin* survivors? **(4pts)**
3. What does Dr Crusher ask Picard if he is wearing? **(3pts)**
4. What gift does Riker present to Angel One's leader on behalf of the Federation? **(4pts)**
5. What are the survivors of the *Odin* not bound by due to their civilian status? **(3pts)**
6. What method of disease transmission does Crusher rule out? **(3pts)**
7. What does the fragrance in the corridor remind Worf of? **(5pts)**
8. What do Klingons appreciate? **(3pts)**
9. What type of government exists on Angel One? **(4pts)**
10. What is the title of the leader on Angel One? **(3pts)**

✪✪ MATHEMATICALLY SPEAKING (25pts)

Answer A to C and then insert the numbers into the formula to solve this problem.

A. How many students were on the field trip? **(5pts)**
B. How many months did it take the survivors from the *Odin* to reach Angel One? **(5pts)**
C. How many days did it take the *Enterprise* to travel from the *Odin* to Angel One? **(5pts)**

$A \times B + C = D$
What is the significance of your answer (D) in relation to the episode? **(10pts)**

ANSWERS

TRIVIA ANSWERS

1. asteroid collision
2. Ramsey
3. cologne
4. Albeni meditation crystal
5. Prime Directive
6. person to person contact
7. Night-Blooming Throgni
8. strong women
9. matriarchal oligarchy
10. The Elected One

MATHEMATICALLY SPEAKING SOLUTION

A. 12
B. 5
C. 2

$12 \times 5 + 2 = 62$

It has been 62 years since the last Federation contact with Angel One.

MISSION PERFORMANCE RATING:

55 – 60 points **Superior:** So you developed the cure and gave it to Crusher!

50 – 54 points **Above Average:** They need you at the Neutral Zone.

40 – 49 points **Average:** Trent will show you to your duty station.

30 – 39 points **Fair:** Go tow the *Odin* to the closest starbase junkyard.

0 – 29 points **Poor:** You are exiled to the farside.

11001001

The *Enterprise* arrives at a starbase for some overdue maintenance by technicians called Bynars. The Bynars communicate directly with the main computer on their home world and are all mentally interconnected.

Many of the crew leave the ship for various forms of recreational pursuit at the starbase. Riker decides to go to a recently enhanced holodeck on the *Enterprise*, and recreates a jazz bar complete with audience, including a pretty brunette named Minuet. Picard joins Riker and they both marvel at the newly enhanced programming.

Problems arise in Engineering and an explosion is imminent. The *Enterprise* is quickly evacuated and programmed to travel away from the starbase on autopilot. As the ship begins to move away from the starbase the situation on board stabilizes, but Starfleet is unable to prevent the *Enterprise* from leaving.

Picard and Riker grow suspicious and leave the holodeck, discovering they are the only ones left on the ship. They retake the bridge and determine that the Bynars have taken the *Enterprise* to their home world of Bynar to avert a disaster. Riker and Picard, assisted by Data at the starbase, complete the task the Bynars started.

TRIVIA QUESTIONS

1. What is the filename for accessing the Bynars' information? **(3pts)**
2. How long is it before a Starfleet vessel will be able to leave the starbase to pursue the *Enterprise*? **(5pts)**
3. In what star system is the Bynars' homeworld located? **(3pts)**
4. What time period does Riker configure the holodeck programme for? **(3pts)**
5. What is the first location Riker chooses to configure the holodeck programme for? **(4pts)**
6. How far away is the closest Starfleet vessel from the stolen *Enterprise*? **(3pts)**
7. What is the name of the bar the holodeck programme creates? **(3pts)**
8. What is the actual time Riker chooses to configure the holodeck programme? **(3pts)**
9. Who is the leading mind in the cybernetics field? **(5pts)**
10. What is Worf developing? **(3pts)**

SPECIAL ASSIGNMENT (10pts)

How much time is left on the LED countdown clock when the autodestruct sequence is cancelled?

MULTIPLE CHOICE QUESTIONS

1. The electromagnetic pulse that threatened the Bynars' main computer resulted from what? **(2pts)**
   A. a black hole passing close by
   B. a star changing into a white dwarf
   C. an unstable pulsar
   D. a star going supernova

2. What possible trouble does Wesley report in Main Engineering? **(3pts)**
   A. problem with magnetic containment field
   B. catastrophic failure of warp propulsion system
   C. imminent ejection of matter/antimatter reaction assembly
   D. a fist fight between two ensigns

3. A piano player on the holodeck tells Riker not to give up what? **(2pts)**
   A. playing the trombone
   B. career in Starfleet
   C. smoking habit
   D. day job

4. What is the actual location Riker chooses to configure the holodeck programme for? **(5pts)**
   A. Kansas City
   B. New Orleans
   C. Austin
   D. New York

5. What is the composition of the band Riker plays with on the holodeck? **(3pts)**
   A. harpsichord, bass, drums, and Riker on trombone
   B. piano, bass, drums, and Riker on trumpet
   C. piano, bass, drums, and Riker on trombone
   D. piano, bass, trumpet, and Riker on drums

ANSWERS

TRIVIA ANSWERS

1. 11001001
2. 18 hours
3. Beta Magellan
4. circa 1958
5. Kansas City
6. 66 hours
7. The Bourbon Street Bar
8. 2am
9. Dr Terence Epstein
10. a sense of humour

SPECIAL ASSIGNMENT SOLUTION

1:58 minutes

Congratulations! Starfleet Command is proud to award you the Starfleet Medal of Honour and 10 extra points.

MULTIPLE CHOICE ANSWERS

1. D. a star going supernova
2. A. problem with magnetic containment field
3. D. day job
4. B. New Orleans
5. C. piano, bass, drums, and Riker on trombone

MISSION PERFORMANCE RATING:

45 – 60 points **Superior:** Champion Parrises Squares player.

40 – 44 points **Above Average:** You've earned a holodeck vacation for two!

30 – 39 points **Average:** C'est la guerre!

20 – 29 points **Fair:** Don't quit your day job!

0 – 19 points **Poor:** Your shoe size is bigger than your score.

HOME SOIL

STARDATE: 41463.9

The *Enterprise* stops at Velara III to inspect the Federation's terraforming project on the planet. They are greeted by a very nervous and unco-operative director. While being shown around the station one of the scientists is mortally wounded by malfunctioning equipment. The piece of equipment also attacks Data when he inspects it to determine the cause of the malfunction.

Upon further investigation Data and Geordi discover some sparkling crystals that prove to be a form of inorganic life. The crystals are brought on board and try to communicate through the *Enterprise*'s translator but are initially unsuccessful.

Picard surmises that the life forms are living in the subsurface water and are inadvertently being killed by the terraformers. The crystal beings declare war on the *Enterprise* and are able to seize control of the ship's computer. Data figures out how the life forms obtain energy and promptly shuts them down. Picard arranges a truce with the life forms and beams them back to the planet.

TRIVIA QUESTIONS

1. What is the last name of the hydraulic specialist? **(5pts)**
2. What must Data destroy in order to save himself? **(3pts)**
3. Which star cluster has the *Enterprise* been mapping? **(4pts)**
4. When do the aliens tell Picard to come back before they would trust humans? **(3pts)**
5. What Federation department is in charge of all terraforming projects? **(3pts)**

MULTIPLE CHOICE QUESTIONS

1. What is the first phase in terraforming? **(4pts)**
    A. developing water supplies
    B. building terraforms
    C. selecting a planet
    D. building a terraforming station on the planet

2. What is the second phase in terraforming? **(5pts)**
    A. developing water supplies
    B. building a terraforming station on the planet
    C. selecting a planet
    D. sending a terraforming ship to the planet

---

3. What is the third phase in terraforming? **(5pts)**
   A. planting vegetation
   B. building a terraforming station on the planet
   C. seeding the oceans with bacteria and viruses
   D. developing water supplies

4. How does the *Enterprise* crew understand the alien life form? **(3pts)**
   A. Foreign Language Bank
   B. Universal Translator
   C. telepathic inversion
   D. interpreter

5. Data and Geordi look at a hydraulic display of what? **(5pts)**
   A. Master Cylinder
   B. Subsurface Sediment Filter Assembly
   C. Master Subsurface Pump
   D. Venae Cavae Circulation Pump

ANSWERS

TRIVIA ANSWERS
1. Malencon
2. the laser drill
3. Pleiades Cluster
4. three centuries
5. Terraform Command

MULTIPLE CHOICE ANSWERS
1. C. selecting a planet
2. B. building a terraforming station on the planet
3. D. developing water supplies
4. B. Universal Translator
5. C. Master Subsurface Pump

MISSION PERFORMANCE RATING:

36 – 40 points **Superior:** Surely, Starfleet will name the aliens after you!

30 – 35 points **Above Average:** You've been reassigned to the Mars Terraforming Project.

20 – 29 points **Average:** You're Starfleet's new ambassador to Velara III.

10 – 19 points **Fair:** Go monitor the quarantine buoys.

0 – 9 points **Poor:** Go check out the laser drill. It's not working properly.

WHEN THE BOUGH BREAKS

STARDATE: 41509.1

The *Enterprise* investigates a trail of strange energy readings that leads to the planet Aldea. The Aldeans greet the *Enterprise* and request a meeting on the surface. The away team discovers that the Aldeans have no children and want to barter their knowledge for *Enterprise* children. The away team says 'no can do', and are returned to the ship instantly by the Aldeans. Selected children are simultaneously taken from the *Enterprise*.

Picard chooses to negotiate the terms of the payment for the children in the hope of rescuing them. The Aldeans demonstrate their power by knocking the *Enterprise* far away from the planet. After the *Enterprise* returns to the planet, crew members disable the Aldeans' defences and the children are rescued.

TRIVIA QUESTIONS

1. What is Aldea's planet-shield similar to? **(3pts)**
2. What knocks the *Enterprise* away from Aldea? **(2pts)**
3. What kind of damage is occurring to the Aldeans? **(4pts)**
4. What activity have Wesley and the other children stopped doing? **(4pts)**
5. What do Data and Riker do to the Aldeans' protective shield? **(3pts)**
6. What Aldean problem is similar to one in the 21st century on Earth? **(4pts)**
7. Wesley teaches the children to use what to make themselves unwanted on Aldea? **(3pts)**
8. How far is the *Enterprise* knocked away from Aldea? **(4pts)**
9. Where do the energy readings the *Enterprise* had been following end? **(5pts)**
10. Radue transports Riker and who else on the first beam down to the planet? **(3pts)**

WHO AM I? **(25pts)**

I reach for the sky and watch the rising star but Mars is my planet and hunger is my strength. Even the mightiest bow before me as a part of me is left behind.

✪✪ SPECIAL ASSIGNMENT **(15pts)**

What is the 'address' of Harry's surrogate parents?

ANSWERS

TRIVIA ANSWERS

1. Romulan cloaking device; 2. repulsor beam; 3. chromosomal; 4. eating; 5. neutralize; 6. deterioration of ozone layer; 7. passive resistance; 8. three days' travel at Warp 9; 9. Epsilon Mynos system; 10. Dr Crusher and Troi

WHO AM I? SOLUTION

Alexandra

EXPLANATION:

I reach for the sky — On Aldea, Alexandra holds her arms up for Picard to pick her up. *and watch the rising star* — Alexandra plays with holographic objects, the one that rose to the top was a star. (Wesley was using the Custodian to view Alexandra). *but Mars is my planet* — The red planet, the colour of Alexandra's hair. *and hunger is my strength.* — Alexandra reaches for some fruit but Wesley tells her they can't eat if they want to go home again and she understands.

Even the mightiest bow before me — On the bridge, Picard drops to his knees to speak to Alexandra. *as a part of me is left behind.* — After giving Picard flowers and hugging him Alexandra walks off but her toy is stuck to Picard's back.

SPECIAL ASSIGNMENT SOLUTION

Unit B 375

Congratulations! Starfleet Command is proud to award you the Starfleet Medal of Honour and 15 extra points.

MISSION PERFORMANCE RATING:

55 – 75 points **Superior:** You could replace the Custodian.

50 – 54 points **Above Average:** The Aldeans can refine your artistic abilities.

40 – 49 points **Average:** The Aldeans left you on the *Enterprise*.

30 – 39 points **Fair:** The Aldeans could use a maintenance drone.

 0 – 29 points **Poor:** Give me 50 pushups!

COMING OF AGE

STARDATE: 41416.2

The *Enterprise* arrives at a Federation planet to allow Wesley to take the Starfleet Academy entrance exam. Admiral Quinn and Remmick, a member of a Starfleet investigating agency, beam aboard the *Enterprise*. Quinn privately tells Picard his ship is under investigation by Remmick. Quinn leaves Picard in the dark as to the reason for the investigation.

Remmick interviews all of the officers on the *Enterprise* and concludes his investigation, finding nothing wrong with the *Enterprise* or its crew. Quinn now tells Picard he suspects a conspiracy in Starfleet and had to know if he could trust Picard. Quinn offers Picard a position of authority at Starfleet who mulls it over and turns it down.

Wesley competes with three other candidates for a single opening at the Academy and loses to a Benzite named Mordock.

TRIVIA QUESTIONS

1. What did Mordock develop that so impressed Wesley? **(3pts)**
2. Starfleet can determine Wesley's deepest fear by analyzing his what? **(2pts)**
3. Lieutenant Commander Remmick is from what Starfleet agency? **(3pts)**
4. What propulsion source is left after Jake loses power in the main shuttlecraft engines? **(3pts)**
5. Which test does Wesley assist Mordock with? **(3pts)**
6. What prevents Lieutenant Yar from locking the shuttlebay doors when Jake steals a shuttlecraft? **(3pts)**
7. Which episode was referred to by Remmick during his interview with Geordi? **(5pts)**
8. Which episode was referred to by Remmick during his interview with Troi? **(5pts)**
9. Which episode was referred to by Remmick during his interview with Picard? **(5pts)**
10. The intermix ratio question was the last of which part of the exam? **(3pts)**

CHARACTER QUOTE
(4pts per word + 9pts for identifying the speaker.)

Unscramble the words below and then identify the character.

'_____ _____ _____ _____.'

EBSCDIEALP   EIALNDOM   MSEIL   ROWM

⭐ SPECIAL ASSIGNMENT (15pts)

At what speed does Picard tell Jake to restart the shuttlecraft engine?

ANSWERS

TRIVIA ANSWERS

1. Mordock Strategy
2. psychological profile
3. Inspector General's Office
4. manoeuvering jets
5. Dynamic Relationships Test
6. Jake initiates a Flight Emergency Override
7. 'Where No One Has Gone Before'
8. 'The Battle'
9. 'Justice'
10. Hyperspace Physics Test

CHARACTER QUOTE SOLUTION

'Despicable Melanoid slime worm.' – Rondon

SPECIAL ASSIGNMENT SOLUTION

.020

Congratulations! Starfleet Command is proud to award you the Starfleet Medal of Honour and 15 extra points.

MISSION PERFORMANCE RATING:

55 – 75 points **Superior:** Congratulations Cadet, see you at the Academy!

50 – 54 points **Above Average:** Sorry, you missed entrance by 2 points.

40 – 49 points **Average:** Better luck on the Starfleet exam next year.

30 – 39 points **Fair:** The Hyperspace Physics Test got you down, huh?

0 – 29 points **Poor:** Even Jake scored better than this!

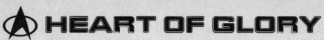
The *Enterprise* investigates a reported battle in the Neutral Zone. Upon arrival in the area they find a badly damaged vessel with three Klingons on board. The away team and the survivors of the ship barely have time to beam back to the *Enterprise* before the vessel explodes. One of the Klingons dies of his injuries while the remaining survivors claim they were attacked by a Ferengi vessel. Although Picard doesn't fully believe their story he allows Worf to escort the Klingons around the ship.

A Klingon ship approaches the *Enterprise* from a distance. The Klingon captain states that the survivors are fugitives and destroyed a Klingon ship sent to capture them. Picard agrees to transfer the Klingons and orders them to be detained in the brig. The Klingons soon escape. On the way to Engineering one of the Klingons is killed. The remaining Klingon trains his disruptor on the warp engines and demands to speak to Worf. Worf is forced to kill him.

TRIVIA QUESTIONS

1. Riker says it smells like a what before beaming over to the *Batris*? **(2pts)**
2. Heat and toxic gases have less effect on whom? **(3pts)**
3. How does Data open the jammed door on the *Batris*? **(2pts)**
4. How many personnel are in the security detail to detain the Klingons? **(4pts)**
5. What does Korris pick up off the floor? **(3pts)**
6. How long will it take to send a message to Starfleet from the Neutral Zone? **(3pts)**
7. Who is the commander of the approaching Klingon cruiser? **(5pts)**
8. What is the name of the approaching Klingon cruiser? **(5pts)**
9. What is the *Enterprise*'s next destination after resolving the Klingon incident? **(5pts)**
10. Worf asks the Klingon commander to send the Klingons to planets in what system? **(3pts)**

MULTIPLE CHOICE QUESTIONS

1. The Starfleet Officer who found Worf lived on this planet. **(3pts)**
   A. Earth
   B. Gault
   C. Cerebus II
   D. Arvada III

2. What is the purpose of the howling during the Klingon Death Ritual? **(2pts)**
   A. a means of expressing grief

B. a warning to the dead that a Klingon warrior is about to arrive

C. a warning to the living enemies that the warrior's death will be avenged

D. to create the proper atmosphere for the rest of the ritual

3. List three important concepts to Klingons. **(2pts)**
   A. duty, truth, and good health
   B. good food, rough women, and dying with honour in battle
   C. duty, honour, loyalty
   D. a fast ship, fast food, and a slow death

4. Who else entered Starfleet Academy with Worf? **(3pts)**
   A. foster brother
   B. half-brother
   C. best friend
   D. adopted sister

5. What is the device called that is wired into Geordi's VISOR? **(5pts)**
   A. Visual Impairment Transmitigator
   B. Visual Acuity Transmitter
   C. Visual Wireless Broadcasting Unit
   D. Visual Enhancement Device

ANSWERS

TRIVIA ANSWERS

1. trap
2. Data
3. he forces it
4. five
5. child
6. 24 hours
7. K'Nera
8. T'Acog
9. Starbase 84
10. Halee system

MULTIPLE CHOICE ANSWERS

1. B. Gault
2. B. a warning to the dead that a Klingon warrior is about to arrive
3. C. duty, honour, loyalty
4. A. foster brother
5. B. Visual Acuity Transmitter

MISSION PERFORMANCE RATING:

45 – 50 points **Superior:** The Klingon Defence Force has a home for you.

40 – 44 points **Above Average:** Go help Worf with hostage negotiations.

30 – 39 points **Average:** Do glorious battles inspire your life no more?

20 – 29 points **Fair:** You've got guard duty. Watch those Klingons in the brig.

0 – 19 points **Poor:** Not even worth talking about.

THE ARSENAL OF FREEDOM

STARDATE: 41798.2

The *Enterprise* is investigating the disappearance of a Federation vessel near the planet Minos where they detected an automated message. An away team is dispatched and subsequently attacked by a robotic device. Before the away team destroys the device, Riker is encased in a force field. While Data attempts to free Riker a second device attacks the party. While fleeing, Picard and Dr Crusher fall into a cavern. Data and Yar are able to destroy the second device and free Riker.

Meanwhile the *Enterprise*, commanded by Geordi, comes under attack by an orbiting device. On the surface the rest of the away team searches for Picard and Dr Crusher. Picard discovers in the cavern the main control panel for the weapons and shuts down the system. Geordi destroys the attacking orbital device and is then able to beam up the away team.

TRIVIA QUESTIONS

1. What hails the *Enterprise* from the planet's surface? **(3pts)**
2. The orbital weapons system attacking the *Enterprise* uses what type of sophisticated device? **(4pts)**
3. Rubbing the roots on the skin changes the skin colour to what hue? **(4pts)**
4. What were the Minotians famous as? **(3pts)**
5. Which officer replaced him at the conn when Geordi took command of the *Enterprise*? **(5pts)**
6. What is lost as the *Enterprise* enters the planet's atmosphere? **(3pts)**
7. Dr Crusher and her grandmother were survivors of which disastrous colony? **(4pts)**
8. Whose image does Riker see on the surface? **(3pts)**
9. Which item couldn't Picard locate in the underground cavern? **(3pts)**
10. Geordi wants to analyze the attacker's what? **(3pts)**

SPECIAL ASSIGNMENT (10pts)

What was the depth of the shaft Picard and Crusher fell into?

MULTIPLE CHOICE QUESTIONS

1. Name the fictitious ship Riker told Rice he was from. **(3pts)**
   - **A.** the *Licorice*
   - **B.** the *Charleston Chew*
   - **C.** the *Lollipop*
   - **D.** the *Tootsie Pop*

2. Data determines Riker is in a state of what? **(2pts)**
   A. depression
   B. stasis
   C. elation
   D. mitosis

3. What has Robotic Attacker No. 3 developed? **(3pts)**
   A. deflector shield
   B. stasis field
   C. metaphasic shield
   D. engine trouble

4. How is the advanced weapons system capable of learning and adapting? **(4pts)**
   A. through alien intelligence
   B. through artificial intelligence
   C. through Dynamic Adaptive Design (DAD)
   D. through Multiple Optimizing Mannerisms (MOM)

5. How does Picard stop the advanced weapons system from killing the away team? **(3pts)**
   A. destroys the main control unit in the cavern
   B. promises to purchase the system
   C. reconfigures the firing sequence
   D. kills the holographic salesman

ANSWERS

TRIVIA ANSWERS
1. automatic hailing system
2. cloaking
3. yellowish
4. arms merchants
5. Lieutenant Solis
6. a deflector
7. Arvada III
8. Captain Paul Rice
9. medical kit
10. firing pattern

SPECIAL ASSIGNMENT
11.75 metres
Congratulations! Starfleet Command is proud to award you the Starfleet Medal of Honour and 10 extra points.

MULTIPLE CHOICE
1. C. the Lollipop
2. B. stasis
3. A. deflector shield
4. C. through Dynamic Adaptive Design (DAD)
5. B. promises to purchase the system

MISSION PERFORMANCE RATING:
45 – 60 points **Superior:** You'd make a good Minotian, if there were any left.
40 – 44 points **Above Average:** You work for a defence contractor, huh?
30 – 39 points **Average:** Don't fall down any mine shafts.
20 – 29 points **Fair:** The holographic salesman has more smarts than you!
  0 – 19 points **Poor:** Don't you want to see the bridge some day?

SKIN OF EVIL

Troi is returning from business elsewhere when her shuttle experiences problems and crashes on a nearby planet. The *Enterprise* tracks down the shuttle and sends an away team to investigate. On the planet the away team discovers a puddle of dark ooze. It turns out to be an intelligent but evil life form named Armus.

Riker and the away team try to negotiate for the release of the shuttle occupants but to no avail. Armus kills Yar when she tries to get to the shuttle.

Picard arrives and orders the away team back to the ship. Armus allows Picard to see Troi in the shuttle. Troi tells Picard what buttons to push to get Armus' energy levels down. Picard tries her suggestions and the ploy works. The shuttle occupants and Picard are beamed up safely.

TRIVIA QUESTIONS

1. What is Armus' nickname for Data? **(3pts)**
2. The planet is declared what? **(3pts)**
3. What is the device Dr Crusher uses on Lieutenant Yar to try to resuscitate her? **(3pts)**
4. What does Armus want? **(3pts)**
5. Whose phaser falls into the black sludge after Riker goes under? **(4pts)**
6. What medical procedure does Dr Crusher try to revive Lieutenant Yar? **(5pts)**
7. What planet does the shuttlecraft crash on? **(4pts)**
8. Who becomes Acting Chief of Security? **(3pts)**
9. What kind of problem does the shuttle pilot report? **(3pts)**
10. What martial arts technique did Lieutenant Yar ask Worf to help her with? **(4pts)**

CHARACTER QUOTE
(3pts per word + 7pts for identifying the speaker.)

Unscramble the words below and then identify the character.

'Tell me _____, how does it ____ to ____ _____ own _____.'
NMTNIA   EFLE CEFA RUYO   ITNTCOXNEI

✪✪ SPECIAL ASSIGNMENT (15pts)

To what level does the force field strength have to drop before Troi and Picard can be beamed out?

ANSWERS

TRIVIA ANSWERS

1. Tinman
2. off-limits to other vessels
3. neural stimulator
4. transport off the planet
5. Geordi's
6. direct reticular stimulation
7. Vagra II
8. Lieutenant Worf
9. on board systems failure
10. Mishiama wristlock and break

CHARACTER QUOTE SOLUTION

'Tell me Tinman, how does it feel to face your own extinction.' – Armus

SPECIAL ASSIGNMENT SOLUTION

Below 2.7

Congratulations! Starfleet Command is proud to award you the Starfleet Medal of Honour and 15 extra points.

MISSION PERFORMANCE RATING:

55 – 75 points **Superior:** I told you way back to apply for Chief of Security!

50 – 54 points **Above Average:** You're favoured to win over Minnerly.

40 – 49 points **Average:** You'll be a shuttle pilot – forever!!!

30 – 39 points **Fair:** Be careful, that's not really an oil slick!

0 – 29 points **Poor:** Armus needs a companion and you just volunteered.

SYMBIOSIS

The *Enterprise* answers a freighter's distress call and saves some of the crew and their cargo. The cargo is supposedly medicine for a plague that has ravaged the Ornarans on the planet below for several hundred years. The Brekkians, the suppliers of the medicine called felicium, claim the medicine has not been paid for and is still theirs.

Dr Crusher examines the Ornarans who are becoming ill and determines that felicium is not a medicine but a drug. All the Ornarans are addicted to the substance. The Brekkians have known all this and so agree to giving the felicium to the Ornarans. Dr Crusher is outraged but Picard is bound by the Prime Directive not to interfere. Picard refuses to supply spare parts for the Ornaran freighters, knowing that eventually the Ornarans will break the habit.

TRIVIA QUESTIONS

1. What was the name of the planet the freighter was in orbit around? **(4pts)**
2. While studying the unusual stellar activity what does Picard order as a precaution? **(3pts)**
3. Where does Yar beam the freighter's cargo? **(2pts)**
4. The barrel of felicium contains enough of the drug for approximately how many doses? **(5pts)**
5. How many hours does felicium effectively mask the effects of the 'plague'? **(3pts)**
6. How many years ago was the only reported contact with the Delos system? **(3pts)**
7. How many years has T'Jon been captain of the freighter? **(5pts)**
8. How many voyages between the two planets has T'Jon been on? **(5pts)**

MULTIPLE CHOICE QUESTIONS

1. Several thousand years ago this planet was technologically sophisticated. **(3pts)**
   - A. Earth
   - B. Ornara
   - C. Aldea
   - D. Brekka

---

2. What appeared on Ornara 200 years ago? **(4pts)**
   A. great prophet
   B. felicium
   C. plague
   D. Romulan warbirds

3. In Langor's grandfather's time an equivalent amount of felicium would have filled five what? **(5pts)**
   A. grain bins
   B. cargo bays
   C. freighters
   D. barrels

4. Where does Security escort the freighter survivors to? **(5pts)**
   A. brig
   B. Captain's ready room
   C. bridge
   D. observation lounge

5. What type of weapons are the survivors of the freighter in possession of? **(3pts)**
   A. disruptors
   B. a natural electrical charge
   C. extremely pungent body odour
   D. telekinetic powers

6. What does Picard call for in the observation lounge? **(3pts)**
   A. silence
   B. security
   C. med alert – medical emergency
   D. staff meeting

7. Wesley reports the deflectors are being hit by what? **(5pts)**
   A. microdust particles
   B. meteor storm
   C. huge bursts of X-rays
   D. dense clouds of hydrogen

8. The *Enterprise* attempts to pull the freighter out of orbit using what? **(2pts)**
   A. transporter
   B. tractor beam
   C. shuttlecraft
   D. reverse polarity repulsor beam

ANSWERS

TRIVIA ANSWERS

1. Ornara
2. yellow alert
3. cargo hold
4. four billion
5. 72 hours
6. 200
7. Seven
8. 26

MULTIPLE CHOICE ANSWERS

1. B. Ornara
2. C. plague
3. B. cargo bays
4. D. observation lounge
5. B. a natural electrical charge
6. C. med alert – medical emergency
7. C. huge bursts of X-rays
8. B. tractor beam

MISSION PERFORMANCE RATING:

55 – 60 points **Superior:** You've got a highly charged personality.

50 – 54 points **Above Average:** Brekkian trader?

40 – 49 points **Average:** At least you beamed off the freighter first!

30 – 39 points **Fair:** You'd better align your electromagnetic coil!

 0 – 29 points **Poor:** I think the felicium is affecting your brain.

WE'LL ALWAYS HAVE PARIS ⏺

STARDATE: 41697.9

Soon after experiencing a time distortion, the *Enterprise* receives a distress call from a Dr Manheim. Picard suspects the two events are connected and investigates further. Manheim's experiments with time have gone awry and many scientists have been killed. Manheim himself is injured. Manheim and his wife are beamed up to sickbay for treatment. It is revealed that Picard had a relationship with Manheim's wife in years past.

The *Enterprise* encounters another time distortion. Data goes to Manheim's lab to fix the problem. As Data prepares to correct the time distortions, several versions of himself appear in the lab. They talk to each other and eventually figure out who is supposed to do what. The rift is repaired and Manheim and his wife return to the station to continue with his work.

TRIVIA QUESTIONS

1. What happens to Manheim after Data seals the time continuum crack? **(3pts)**
2. What contraction did Data use at the end of the episode in the lab? **(4pts)**
3. How long did Manheim search for a proper location to work on his experiments? **(3pts)**
4. What was the name of another star system feeling the effects of the time distortion? **(4pts)**
5. What is the minimum range of the time distortions? **(3pts)**
6. Which farming colony reported an episode of time distortion? **(5pts)**
7. Which holodeck did Picard use? **(3pts)**
8. What is the name of the restaurant in Paris for which Picard configures the holodeck programme? **(4pts)**
9. Picard configures the holodeck programme for how many years ago? **(3pts)**
10. How soon before reaching the source of the emergency signal does Picard wish to be notified? **(3pts)**

SPECIAL ASSIGNMENT (10pts)

Picard configures the holodeck programme for what date?

MULTIPLE CHOICE QUESTIONS

1. While Data is in Manheim's lab, what does he need Geordi to do? **(3pts)**
   A. hand him a wrench
   B. give him a 27 second countdown
   C. beam down a matter/antimatter pod
   D. move the *Enterprise* to the other side of the planet in case something goes wrong

2. Picard appears on the bridge wearing what? **(2pts)**
   A. fencing outfit
   B. dress uniform
   C. bathrobe
   D. emergency decon unit

3. Manheim says they opened what into another dimension? **(3pts)**
   A. door
   B. can of worms
   C. window
   D. rift

4. What is the name of the club on Sarona VIII that serves blue coloured drinks? **(5pts)**
   A. Blue Bonnet Cafe
   B. Blue Parrot Cafe
   C. The Parrots Claw Cafe
   D. Blue Donkey Cafe

5. What landmark can be seen in the distance from the holodeck restaurant? **(2pts)**
   A. Office of the President of the Federation Council
   B. Eiffel Tower
   C. Café des Artistes
   D. WWII war memorial

ANSWERS

TRIVIA ANSWERS

1. complete recovery
2. It's (instead of saying 'It is me.')
3. two years
4. Ilecom
5. Several thousand light years
6. Coltar IV
7. Holodeck 3
8. Café des Artistes
9. 22 years
10. 30 minutes

SPECIAL ASSIGNMENT SOLUTION

9 April

Congratulations! Starfleet Command is proud to award you the Starfleet Medal of Honour and 10 extra points.

MULTIPLE CHOICE ANSWERS

1. B. give him a 27 second countdown.
2. A. fencing outfit
3. C. window
4. B. Blue Parrot Cafe
5. B. Eiffel Tower

MISSION PERFORMANCE RATING:

45 – 60 points **Superior:** Dr Manheim is looking for a few good people.

40 – 44 points **Above Average:** You're Picard's next fencing partner.

30 – 39 points **Average:** Didn't you use to work at the Blue Parrot Cafe?

20 – 29 points **Fair:** You're in your own little dimension.

0 – 19 points **Poor:** Been playing with too many time distorting substances?

CONSPIRACY

STARDATE: 41775.5

Picard meets covertly with a trusted friend who warns him of a conspiracy within Starfleet. When this informant mysteriously dies, Picard makes Data study recent Starfleet reports and communications for any signs of unusual activity. Data soon uncovers evidence of the conspiracy.

Picard decides to go to the heart of the Federation for answers and the *Enterprise* returns to Earth. Picard beams down for dinner with several admirals while Admiral Quinn beams aboard to look around. Quinn attempts to compromise a key member of the *Enterprise* crew with a parasitic life form but is thwarted. Dr Crusher discovers that Quinn is controlled by a similar parasite.

Picard checks in with the *Enterprise* and is warned of the parasites. Picard realizes that everyone in the room has been compromised. With the help of Riker, Picard is able to neutralize the threat and uncover the leader of the conspiracy.

TRIVIA QUESTIONS

1. A Code 47 message is only for whom? **(3pts)**
2. What is not kept on a Code 47 message? **(3pts)**
3. Data reads three life forms on Dytallix B near what? **(3pts)**
4. What does Dr Crusher find in Admiral Quinn's body? **(3pts)**
5. The alien parasites were discovered on an uncharted planet by whom? **(3pts)**
6. Where did Rixx first meet Picard? **(3pts)**
7. Where in the nearby quadrant did Worf detect a disturbance? **(5pts)**
8. What type of star is Mira? **(4pts)**
9. Who owns Dytallix B and the other six planets in the star system? **(3pts)**
10. Where did Picard first meet Walker Keel? **(5pts)**

WHO AM I? (25pts)

I never found fault with you. I thought we all could just get along. I was only ETing but you blew my mind anyway.

✪✪ SPECIAL ASSIGNMENT (15pts)

List the three Starfleet personnel who died mysteriously.

ANSWERS

TRIVIA ANSWERS

1. Captain's Eyes Only
2. computer record
3. mining shaft
4. alien parasite
5. survey team
6. Altarian Conference
7. Sector 63
8. red giant
9. Dytallix Mining Company
10. bar on Tau Ceti III

WHO AM I? SOLUTION

Remmick

EXPLANATION:

I never found fault with you. – In 'Coming Of Age', Remmick's investigation found nothing wrong with the *Enterprise* and its crew.

I thought we all could get along. – Remmick claims the alien parasites 'seek peaceful coexistence'.

I was only ET'ing – 'ET phone home.' Remmick was sending a homing beacon to the aliens' base.

but you blew my mind anyway. – Picard and Riker phaser Remmick, exploding his head.

SPECIAL ASSIGNMENT SOLUTION

McKinney; Ryan Sipe; Onna Karapleedez

Congratulations! Starfleet Command is proud to award you the Starfleet Medal of Honour and 15 extra points.

MISSION PERFORMANCE RATING:

55 – 75 points **Superior:** Thanks to you the conspiracy is crushed!

50 – 54 points **Above Average:** Code 47 message for you. Well maybe not yet!

40 – 49 points **Average:** Close your mouth before you eat a big bug!

30 – 39 points **Fair:** Howd' you get off the *Horatio*?

0 – 29 points **Poor:** You like crunchy little worms for dinner, don't you?

THE NEUTRAL ZONE

STARDATE: 41986.0

While the *Enterprise* is waiting for Picard to return from an emergency meeting, an ancient spacecraft floats by. Data and Worf beam over and discover lots of frozen bodies, three of which are still preserved. Data and Worf return to the *Enterprise* with the three bodies as Picard arrives from the conference.

The *Enterprise* heads for the Neutral Zone to investigate the destruction of several Federation outposts. Meanwhile, Dr Crusher resuscitates the frozen humans found on the derelict craft. The three humans, from the late 21st century, undergo a bad case of time lag.

A Romulan warbird suddenly appears in front of the *Enterprise*. They have also had outposts destroyed but have no idea who is responsible. With the help of one of the thawed-out passengers, Picard persuades the Romulans to work together with the Federation to determine what is happening. The *Enterprise* later meets with another starship that will take the humans back to Earth.

TRIVIA QUESTIONS

1. Which shuttlebay does Picard land in? **(3pts)**
2. How old was Claire Raymond when she died and was frozen? **(4pts)**
3. What is the name of the first outpost the *Enterprise* comes across that is totally destroyed? **(5pts)**
4. At Warp 8 the *Enterprise* could be at which starbase in five days from the Neutral Zone? **(5pts)**
5. What is the name of the second destroyed outpost the *Enterprise* encounters? **(5pts)**
6. How fast does the *Enterprise* travel to the Neutral Zone? **(5pts)**
7. Where were the two Federation outposts that were destroyed? **(3pts)**
8. On its current heading what is the projected destination of the ancient cryosatellite? **(5pts)**

✪✪ SPECIAL ASSIGNMENT (15pts)

There has been no contact with any starbases in Sector 31 since what stardate?

MULTIPLE CHOICE QUESTIONS

1. What does Sonny first order from the replicator? **(5pts)**
   A. thick T-bone steak, country fried potatoes, and a mess of mustard greens
   B. Kansas City steak, french fries, and a mess of peas
   C. thick Kansas City steak, country fried potatoes, and a mess of greens
   D. Quarter Pounder with cheese, large order of fries, and a big coke

2. Offenhouse wants a copy of what? **(3pts)**
   A. *War and Peace*
   B. *Wall Street Journal*
   C. *New York Times*
   D. *Forbes*

3. Which slang term did Sonny use that Data and Riker had no idea what it meant? **(3pts)**
   A. high stepping pit hound
   B. high mileage pit woofer
   C. low priced pit bull
   D. low mileage pit woofie

4. Offenhouse compares the *Enterprise* to what? **(2pts)**
   A. QE-2
   B. DS-9
   C. TOS
   D. ICU

5. What term does Raymond use that Troi isn't familiar with? **(2pts)**
   A. tempus fugit
   B. How's by you?
   C. local shrink
   D. mess of greens

ANSWERS

TRIVIA ANSWERS

1. main shuttlebay
2. 35 years old
3. Science Station Delta Zero Five
4. Starbase 39-Sierra
5. Tarod IX
6. Warp 8
7. Sector Three Zero
8. Kazis Binary system

SPECIAL ASSIGNMENT SOLUTION

41903.2

Congratulations! Starfleet Command is proud to award you the Starfleet Medal of Honour and 15 extra points.

MULTIPLE CHOICE ANSWERS

1. C. thick Kansas City steak, country fried potatoes, and a mess of greens
2. B. *Wall Street Journal*
3. D. low mileage pit woofie
4. A. QE-2
5. C. local shrink

MISSION PERFORMANCE RATING:

45 – 65 points **Superior:** You must know who destroyed all those outposts.

40 – 44 points **Above Average:** Ex-cryoengineer?

30 – 39 points **Average:** Just thawed out? Well it's still the 21st century!

20 – 29 points **Fair:** A little frostbite damage around the edges of your brain?

0 – 19 points **Poor:** Report to the cryosatellite for extended duty.

CHARACTER TRIVIA

For over seven seasons you have been observing the crew of the *Enterprise* as they deal with the worst the galaxy can throw at them. You think you know them quite well by now. But how well do you really know them? Answer the questions below and find out.

PICARD

1. In which two episodes does Picard play the Ressikan flute he receives in 'The Inner Light'? **(10pts)**
2. What does Picard prefer for breakfast? **(10pts)**
3. How many candidates did Picard have to choose from to fill the first officer position? **(20pts)**
4. What is Picard's serial number? **(20pts)**
5. What was Picard's graduating class from the Academy? **(10pts)**
6. What is the name of Picard's ancestor who was a Spanish soldier in the 1690s? **(30pts)**
7. Picard's family roots in Western Europe can be traced back to what time? **(10pts)**
8. How does Picard prefer to view the future? **(10pts)**

RIKER

1. Which are the only two episodes where Riker is called Bill? **(30pts)**
2. What graduating class is Riker from? **(15pts)**
3. What is Riker's Starfleet number? **(20pts)**
4. Which three starships has Riker been offered to command? **(15pts)**
5. Why did Riker grow a beard? **(10pts)**

DATA

1. How much does Data weigh? **(10pts)**
2. Why does Data have a functional respiratory system? **(10pts)**
3. Data's circulatory system produces what? **(10pts)**
4. How did Dr Soong and Juliana finally get Data to wear clothes? **(10pts)**
5. What happened to Data when he once tried to swim on Lake Navalo? **(10pts)**
6. What play (including act and scene) is Data practising on the holodeck during the pretitle sequence of 'Emergence'? **(30pts)**

DR CRUSHER

1. Dr Crusher has a fear of what? (10pts)
2. Where did Jack and Beverly take Wesley on his first camping trip? (15pts)
3. At what age did Dr Crusher change her hair colour to brunette? (15pts)
4. With which two historical figures did Dr Crusher once have dinner on the Orient Express? (20pts)

GEORDI

1. What is Geordi's Starfleet speciality according to Data? (15pts)
2. What traumatic event did Geordi experience and how old was he? (15pts)
3. What range of frequencies does Geordi's VISOR scan? (15pts)
4. Name a language Geordi learned from his travels growing up with his family. (30pts)
5. What does Geordi's father do in Starfleet? (10pts)

WORF

1. On what day was Alexander born? (30pts)
2. What does the Klingon Rite of MajQa that Worf participated in as a child entail? (20pts)
3. What caused the scar on Worf's left arm? (20pts)

TROI

1. How does Troi know so much about the Ancient West? (10pts)
2. How old was Troi when her father died? (20pts)
3. What song did Troi always want her father to sing before she went to sleep? (20pts)

MISCELLANEOUS

1. Who is the only other member of the crew besides Data that Spot seems to like? (10pts)
2. How does O'Brien drink his coffee? (15pts)
3. Which is the only *TNG* episode when the viewer has seen a Klingon's bare feet? (30pts)
4. What did O'Brien often eat with his eggs for breakfast while growing up? (15pts)
5. Which three episodes of the original *Star Trek* series, by title, were alluded to by Scotty? (30pts)

Along the left margin: **SPECIAL SECTION**

ANSWERS

PICARD TRIVIA ANSWERS

1. 'Lessons' and 'A Fistful of Datas'; 2. coffee and croissants ('Attached'); 3. 50 ('The Pegasus'); 4. SP-937-215 ('Chain Of Command – Part I'); 5. Class of '27 ('Tapestry'); 6. Javier Maribona-Picard ('Journey's End'); 7. Charlemagne ('Journey's End'); 8. as something not written in stone ('All Good Things …')

RIKER TRIVIA ANSWERS

1. 'The Naked Now', 'Haven'; 2. Class of '57 ('Chain Of Command – Part I'); 3. 231-427 ('Gambit – Part I'); 4. USS Drake ('Arsenal Of Freedom'), USS Aries ('The Icarus Factor'), USS Melbourne ('The Best Of Both Worlds – Part I'); 5. he got tired of hearing how young he looked ('The Pegasus')

DATA TRIVIA ANSWERS

1. 100 kilograms ('Inheritance'); 2. to maintain thermal control of his internal systems ('Birthright – Part I'); 3. biochemical lubricants ('Birthright – Part I'); 4. they had to write a modesty subroutine ('Inheritance'); 5. he sank to the bottom (lack of buoyancy) and had to walk underwater to the shore ('Descent – Part II'); 6. Shakespeare's The Tempest, Act V, Scene i ('Emergence')

DR CRUSHER TRIVIA ANSWERS

1. fear of heights or acrophobia ('Attached'); 2. Balfour Lake ('Attached'); 3. 13 years old ('The Quality Of Life'); 4. Sigmund Freud and Gertrude Stein ('Emergence')

GEORDI TRIVIA ANSWERS

1. antimatter power and dilithium regulators ('Elementary, Dear Data'); 2. He was caught in a fire for several minutes when he was five years old ('Hero Worship'); 3. 1 Hz to 100,000 Terahertz ('The Masterpiece Society'); 4. Hahliian ('Aquiel'); 5. exo-zoologist ('Imaginary Friend')

WORF TRIVIA ANSWERS

1. on the 43rd day of Maktag ('New Ground'); 2. deep meditation in the lava caves on No'Mat ('Birthright – Part I'); 3. Worf grabbed a beast with his bare hands during a ritual hunt when he was young ('Birthright – Part I')

TROI TRIVIA ANSWERS

1. her father used to read her stories about the Ancient West when she was little ('A Fistful Of Datas'); 2. when she was seven years old ('Dark Page'); 3. Down In The Valley ('Dark Page')

MISCELLANEOUS TRIVIA ANSWERS

1. Barclay ('Genesis'); 2. black, double sweet ('Rascals'); 3. Worf's feet in the episode 'Ethics' as he is recuperating from his spinal injuries; 4. corned beef ('The Wounded'); 5. 'Elaan of Troyius', 'Wolf In the Fold', 'The Naked Time' ('Relics')

MISSION PERFORMANCE RATING:

550 – 655 points	**Superior:** You know the crew better than yourself! (SEE BELOW)
450 – 549 points	**Above Average:** You are most observant.
300 – 449 points	**Average:** Not bad, all things considered.
150 – 299 points	**Fair:** You know a whole lot about nothing.
0 – 149 points	**Poor:** You don't even know who you are, let alone the crew.

If you have received a SUPERIOR Mission Performance Rating –

Congratulations!
Starfleet Command is proud to award you
the Palm Leaf of Axanar Peace Mission and 50 extra points.

SEASON TWO

THE CHILD

STARDATE: 42073.1

The *Enterprise* is transporting hazardous samples needed at a research facility trying to develop a vaccine against a deadly plague. The samples are stored in special containment modules for the duration of the trip.

An energy source enters the *Enterprise* and impregnates Troi. After a speedy pregnancy, Troi delivers a baby boy named Ian. The boy continues to mature at a fantastic rate. It is revealed that Ian is an energy being curious about humans and has assumed human form to learn about them.

A plague sample begins to grow during the transportation. If not stopped, the sample will break out of the containment area and kill everyone on board the *Enterprise*. A special type of radiation is determined to be the cause of the plague sample growth. Troi's child is found to be the source of the problem and leaves the ship in order to save the *Enterprise*.

TRIVIA QUESTIONS

1. What is the normal gestation period for a Betazoid? **(3pts)**
2. Which bridge station is Data at when he observes a random energy transference? **(3pts)**
3. How old does Ian appear to be one day after his birth? **(3pts)**
4. Which quadrant does the *Enterprise* head for after delivering the plague samples. **(4pts)**
5. What is the Starfleet registry number on the side of the shuttlecraft leaving the *Enterprise*? **(5pts)**
6. How cold is it in the containment modules? **(4pts)**
7. Which transporter room is Data needed in? **(3pts)**
8. Which plague module is growing? **(4pts)**
9. What is the length of Troi's gestation period? **(3pts)**
10. Wesley tells Guinan the crew thinks she is from where? **(3pts)**

✪ SPECIAL ASSIGNMENT (15pts)

Cyanoacrylates is an actual chemical term describing several kinds of products. Name the general category of products **(7pts)** and then one specific name brand **(8pts)**.

MULTIPLE CHOICE QUESTIONS

1. Troi felt no _____ during the delivery. **(2pts)**
   - **A.** remorse
   - **B.** pain
   - **C.** joy
   - **D.** sadness

---

2. What breed of puppies were in the nursery? **(3pts)**
   A. German shepherd
   B. pit bull terrier
   C. golden retriever
   D. Norwegian elkhound

3. Plague specimens are 20% ... **(5pts)**
   A. dead
   B. grafted biological specimens
   C. genetically deconstructed life forms
   D. genetically engineered biological life forms

4. Which phrase did Data not understand? **(3pts)**
   A. don't let the bedbugs bite
   B. eager beaver
   C. the early bird gets the worm
   D. a targ a day keeps the doctor away

5. What assignment did Dr Crusher accept? **(2pts)**
   A. Chief Medical Officer for *USS Berlin*
   B. personal physician for the Federation Council President
   C. head of Starfleet Medical
   D. head of TB screening clinic on Tavit D

ANSWERS

TRIVIA ANSWERS
1. 10 months
2. Science I
3. four Earth years
4. Morgana
5. NCC-2544
6. 97 °Kelvin
7. Transporter Room 3
8. L73
9. 47 hours
10. Novacron

SPECIAL ASSIGNMENT
fast-bonding adhesives (general category)
Krazy Glue (specific name brand)
Congratulations! Starfleet Command is proud to award you the Starfleet Medal of Honour and 15 extra points.

MULTIPLE CHOICE
1. B. pain; 2. C. golden retriever;
3. D. genetically engineered biological life forms;
4. B. eager beaver;
5. C. head of Starfleet Medical

MISSION PERFORMANCE RATING:
45 – 65 points **Superior:** Used any good cyanoacrylates lately?
40 – 44 points **Above Average:** Genetic engineering background, huh?
30 – 39 points **Average:** You'd better request to stay on board the *Enterprise*!
20 – 29 points **Fair:** Report to Science Station Tango Sierra.
0 – 19 points **Poor:** Go sit with the containment modules, one's ready to burst.

WHERE SILENCE HAS LEASE

STARDATE: 42193.6

The *Enterprise* encounters a strange void while mapping a new quadrant. The ship is soon caught in the void and cannot break free. An enemy ship suddenly appears and attacks the *Enterprise*. Next, a Federation vessel mysteriously approaches the *Enterprise*. Picard and the bridge crew finally realize they are being tested by some form of entity in the void.

The entity is fascinated with the limited life spans of humans and wants to experiment with a large part of the crew, killing them in the process. Picard prepares to destroy the *Enterprise*, rather than allow his crew to be tortured to death by this entity. At the last moment possible the entity lets the *Enterprise* go free.

TRIVIA QUESTIONS

1. The hole in space the *Enterprise* discovers is void of what? **(3pts)**
2. Of what type is the second probe which is launched into the void? **(5pts)**
3. How many of the *Enterprise* crew does the alien entity want to kill? **(3pts)**
4. What course at Starfleet Academy does Riker mention in the episode? **(3pts)**
5. The *Yamato* is the *Enterprise*'s what? **(3pts)**
6. Behind the tactical station, for what purpose is the far right aft station? **(4pts)**
7. According to inertial guidance, how far did the *Enterprise* travel within the void? **(5pts)**
8. According to Data, what is absent on the *Yamato*? **(3pts)**
9. What does the *Enterprise* use to try to determine their position within the void? **(3pts)**
10. What type of ship appeared and attacked the *Enterprise*? **(3pts)**

CHARACTER QUOTE
(5pts per word + 10pts for identifying the speaker.)

Unscramble the words below and then identify the character.

'Yes, _____, I do _____ _____, _____!'
    UATYLBEOLS   EIEDND UNCCRO ETLWEYLHEHODRA

ANSWERS

TRIVIA ANSWERS

1. matter and energy
2. class-1 probe with full sensor array.
3. 1/3 to1/2 of the crew.
4. Ancient History
5. sister ship
6. Engineering
7. 1.4 parsecs
8. life signs
9. stationary beacon
10. Romulan warbird

CHARACTER QUOTE SOLUTION

'Yes, absolutely, I do indeed concur, wholeheartedly!' – Riker

---

MISSION PERFORMANCE RATING:

55 – 65 points **Superior:** You've been through Nagilum's laboratory before!

45 – 54 points **Above Average:** Nagilum finds you most curious!

30 – 44 points **Average:** There's a relief conn officer position available.

15 – 29 points **Fair:** You're being transferred to the *Yamato*.

0 – 14 points **Poor:** Nagilum needs one more subject for today's experiment.

ELEMENTARY, DEAR DATA

STARDATE: 42286.3

Geordi and Data visit the holodeck, choosing to indulge in a Sherlock Holmes mystery. Almost immediately Data solves the mystery after meeting the first holodeck characters. On hearing of the android's accomplishment, Dr Pulaski bets that Data can't solve a true mystery; one he has not already memorized. Data accepts the bet and Dr Pulaski joins them in the holodeck.

Geordi accidentally programmes the computer to create a nemesis Data can't defeat, Professor Moriarty. Moriarty eventually becomes self aware and seizes control of the holodeck. Moriarty demands to leave the holodeck. Picard explains the impossibility of this request but tells Moriarty that he could be stored in memory. Moriarty agrees to this in the hope that some day a way will be found to allow him to live a more permanent existence outside the holodeck.

TRIVIA QUESTIONS

1. What does Geordi say is the proper way to move a ship? **(3pts)**
2. Whose arm does Dr Pulaski take while walking down the street in holographic London? **(3pts)**
3. What is the Inspector's name? **(3pts)**
4. What is the name of the prison the dead man was released from? **(4pts)**
5. Which Sherlock Holmes adventure mentioned by Data involved a secret code? **(4pts)**
6. Which book does Data find which provided Holmes with the key to a secret code? **(5pts)**
7. How much did Holmes pay for his violin? **(3pts)**
8. The first Sherlock Holmes mystery Data solves involved the king of what country? **(4pts)**
9. Where did Sherlock Holmes die? **(3pts)**
10. Mr Wilson was an employee of whom? **(3pts)**

MULTIPLE CHOICE QUESTIONS

1. Which old naval phrase is mentioned which means 'everything in perfect order'? **(2pts)**
   A. quid nunc
   B. shipshape
   C. fine and dandy
   D. Bristol fashion

---

2. What ship's function was transferred temporarily to the holodeck? **(5pts)**
   A. attitude and stabilization control
   B. life support
   C. navigational control
   D. warp drive system

3. What was the purpose of the photograph hidden in the coat? **(3pts)**
   A. keepsake
   B. present
   C. blackmail
   D. amusement

4. What is one of Data's strengths according to Geordi? **(3pts)**
   A. his computational speed
   B. his deductive reasoning
   C. his objectivity
   D. his ability to understand humour

5. Which holodeck safety feature has probably been overridden? **(2pts)**
   A. random violence squelcher
   B. pain threshold stabilizer
   C. character self awareness lockout
   D. mortality failsafe

ANSWERS

TRIVIA ANSWERS
1. using wind and sail
2. Geordi's
3. Lestrade
4. Dartmoor
5. The Valley of Fear
6. Whitaker's Almanac
7. 55 shillings
8. Bohemia
9. Reichenbach Falls
10. Red Headed League

MULTIPLE CHOICE ANSWERS
1. D. Bristol fashion
2. A. attitude and stabilization control
3. C. blackmail
4. B. his deductive reasoning
5. D. mortality failsafe

MISSION PERFORMANCE RATING:
45 – 50 points **Superior:** I do believe it's Sherlock Holmes himself!
40 – 44 points **Above Average:** A student of Professor Moriarty!
30 – 39 points **Average:** You're not even an average Watson.
20 – 29 points **Fair:** The bobbies are looking for you!
 0 – 19 points **Poor:** The holodeck characters did better than you!

THE OUTRAGEOUS OKONA

STARDATE: 42402.7

The *Enterprise* helps a distressed vessel and offers to repair the damaged system. Okona, the captain of the vessel, beams on board while the *Enterprise* crew carries out repairs. Soon several other ships approach the *Enterprise* bearing the leaders of two nearby planets. One leader accuses Okona of being a thief; the other leader accuses him of being the father of his daughter's child. Each leader wants custody of Okona immediately.

Picard sets up a meeting on the *Enterprise* between all interested parties. Okona turns himself over to the disgraced father. Eventually the son of the other leader steps forward and claims the child as his own. Okona is exonerated and leaves on his ship as the other two vessels depart as well.

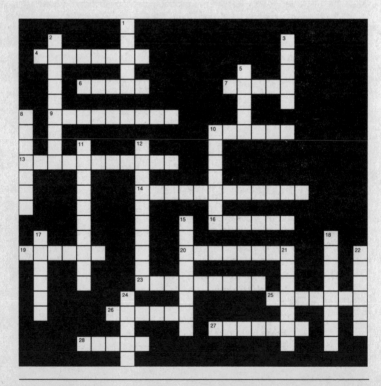

CROSSWORD PUZZLE CLUES

ACROSS

4. Okona wears a _____. (2pts)
6. A remembrance. (3pts)
7. Orders Picard to prepare to be boarded. (1pt)
9. Complement of a class-7 interplanetary vessel. (3pts)
10. Actual father of baby. (1pt)
13. What Okona supposedly did to Debin's daughter. (1pt)
14. Occurred on Atlec and Straleb some two hundred years ago. (1pt)
16. Data discusses his inability to understand humour with _____. (1pt)
19. Two planets form the Coalition of _____. (3pts)
20. Malfunctioning system on Okona's vessel. (1pt)
23. Name of Okona's vessel. (3pts)
25. Data's timing is _____. (2pts)
26. Riker says Okona has a healthy _____. (1pt)
27. A security vessel from the planet _____ is the last to arrive. (2pts)
28. Name of Debin's daughter. (2pts)

DOWN

1. Okona is accused of being a _____ by Secretary Kushell. (1pt)
2. Okona asks Data if he's seen any good looking _____ lately. (1pt)
3. Data can never become _____ off alcohol. (1pt)
5. Worf retrieves Okona from the arms of a beautiful woman on deck _____. (3pts)
8. Okona's first name. (3pts)
10. A monk, a clone and a Ferengi decide to go _____ together. (3pts)
11. Mode viewscreen is set to view multiple images simultaneously. (3pts)
12. Material Geordi uses to repair Okona's ship. (3pts)
15. Secretary Kushell is from the political entity called the _____ of Unity. (3pts)
17. Type of weapons found on the class-7 vessel. (1pt)
18. Okona has been reported at three different crew _____. (1pt)
21. Okona must shut down his _____ before the Enterprise can lock a tractor beam on his ship. (1pt)
22. Engages the tractor beam on Okona's vessel. (2pts)
24. Data holds a _____ while telling jokes to Guinan. (2pts)

✪✪ **SPECIAL ASSIGNMENT (15pts)**

What room number is Okona looking for when he speaks to Data in the corridor?

SPECIAL ASSIGNMENT SOLUTION

Room 806

Congratulations! Starfleet Command is proud to award you the Starfleet Medal of Honour and 15 extra points.

MISSION PERFORMANCE RATING:

50 – 70 points **Superior:** You must enjoy quantum mathematics.

40 – 49 points **Above Average:** Swashbuckler at heart.

30 – 39 points **Average:** You have an eye for detail but not much else.

20 – 29 points **Fair:** You'd make good material for Joe Piscopo's next show.

0 – 19 points **Poor:** Lasers at 20 paces!

THE SCHIZOID MAN

STARDATE: 42437.5

The *Enterprise* travels to the aid of a prominent Federation scientist, Dr Ira Graves who is terminally ill. Graves, a leading expert in cybernetics, sees Data's presence as a great opportunity to extend his life and further his research. He transfers his consciousness into Data before dying.

Back on board the starship, Data begins to act strangely and even displays violent emotional outbursts. Soon the crew realizes that Graves' personality is struggling for control of Data's body. Picard argues with Graves that Data is a sentient being and also deserves the right to live. Graves finally decides to leave Data's body and he does a core dump into the *Enterprise*'s computers.

TRIVIA QUESTIONS

1. Of what race is Lieutenant Selar? **(3pts)**
2. Data/Graves says his ears are better than what? **(3pts)**
3. Where is Graves' body transported to? **(3pts)**
4. Picard orders Dr Selar to report where? **(3pts)**
5. Who is initially injured by Data/Graves in Engineering? **(3pts)**
6. What does Data disclose to Graves? **(3pts)**
7. How many people were injured on the distressed Federation vessel? **(5pts)**
8. What tune does Graves keep whistling and which movie is it from? **(4pts)**
9. What is the name of the doctor on the away team to Graves' planet? **(4pts)**
10. Graves says he's as healthy as what? **(4pts)**

✪✪ SPECIAL ASSIGNMENT (15pts)

During the mental examination Data/Graves views an image of a 'wolf in sheep's clothing'. Who is it and which two episodes was the character in?

MULTIPLE CHOICE QUESTIONS

1. Which two traits does Graves say are responsible for his genius? **(2pts)**
    A. superior intellect and nerves of duranium
    B. rigid backbone and daring bravado
    C. iron will and nerves of steel
    D. egocentric thinking and hedonistic lifestyle

---

2. What is Graves' body placed in for burial? **(3pts)**
   A. open-faced tritanium casket
   B. modified dilithium shipping container
   C. unarmed photon torpedo
   D. modified haz-mat storage receptacle

3. What disease does Graves have? **(5pts)**
   A. Bendii Syndrome
   B. Iverson's disease
   C. Anchilles fever
   D. Darney's disease

4. What examination do all cadets at Starfleet Academy take before graduating? **(3pts)**
   A. Mental Competency Examination
   B. Psychotronic Stability Examination
   C. Neuraltronic Mental Ability Examination
   D. Psychosomatic Agility Examination

5. How does Graves classify humans? **(2pts)**
   A. doers, dreamers, and those who watch the other two
   B. people, women, and lawyers
   C. human beings, doctors, and politicians
   D. women, people, and doctors

ANSWERS

TRIVIA ANSWERS

1. Vulcan
2. the average dog's
3. depths of space
4. Captain's ready room
5. Geordi and an assistant
6. existence of his On/Off switch
7. 46
8. 'If I Only Had A Heart', Wizard of Oz
9. Dr Selar
10. A Rigelian ox

SPECIAL ASSIGNMENT SOLUTION

Lieutenant Commander Remmick – he was infected with a parasitic alien being.

He was featured in the episodes 'Coming Of Age' and 'Conspiracy'.

Congratulations! Starfleet Command is proud to award you the Starfleet Medal of Honour and 15 extra points.

MULTIPLE CHOICE ANSWERS

1. C. iron will and nerves of steel
2. C. unarmed photon torpedo
3. D. Darney's disease
4. B. Psychotronic Stability Examination
5. D. women, people, and doctors

MISSION PERFORMANCE RATING:

45 – 65 points **Superior:** Your great intellect wouldn't fit in Data's brain.

40 – 44 points **Above Average:** Did you really wrestle a Klingon targ?

30 – 39 points **Average:** Maybe you should take the Psycho Stab Exam.

20 – 29 points **Fair:** Your face rang a bell.

0 – 19 points **Poor:** Oops, your brain materialized in a wall during transport.

LOUD AS A WHISPER

STARDATE: 42477.2

The *Enterprise* transports Riva, a Federation negotiator, to Solari V to work out a peace agreement between the warring factions. Riva, who is deaf, uses three interpreters who sense his thoughts and emotions. An away team beams down with Riva and his interpreters to Solari V. Soon emissaries from the two sides arrive at the meeting place. Suddenly, one of them discharges their weapon into the group of interpreters, vaporizing them instantly. The away team quickly beams back to the *Enterprise*.

Riva is lost and isolated without his interpreters. He refuses to go back to the surface to negotiate a settlement. The military situation is worsening on the planet and Troi gets Picard to allow her to go to the surface and begin peace talks. Troi asks Riva for any advice he can give. Eventually she is able to persuade Riva to use his inability to communicate with the inhabitants to his advantage. He returns to the meeting place to teach his sign language to the combatants.

TRIVIA QUESTIONS

1. What functions similarly to Riva's chorus? **(3pts)**
2. What is in the middle of the negotiating table? **(3pts)**
3. After Riva's interpreters are killed, what does the *Enterprise* monitor on the planet? **(4pts)**
4. Riva declines what? **(4pts)**
5. How long have the Solari been at war? **(4pts)**
6. On what topic has Picard arranged a briefing for Riva? **(3pts)**
7. Which transporter room does Picard use to beam down to Ramatis III? **(4pts)**
8. How fast does the *Enterprise* travel to the warring planet? **(4pts)**
9. Riva's translators speak not only his thoughts but what else? **(3pts)**
10. What sound does Riva find quite remarkable? **(3pts)**

✪ SPECIAL ASSIGNMENT (15pts)

What culture (and planet) developed a written language before a gestural one?

MULTIPLE CHOICE QUESTIONS

1. Riker says Riva is very what? **(2pts)**
    A. pompous
    B. arrogant
    C. self-assured
    D. zealous

---

2. What does Riva says is the real secret to negotiating? **(2pts)**
   A. turning disadvantage into advantage
   B. carrying a big stick
   C. being empathetic
   D. being able to bluff

3. Picard tells Riker he's being a what? **(3pts)**
   A. mother hen
   B. old maid
   C. nitpicker
   D. fussbudget

4. What does Riva call Data? **(3pts)**
   A. an interesting piece of machinery
   B. a unique individual
   C. a tragedy in the making
   D. a truly extraordinary android

5. Which Picard speech does Riker steal? **(5pts)**
   A. Our job is to promote peace not war.
   B. The Prime Directive must be held sacrosanct.
   C. We must respect other life forms no matter how strange their customs are.
   D. Our job is not to police the galaxy.

ANSWERS

TRIVIA ANSWERS
1. Geordi's VISOR
2. hole
3. increased military activity
4. security team
5. 1,500 years
6. Solaris wars
7. Transporter Room 5
8. Warp 8
9. emotional intent
10. The Enterprise travelling through space

SPECIAL ASSIGNMENT
Leyrons of Malkus IX
Congratulations! Starfleet Command is proud to award you the Starfleet Medal of Honour and 15 extra points.

MULTIPLE CHOICE ANSWERS
1. C. self-assured
2. A. turning disadvantage into advantage
3. A. mother hen
4. B. a unique individual
5. D. Our job is not to police the galaxy.

MISSION PERFORMANCE RATING:
45 – 65 points **Superior:** You're a talented and skilled negotiator.
40 – 44 points **Above Average:** You know many gestural languages.
30 – 39 points **Average:** You know only one gestural language.
20 – 29 points **Fair:** Your chorus was on vacation.
  0 – 19 points **Poor:** Dr Pulaski wants to try to regenerate your brain tissue.

UNNATURAL SELECTION

STARDATE: 42494.8

The *Enterprise* attempts to come to the aid of the *USS Lantree* but finds the crew all dead. A contagious disease that speeds the ageing process appears responsible for their deaths. The *Enterprise* travels to the *Lantree's* last port of call, the Darwin Genetic Research Station. Upon arrival at the station the *Enterprise* finds everyone there also rapidly ageing. Only the genetically engineered children, who were kept in isolation, are unaffected.

Picard allows Dr Pulaski to beam over one child to sickbay for examination using optimum safety precautions. After examining the boy Dr Pulaski feels he is not infected and wants to remove a protective covering from around the boy. Picard will allow Dr Pulaski to do this inside a shuttle to prevent any possibility of spreading the disease to the *Enterprise's* crew. Soon Dr Pulaski starts to show signs of the disease.

Data, also on board, pilots the shuttle to Darwin Station and works with their scientists to find a cure. He determines that the children and their advanced immune systems are the cause of the disease. The crew is able to reconfigure the transporters using a sample of DNA from Dr Pulaski. The transporter is used to reverse the disease process, curing the doctor.

TRIVIA QUESTIONS

1. The *Enterprise's* original mission was to meet where? **(3pts)**
2. With whom is the *Enterprise* supposed to rendezvous? **(4pts)**
3. Dr Pulaski becomes exasperated whenever Picard does what? **(3pts)**
4. What channel does the *Enterprise* use to contact Dr Pulaski's former captain? **(4pts)**
5. What do Data and Riker find in Dr Pulaski's quarters? **(3pts)**
6. Which shuttlebay is the shuttle launched from? **(4pts)**
7. What does Dr Pulaski keep reminding Data of? **(3pts)**
8. What is the child encased in? **(3pts)**
9. Of what book is Dr Pulaski the author? **(5pts)**
10. What is the first thing the *Enterprise* does upon gaining control of the *Lantree*? **(3pts)**

✪✪ MATHEMATICALLY SPEAKING (25pts)

Add the following numbers together:

1. After arriving at the *Lantree*, sensors show no other vessels within how many parsecs? **(4pts)**

2. At what warp speed does the *Enterprise* travel to intercept the *Lantree*? **(4pts)**
3. How many years old is the child transferred for exam said to be? **(4pts)**
4. How many weeks ago did the *Lantree* crew have medical exams? **(4pts)**
5. What class of ship is the *USS Lantree*? **(4pts)**

Total: _____

What is the significance of this number in relation to the episode? **(5pts)**

ANSWERS

TRIVIA ANSWERS

1. Star Station India
2. Starfleet medical courier
3. quotes Starfleet regulations
4. Subspace Captain's Priority Channel
5. a hair with a follicle
6. Shuttlebay 3
7. that he is a machine
8. #6 Styrolite
9. *Linear Models of Viral Propagation*
10. shut down her engines

MATHEMATICALLY SPEAKING SOLUTION

1. 2
2. 7
3. 12
4. 8
5. 6

Total: 35
Dr Kingsley is 35 years old.

MISSION PERFORMANCE RATING:

30 – 60 points	**Superior:** The children at Darwin Station are your siblings.
25 – 29 points	**Above Average:** You're wise beyond your age.
20 – 24 points	**Average:** Are those wrinkles developing around your eyes?
10 – 19 points	**Fair:** You're aged beyond your wisdom.
0 – 9 points	**Poor:** At this rate you'll stay an ensign!

A MATTER OF HONOR

STARDATE: 42506.5

The *Enterprise* picks up some new crew members at a starbase. A Benzite named Mendon is included in the group as part of an exchange programme while Riker serves on a Klingon vessel temporarily. Mendon notices a strange organism on the Klingon ship's hull and studies it. The Klingon ship soon leaves for patrol, unaware of any problems.

Later, the *Enterprise* detects a similar organism growing on its hull. Mendon explains his discovery of an identical growth on the Klingon vessel. Picard tells him to figure out how to stop it from eating through the hull while the *Enterprise* moves to intercept the Klingon vessel.

Initially, Riker earns the respect of the Klingon crew. Then the Klingon captain discovers the parasite on their hull and suspects a new weapon being tested by the Federation. He prepares to do battle with the unsuspecting *Enterprise*. Riker, acting quickly, arranges to have the Klingon captain removed from command according to Klingon military custom. The *Enterprise* figures out how to remove the organisms from both vessels.

TRIVIA QUESTIONS

1. Which starbase does the *Enterprise* stop at for the crew transfer? **(3pts)**
2. At which bridge station did Mendon work? **(3pts)**
3. According to Data's estimate, what size is the opening in the Klingon ship's hull? **(4pts)**
4. How quickly can the microbes double in size? **(3pts)**
5. What does Picard dislike although he knows they turn up from time to time? **(3pts)**
6. Which battle did the Klingon officer's father die at? **(5pts)**
7. Who is the second officer on the Klingon vessel? **(3pts)**
8. Which Klingon dish did Riker find delicious on the Klingon vessel? **(4pts)**
9. According to the Klingon tactics officer, how long did the *Enterprise* concentrate an intense scanning beam at the damaged area on the hull? **(3pts)**
10. The new crew members picked up at the starbase are to report to whom? **(4pts)**

WHO AM I? (20pts)

I ventured into terra incognita. I assumed only one thing for I am heartier than most. The raptor swallowed me up.

MULTIPLE CHOICE QUESTIONS

1. What is the expectation of any Klingon officer? **(2pts)**
    - A. to be ordered to die at any time
    - B. to die with honour
    - C. to be promoted to Captain
    - D. to lead a comfortable life

2. What easier alternative is suggested by Riker's second officer as a means of obtaining nourishment? **(3pts)**
    - A. Riker could use the replicator to recreate Federation food.
    - B. Riker could eat some surplus Federation rations that the Klingons have on board.
    - C. The ship could stop at a nearby Ferengi trading post and buy some stolen Federation food.
    - D. The second officer could have a female Klingon breast-feed Riker.

3. Picard tells Mendon that the *Enterprise* crew use what? **(2pts)**
    - A. common courtesy
    - B. chain of command
    - C. holodeck
    - D. information exchange as a basis for communication

4. A Klingon captain killed and replaced by his first officer is considered to have had what? **(3pts)**
    - A. an honourable retirement
    - B. an accident
    - C. a bad day
    - D. contretemps

5. What is a Benzite trait? **(5pts)**
    - A. anal retentiveness
    - B. questioning orders
    - C. eagerness to please
    - D. tardiness

ANSWERS

TRIVIA ANSWERS

1. Starbase 179; 2. Science Station 1; 3. 12 cm; 4. every 15 minutes
5. errors; 6. Tranome Sar; 7. Lieutenant Klag; 8. rokeg blood pie
9. two minutes; 10. Lieutenant Lewis

WHO AM I? SOLUTION

Riker

EXPLANATION:

I ventured into terra incognita. – Riker was the first Federation officer to serve aboard a Klingon ship.

I assumed only one thing. – Riker assumed command of the Klingon vessel.

for I am heartier than most. – Riker ate Heart of Targ on the *Enterprise.*

The raptor swallowed me up. – Riker served on board a Klingon bird-of-prey.

MULTIPLE CHOICE ANSWERS

1. A. to be ordered to die at any time
2. D. The second officer could have a female Klingon breast-feed Riker.
3. B. chain of command
4. A. an honourable retirement
5. C. eagerness to please

MISSION PERFORMANCE RATING:

55 – 70 points **Superior:** You'll make a good Klingon!

45 – 54 points **Above Average:** You know when not to duck.

30 – 44 points **Average:** There are no average Klingons.

15 – 29 points **Fair:** You can't even bake a rokeg blood pie.

0 – 14 points **Poor:** The Klingons will dishonourably discharge you.

THE MEASURE ⏃
OF A MAN

STARDATE: 42523.7

The *Enterprise* takes on board Commander Maddox, a Federation scientist who wants to study Data. The problem is that Maddox will have to disassemble Data in order to study him. Picard refuses to allow Maddox to experiment on Data. Maddox produces transfer orders for Data who attempts to resign from Starfleet to avoid the transfer.

Picard becomes embroiled in a legal proceeding with Maddox to determine whether Data is Starfleet property or a sentient being. Riker is forced to act as the prosecutor. Picard talks to Guinan during a court recess and realizes that the real issue at hand is the enslavement of a new race of beings. Picard returns to the courtroom with new zeal, arguing successfully in Data's favour.

TRIVIA QUESTIONS

1. Where does Maddox hold an associate chair of robotics? **(4pts)**
2. What is Commander Maddox's first name? **(3pts)**
3. Who is the initial dealer in the poker game? **(3pts)**
4. What is Data's ultimate storage capacity? **(5pts)**
5. How fast can Data access information? **(4pts)**
6. What is Prosecution Exhibit A? **(3pts)**
7. What is standard procedure when a ship is lost? **(3pts)**
8. What is the first thing we see Data packing? **(4pts)**
9. Picard is surprised that the new starbase is so close to what? **(3pts)**
10. What does JAG stand for? **(3pts)**

✪✪ SPECIAL ASSIGNMENT (15pts)

What is Riker's computer access code?

MULTIPLE CHOICE QUESTIONS

1. Maddox has yet to resolve the problem of electron resistance across what? **(4pts)**
   A. neural filaments
   B. neural networks
   C. primary neural field links
   D. trilateral secondary anterior nephron filaments

---

2. What are the three qualities necessary for sentience? **(2pts)**
   A. intelligence, unconsciousness, self-determination
   B. ability to: sit on a couch, push remote control buttons, raise beer can to mouth
   C. independence, intelligence, ambition
   D. intelligence, self-awareness, consciousness

3. Which dictionary does Data quote the definition of android from? **(3pts)**
   A. *Webster's 23rd Century Dictionary, 3th Edition*
   B. *Webster's 24th Century Dictionary, 5th Edition*
   C. *Random House 24th Century Dictionary, 2nd Edition*
   D. *tlhIngan mu'ghom, Federation Revised Special Edition*

4. What book (name and author) did Worf give Data as a going away present? **(4pts)**
   A. *I Dream Of The Fire* by Kahless
   B. *Poisoned By The Fire* by K'mpec
   C. *The Dream Of The Fire* by K'Ratak
   D. *I Scream By The Fire* by K'Ehleyr

5. Maddox opposed Data's entry into the Academy because he said Data wasn't _____. **(2pts)**
   A. a sentient being
   B. emotionally well adjusted
   C. tall enough
   D. a Federation citizen

ANSWERS

TRIVIA ANSWERS

1. Daystrom Technological Institute
2. Bruce
3. Riker
4. 800 quadrillion bits
5. Data's total computational speed is 60 trillion operations per second
6. rod of plasteel
7. court martial
8. holographic statue of Lieutenant Yar
9. the Neutral Zone
10. Judge Advocate General

SPECIAL ASSIGNMENT SOLUTION

theta, alpha, 2 737, blue, enable

Congratulations! Starfleet Command is proud to award you the Starfleet Medal of Honour and 15 extra points.

MULTIPLE CHOICE ANSWERS

1. A. neural filaments
2. D. intelligence, self-awareness, consciousness
3. B. Webster's 24th Century Dictionary, 5th Edition
4. C. The Dream Of The Fire by K'Ratak
5. A. a sentient being

MISSION PERFORMANCE RATING:

45 – 65 points **Superior:** Maddox can use your help on resolving the resist . . .

40 – 44 points **Above Average:** What's your ultimate storage capacity?

30 – 39 points **Average:** You have the three qualities necessary for sentience!

20 – 29 points **Fair:** You have one quality of sentience, but it's not intelligence.

0 – 14 points **Poor:** Wesley will make lieutenant before you do!

THE DAUPHIN

STARDATE: 42568.8

The *Enterprise* transports Salia and her guardian, Anya, to the planet Daled IV. Salia is to be the new leader of Daled IV, a planet racked by war. Soon after arriving Salia meets Wesley and he becomes infatuated with her.

Later, Salia slips past Anya and goes to Wesley's quarters. While the two kiss, Anya appears and transforms herself into an alien creature. Salia also changes into a threatening beast and challenges Anya. Wesley is crushed, the love of his life is not what she appeared to be.

As the *Enterprise* arrives at Daled IV, Salia tries to say good-bye to Wesley but he isn't having any of it. Disappointed she goes to the transporter room. Just before Salia is transported to the planet Wesley turns up and gives her a proper good-bye.

TRIVIA QUESTIONS

1. Rousseau V is what? **(3pts)**
2. Where is Anya's home? **(4pts)**
3. How fast does the *Enterprise* travel to Daled IV after warp drive is restored? **(5pts)**
4. What does Worf call Anya? **(3pts)**
5. Where does Thalian Chocolate Mousse originate? **(3pts)**
6. What is the name of the patient in sickbay? **(4pts)**
7. In what catalogue is a shape-shifting race listed? **(4pts)**
8. How long are the cocoa beans aged for Thalian Chocolate Mousse? **(3pts)**
9. What does Worf demonstrate to Wesley? **(3pts)**
10. What do female Klingons do to intended mates? **(3pts)**

WHO AM I? (25pts)

One understood my meaning, though I am part of a larger family. Those who misuse me, pale before me. I was picked up by the lowest rung and brought before he who had requested me.

ANSWERS

TRIVIA ANSWERS

1. asteroid belt
2. 3rd moon from Daled IV
3. Warp 8.8
4. a worthy opponent
5. Thalos VII
6. Henessey
7. *Galactic Zoological Catalogue*
8. 400 years
9. a female Klingon's mating scream
10. hurl heavy objects at them

WHO AM I? SOLUTION

SCM Model 3 (superconducting magnet)

EXPLANATION:

One understood my meaning. — Salia correctly identified the SCM Model 3 that Wesley carried.

though I am part of a larger family. — There are many makes and models of superconducting magnets.

Those who misuse me pale before me. — Salia joked that the magnet could rip iron out of blood cells.

I was picked up by the lowest rung — Wesley picks up the magnet. He is an ensign, the lowest rung.

and brought before him who had requested me. — Geordi needed the magnet for repairs.

MISSION PERFORMANCE RATING:

36 – 60 points	**Superior:** You unite the factions and bring peace in your home.
30 – 35 points	**Above Average:** You know a magnet when you see one.
20 – 29 points	**Average:** What species are you?
10 – 19 points	**Fair:** You can't seem to hold your shape, you must be part Allaso.
0 – 9 points	**Poor:** You've just been assigned to watch the cocoa beans age.

CONTAGION

STARDATE: 42609.1

The *Enterprise* comes to the aid of the *USS Yamato* in the Neutral Zone but the ship explodes before Picard can render assistance. Picard continues the *Yamato*'s investigation into the location of the mythical Iconian home world. The *Yamato* feared the Romulans would obtain the advanced Iconian technology and gain an edge over the Federation.

While in orbit around Iconia, a probe is launched from the planet. The *Enterprise* crew destroys the probe, but soon discover that they have been infected with a computer virus from the *Yamato*. The Iconian virus is rewriting the *Enterprise*'s programming, causing plenty of trouble.

On the planet, the away team discovers a control station where the probes are launched from. Picard decides the technology is too hot to fall into Romulan hands and sets the station to overload, barely escaping in time. Meanwhile, Geordi figures out how to rid the *Enterprise* of the virus and restore things to normal.

TRIVIA QUESTIONS

1. The *Yamato* is the *Enterprise*'s what? **(2pts)**
2. What is the launch code sequence for the Iconian probes? **(4pts)**
3. What is activated on the Romulan ship? **(3pts)**
4. Name two ancient languages that begin with the letter 'D' derived from the parent tongue of Iconian. **(4pts each)**
5. How long ago was Iconia destroyed? **(4pts)**
6. What does Picard order from the food replicator? **(3pts)**
7. What type of problem is suspected initially after the *Yamato* explodes? **(2pts)**
8. What analogy does Varley use in describing the complexity of the Iconian artifact? **(3pts)**
9. What are decaying on the *Yamato*? **(3pts)**
10. What did Riker say that puzzled Data? **(3pts)**

✪✪ SPECIAL ASSIGNMENT (15pts)

How many emergency calls has Dr Pulaski had and where?

MULTIPLE CHOICE QUESTIONS

1. How can Geordi reload the *Enterprise*'s computer programmes? **(4pts)**
   - **A.** by using the shuttlecraft's computer
   - **B.** by accessing the secondary archives on Deck 10
   - **C.** by using the 12,397 backup floppy disks
   - **D.** by using the protected archives in the main core

2. Which conversation has Riker had a hundred times before? **(2pts)**
   - **A.** Will you go to dinner with me?
   - **B.** Captain you shouldn't lead the away team!
   - **C.** Deanna, get out of my head!
   - **D.** Why can't you get the shields working Ensign Crusher?

3. What doesn't Dr Pulaski trust? **(2pts)**
   - **A.** turbolifts
   - **B.** the Romulans
   - **C.** bioscanners
   - **D.** her abilities

4. Where is the planet Iconia? **(4pts)**
   - **A.** close to the Romulan side of the Neutral Zone
   - **B.** near the Rubicun system
   - **C.** Alpha Quadrant
   - **D.** close to the Federation side of the Neutral Zone

5. What does Varley call the Iconian artifact? **(3pts)**
   - **A.** galactic Rosetta stone
   - **B.** tricorder
   - **C.** portable Stonehenge
   - **D.** key to the Iconian legends

ANSWERS

TRIVIA ANSWERS

1. sister ship
2. blue – amber – amber – red
3. self-destruct sequence
4. Dinasian, Dewan
5. 200,000 years
6. tea, Earl Grey, hot
7. design flaw
8. it's like a caveman confronted by a tricorder
9. magnetic seals on the antimatter containment field
10. 'Have you nailed down our little hiccup yet?'

SPECIAL ASSIGNMENT SOLUTION

35 emergency calls scattered across 12 decks

Congratulations! Starfleet Command is proud to award you the Starfleet Medal of Honour and 15 extra points.

MULTIPLE CHOICE ANSWERS

1. D. by using the protected archives in the main core
2. B. Captain you shouldn't lead the away team!
3. A. turbolifts
4. A. close to the Romulan side of the Neutral Zone
5. A. galactic Rosetta stone

MISSION PERFORMANCE RATING:

45 – 65 points **Superior:** So you're the Iconian travel agent I heard about.

40 – 44 points **Above Average:** Now you know you're not colour blind.

30 – 39 points **Average:** Was that blue – amber – blue, or blue – blue – blue?

20 – 29 points **Fair:** Check out life support on Deck 13. Is the air breathable?

0 – 19 points **Poor:** You've been transferred to the *Yamato* – find a piece of it!

The *Enterprise* checks out reports of spacecraft debris orbiting Theta VIII and a chunk of debris is beamed aboard. The crew determines the vessel is from 21st century Earth. A structure resembling a 20th century Earth casino-hotel is discovered on the surface of the planet surrounded by a pocket of breathable air. An away team beams down and discovers that they cannot leave the structure once inside.

Exploring inside the hotel, the away team comes across the remains of Colonel Richey who was aboard the centuries-old spacecraft from Earth when it encountered aliens. All of the crew were accidentally killed except Richey. The aliens, trying to make amends, created this casino-hotel based on a novel found aboard the spacecraft. The away team determines that events are occurring as they did in the novel. To escape, the away team must buy the casino-hotel. Data uses his unique talents at gambling to raise the money. The away team purchases the casino-hotel and is then able to leave.

TRIVIA QUESTIONS

1. What phrase does Data use at the crap table? **(3pts)**
2. On what page does Mickey D. kill the bellboy and walk out? **(5pts)**
3. What are the first seven words of the novel, *Hotel Royale*? **(3pts)**
4. What type of car did the Texan drive and how many miles were on it? **(4pts)**
5. What is the sale price of the Hotel Royale? **(4pts)**
6. The Texan asks Data if he knows what the odds are on what? **(4pts)**
7. What does Worf say is a terrible way to die? **(3pts)**
8. What do the away team members receive when they check into the hotel? **(3pts)**
9. Who was the assistant manager expecting at the hotel? **(3pts)**
10. What is written on the recovered piece of wreckage? **(3pts)**

✪✪ MATHEMATICALLY SPEAKING (25pts)

Answer A to D and then insert the numbers into the formula to solve this problem.

A. What is the surface temperature of Theta VIII in degrees Celsius? **(4pts)**
B. How fast are the surface winds on Theta VIII in metres per second? **(4pts)**
C. Number of seconds away team will live if *Enterprise* slices through envelope around hotel. **(4pts)**

D. Data detects human DNA how far above and to the right of the away team? (round answer down to nearest metre) **(4pts)**

A + B x C + D = E

What is the significance of your answer (E) in relation to the episode? **(9pts)**

ANSWERS

TRIVIA ANSWERS

1. Baby needs a new pair of shoes.
2. page 244
3. 'It was a dark and stormy night'
4. 1991 Cadillac with only 80,000 miles on it
5. $12.5 million
6. a five card Charlie (5 cards adding up to 21)
7. in your sleep
8. room keys and complimentary casino chips
9. a trio of foreign gentlemen
10. NASA

MATHEMATICALLY SPEAKING SOLUTION

A.–291
B. 312
C. 12
D. 31
–291 + 312 x 12 + 31 = 283
Colonel Richey has been dead for 283 years.

MISSION PERFORMANCE RATING:
30 – 60 points **Superior:** You could have written a better episode.
25 – 29 points **Above Average:** NASA engineer (how did that ship get there?).
20 – 24 points **Average:** Been to Vegas, huh.
10 – 19 points **Fair:** You must write pulp fiction.
 0 – 9 points **Poor:** Go clean up the Colonel's suite!

TIMES SQUARED ⚓

The *Enterprise* comes across a shuttlecraft drifting in space. The unconscious occupant of the shuttle appears to be identical to Picard. Geordi downloads the shuttle's logs and determines it is from the near future. According to the logs, the *Enterprise* is destroyed by a vortex of some type and only Picard is saved.

Several hours later the *Enterprise* encounters the vortex seen in the shuttle logs and is unable to pull away. Picard goes to sickbay where Picard 2 is conscious and somewhat aware of where he is. Picard takes Picard 2 to the shuttlebay. Picard tries to determine what other options he has but Picard 2 is intent only on leaving the ship. Picard 2 is locked into a decision loop and can't do anything different. Picard figures out he must fly through the vortex. He dispatches Picard 2 to prevent the *Enterprise* from being destroyed again. The *Enterprise* flies through the vortex and pops out into normal space.

TRIVIA QUESTIONS
1. How many phasers were in the wall cabinet in Shuttlebay 2? **(3pts)**
2. How long before the *Enterprise* is destroyed, based on the shuttle log and the time of the staff meeting? **(3pts)**
3. What does the shuttlebay crew engage to finish the retrieval process? **(3pts)**
4. What percentage are the warp engines running at when Geordi engages Warp 9 to try to leave the vortex? **(4pts)**
5. Who is seen standing in the shuttlebay as the shuttle log is played back? **(3pts)**
6. What inverter setting is the correct one for the shuttlecraft? **(4pts)**
7. When is the *Enterprise* due to arrive in the Endicor system? **(3pts)**
8. What is the name and number on the recovered shuttlecraft? **(5pts)**
9. Where did Riker get the eggs? **(4pts)**
10. How soon is it before the *Enterprise* intercepts the shuttlecraft? **(3pts)**

MULTIPLE CHOICE QUESTIONS
1. What did Dr Pulaski bring to the meal? **(3pts)**
   - A. tranquillizers
   - B. ale from Ennan VI
   - C. eggs from Starbase 12
   - D. Teflon coated cooking skillet

2. What does Troi sense from the energy vortex? **(3pts)**
   - A. an instinctual consciousness
   - B. a highly intelligent malevolent being
   - C. a curious energy entity
   - D. a vast unreadable void of incredible energy

---

3. Which two methods would theoretically allow time travel? (2pts each)
    A. accelerating past Warp 10
    B. engaging a multiphasic warp attenuator at maximum speed
    C. touch-and-go downwarping near a supernova
    D. using the gravitational pull of a star to create a slingshot effect

4. What does the shuttlecraft's on-board clock indicate? **(3pts)**
    A. it has not been reset for daylight saving time
    B. the shuttlecraft is 6 hours ahead of *Enterprise* time
    C. the shuttlecraft was drained of power 5 hours and 27 minutes before it was discovered
    D. the shuttlecraft is 6 hours behind *Enterprise* time

5. When did Riker's mother die? **(2pts)**
    A. straight after he graduated from the Academy
    B. just before he entered the Academy
    C. when he was very young
    D. before he was born

ANSWERS

TRIVIA ANSWERS
1. four
2. 3 hours, 19 minutes
3. secondary tractor beam
4. 91%
5. Riker
6. 2% negative
7. 3 days
8. El-Baz, 05
9. Starbase 73
10. 3 minutes

MULTIPLE CHOICE ANSWERS
1. B. ale from Ennan VI
2. A. an instinctual consciousness
3. A. accelerating past Warp 10; D. using the gravitational pull of a star to create a slingshot effect
4. B. shuttlecraft is 6 hours ahead of *Enterprise* time
5. C. when he was very young

MISSION PERFORMANCE RATING:
45 – 50 points **Superior:** You know your options without having to ask anyone.
40 – 44 points **Above Average:** You probably make a heck of an omelette.
30 – 39 points **Average:** Flown through any good vortices lately?
20 – 29 points **Fair:** Hopefully there's only one of you floating around.
0 – 19 points **Poor:** Picard 2 needs a shuttle pilot, no experience necessary.

THE ICARUS FACTOR

STARDATE: 42686.4

The *Enterprise* stops at a starbase where Riker is offered his own command. The briefing officer turns out to be his father, Kyle Riker, whom Will has not seen in quite some time. Their relationship is very troubled but Kyle had come seeking reconciliation with his son. They finally work things out after a martial arts bout between the two of them.

Meanwhile, Worf reaches an important anniversary in his life with no Klingons to share in the celebration. Wesley sets up a holographic celebration for Worf, and his fellow crew members share in the ritual along with a bunch of holographic Klingons. Will Riker finally decides against taking the promotion and stays aboard the *Enterprise*.

TRIVIA QUESTIONS

1. How long a layover will the *Enterprise* have at the starbase? **(3pts)**
2. How long have Kyle and Will Riker played Anbo-jytsu? **(3pts)**
3. What was Kyle Riker at a starbase attacked by hostile aliens? **(3pts)**
4. For how long does Kyle Riker say he hung in there? **(5pts)**
5. What is Worf's problem? **(3pts)**
6. What is the Klingon Age of Ascension? **(3pts)**
7. For how long has Will Riker been on his own? **(4pts)**
8. What is the uncanny linguistic skill that the *Aries'* first officer possesses? **(4pts)**
9. How old is Will Riker in the pictures he's viewing in his quarters? **(3pts)**
10. What kind of predisposition do Klingons have? **(4pts)**

SPECIAL ASSIGNMENT (10pts)

Name the crew member Kyle Riker called by name in Ten-Forward.

MULTIPLE CHOICE QUESTIONS

1. O'Brien once saw a Klingon painstik used on what animal? **(5pts)**
   - **A.** Bulgallian rat
   - **B.** 2 ton Rectyne monopod
   - **C.** Denebian slime devil
   - **D.** Tarcassian razor beast

2. What is considered a Klingon spiritual test? **(2pts)**
   - **A.** enduring physical suffering
   - **B.** fasting for 21 days
   - **C.** being placed in a locked room with Wesley for 24 hours
   - **D.** defeating one's enemies in battle

---

3. Where did Wesley find the solution to Worf's problem? **(2pts)**
   A. *Ripley's Believe It or Not, Klingon Edition*
   B. Klingon/Romulan Crosscultural Index
   C. Complete Klingon Cultural Database
   D. *Barlowe's Guide to Extraterrestrials*

4. What does Worf want to do if Riker takes the promotion? **(3pts)**
   A. apply for the first officer's position on the *Enterprise*
   B. resign from Starfleet
   C. assist Picard in reviewing new applicants for Riker's former position
   D. transfer to the *Aries* with Riker

5. What does PCS stand for? **(3pts)**
   A. Potassium Coronary Solution
   B. Pulaski's Chicken Soup
   C. Plasma Cordrazine Serum
   D. Polymer Caustic Syrup

ANSWERS

TRIVIA ANSWERS

1. 12 hours
2. since Will Riker was eight years old
3. sole survivor
4. 13 years
5. it's the 10th Anniversary of Worf's Age of Ascension
6. a rite of initiation into a new level of Klingon spirituality
7. since he was 15 years old
8. can speak 40 languages
9. nine years old
10. a genetic predisposition toward hostility

SPECIAL ASSIGNMENT SOLUTION

Graham.

Congratulations! Starfleet Command is proud to award you the Starfleet Medal of Honour and 10 extra points.

MULTIPLE CHOICE ANSWERS

1. B. 2 ton Rectyne monopod
2. A. enduring physical suffering
3. C. Complete Klingon Cultural Database
4. D. transfer to the Aries with Riker
5. B. Pulaski's Chicken Soup

MISSION PERFORMANCE RATING:

45 – 60 points **Superior:** We bow to you, oh Anbo-jytsu Grand Master!

40 – 44 points **Above Average:** You must be a Starfleet strategist.

30 – 39 points **Average:** What's the matter? Do you need some PCS?

20 – 29 points **Fair:** You must have jettisoned the intellectual baggage you had.

0 – 19 points **Poor:** I've got a Klingon painstik with your name on it.

The *Enterprise* investigates unusual geothermal activity throughout a whole sector. Data, while enhancing the sensors, picks up an alien transmission from one of the nearby planets. Data ends up communicating with a little girl on one of the endangered planets.

Data goes to Picard for help when her family becomes threatened by the violent phenomenon. Although Data has broken the Prime Directive, Picard ultimately decides to help the girl's civilization survive.

A research team headed by Wesley figures out a solution to the geological problems and modifies some probes to help quiet the seismic activity. Data ends up having to beam the little girl up to the safety of the *Enterprise*. Dr Pulaski erases the girl's memory thus setting things right once again. Wesley's plan works and the planet is saved.

TRIVIA QUESTIONS

1. What is Picard doing on the holodeck when Data talks to him? **(3pts)**
2. What is not a matter of degrees but is absolute? **(3pts)**
3. What does Dr Pulaski have on her desk? **(4pts)**
4. How will the modified probes work? **(5pts)**
5. What does Picard order from the replicator? **(3pts)**
6. What English saying does Picard use while talking to Data? **(4pts)**
7. Where does Data find Picard? **(3pts)**
8. When does Data say he received his first message? **(4pts)**
9. What does Ensign Davies like to do? **(3pts)**
10. Picard respects an officer who does what? **(3pts)**

MULTIPLE CHOICE QUESTIONS

1. What is Wesley placed in charge of? **(2pts)**
    A. latrines
    B. planetary mineral survey
    C. all science away team missions
    D. Selcundi Drema census survey

2. What happened to one of the planets in the Sekundi Drema system? **(5pts)**
    A. volcanic activity melted ice caps, submerging most land masses on the planet
    B. it disintegrated and turned into an asteroid belt
    C. all life died on the planet and it became a desert world
    D. volcanic activity created a nuclear winter effect killing off most life forms

3. Drema IV has the largest _____ ever recorded. **(3pts)**
   A. deposits of dilithium ore
   B. oceans
   C. deposits of tritanium ore
   D. wind storms

4. What does Riker say is the difference between sending the message and delivering it personally? **(2pts)**
   A. not a whole lot
   B. like comparing apples and oranges
   C. a whopping big one
   D. substantial

5. What is Data's personal project? **(3pts)**
   A. to find Wesley a girlfriend
   B. to reset the sensors to scan for frequencies outside their usual range
   C. to reprogramme the food replicators to include more Klingon food
   D. to adjust the holodeck's omnidirectional holo diode clusters

ANSWERS

TRIVIA ANSWERS

1. riding a horse
2. Prime Directive
3. Elanian singer stone
4. they'll emit harmonic vibrations that will shatter the crystal structure
5. tea, Earl Grey, hot
6. 'In for a penny, in for a pound.'
7. Holodeck 3
8. eight weeks ago
9. break up married teams when assigning them for special duties
10. is prepared to admit ignorance and ask a question

MULTIPLE CHOICE ANSWERS

1. B. planetary mineral survey
2. B. it disintegrated and turned into an asteroid belt
3. A. deposits of dilithium ore
4. C. a whopping big one
5. B. to reset the sensors to scan for frequencies outside their usual range

MISSION PERFORMANCE RATING:

45 – 50 points **Superior:** You knew the problem on the planet without looking.
40 – 44 points **Above Average:** Ham radio operator, not bad.
30 – 39 points **Average:** Can't you set up a simple ico-spectogram?
20 – 29 points **Fair:** You've been reassigned as a dilithium miner.
0 – 19 points **Poor:** At this rate you'll never even report to Wesley Crusher.

The *Enterprise* encounters Q once again. Q wants to join the *Enterprise* crew but Picard says no. Q then decides to transport the *Enterprise* into uncharted territory. A strange cube-shaped vessel soon approaches the *Enterprise*. It is from a race known as the Borg, a humanoid race blended with an artificial intelligence and enhanced with biomechanical implants.

The Borg survey the *Enterprise*'s capabilities, then decide to attack. In the ensuing battle both ships are damaged. An away team that beams over to the Borg ship to investigate further sees evidence that the Borg are repairing their vessel. The *Enterprise* tries to outrun the Borg but is pursued relentlessly. The *Enterprise* is about to be destroyed when Picard pleads to Q for help. Q is happy to oblige the shaken Picard and whisks the ship away from the clutches of the Borg.

TRIVIA QUESTIONS

1. What are the Borg born as? **(3pts)**
2. Guinan says the Borg have been developing for how long? **(3pts)**
3. How many crew members are MIA after the first Borg attack? **(4pts)**
4. What percentage of the Borg ship is damaged after the first attack? **(3pts)**
5. What happens after the *Enterprise* loses its shields during the first Borg attack? **(3pts)**
6. How does Riker describe the first Borg attack? **(3pts)**
7. What is Q's name for the Borg? **(4pts)**
8. The damage done to the class-M planet in Borg Land is identical to what? **(3pts)**
9. How far has Q propelled the *Enterprise* through space? **(5pts)**
10. Where did the *Enterprise* finally stop after Q sent the ship through space? **(4pts)**

MULTIPLE CHOICE QUESTIONS

1. What does Ensign Gomez do the first time she meets Captain Picard? **(2pts)**
   - **A.** kisses him
   - **B.** shakes his hand
   - **C.** spills her hot chocolate on him
   - **D.** mispronounces his name

2. What are food replicators listed as? **(3pts)**
   - **A.** intelligent circuitry
   - **B.** molecular matrix circuitry
   - **C.** artificial intelligence circuitry
   - **D.** recyclable nutrient flow circuitry

3. While in pursuit of the *Enterprise*, the Borg ship fires a weapon designed to do what? **(3pts)**
   A. disable the warp engines
   B. destroy the *Enterprise*
   C. slice through the hull
   D. drain the shields

4. What are indications of a highly industrialized civilization on the class-M planet? **(2pts)**
   A. radioactive wastelands
   B. ozone depleted atmosphere
   C. series of roads
   D. huge smog producing megacities

5. At what planet can Starfleet engineers perform phase work on antimatter? **(5pts)**
   A. Ramatis III
   B. Raynus VI
   C. Risa
   D. Ruah IV

ANSWERS

TRIVIA ANSWERS

1. biological life forms
2. thousands of centuries
3. 18 crew missing
4. 20%
5. a type of laser weapon slices through the hull in the saucer section
6. 'They're carving us up like a roast.'
7. enhanced humanoids
8. damage done to the Federation outposts near the Neutral Zone
9. 7,000 light years
10. System J-25

MULTIPLE CHOICE ANSWERS

1. C. spills her hot chocolate on him
2. A. intelligent circuitry
3. D. drain the shields
4. C. series of roads
5. B. Raynus VI

MISSION PERFORMANCE RATING:

45 – 50 points **Superior:** You're Starfleet's top Borg Hunter/Killer.
40 – 44 points **Above Average:** Stay cool and you might survive a Borg attack.
30 – 39 points **Average:** You'll make an average Borg.
20 – 29 points **Fair:** Fresh meat for the Borgs.
 0 – 19 points **Poor:** Even the Borg won't have anything to do with you.

SAMARITAN SNARE ⟨A⟩

Picard and Wesley leave the *Enterprise* to travel to a nearby starbase via shuttlecraft when the *Enterprise* receives a distress call. Geordi beams over to a seemingly crippled Pakled ship. He fixes several problems on their craft but is prevented from leaving. They hold Geordi hostage, demanding access to the *Enterprise*'s computer records.

Meanwhile, the shuttlecraft makes it to the starbase where Picard is to undergo surgery to correct a problem with his artificial heart. Complications arise during surgery and Dr Pulaski is sent for.

The Pakleds force Geordi to make their weapons more powerful but not before Riker cryptically tells Geordi what to do. Geordi tricks the Pakleds into thinking the *Enterprise* has disabled their new weapons. The Pakleds now respect the *Enterprise*'s power and release Geordi. The *Enterprise* warps to Picard's rescue with Dr Pulaski successfully completing the surgery.

TRIVIA QUESTIONS

1. Where was Picard ranked in his Starfleet Academy class? **(3pts)**
2. How long will Picard be in the recovery room after the surgery? **(3pts)**
3. Who was the author of the book Picard gave to Wesley? **(3pts)**
4. When the young Picard was impaled he was shocked by what? **(3pts)**
5. What starbase did the young Picard go to during his leave? **(5pts)**
6. What had not yet occurred when the young Picard had his altercation? **(4pts)**
7. What does Picard offer Wesley on the shuttle trip? **(3pts)**
8. What is the name of the Pakled in charge of Engineering? **(4pts)**
9. The *Enterprise* will be performing an astronomical survey of what? **(3pts)**
10. Where does Wesley have to go to take his exams? **(4pts)**

SPECIAL ASSIGNMENT (10pts)

What is the mortality rate on the cardiac replacement procedure Picard is to undergo?

MULTIPLE CHOICE QUESTIONS

1. Picard says there's no greater challenge than what? **(3pts)**
   A. marriage
   B. the study of philosophy
   C. eating Klingon food
   D. trying to outwit the Pakleds

2. The young Picard was on leave at which facility? **(5pts)**
   A. Hotel Royale
   B. Earth Station McKinley
   C. Bonestell Recreation Facility
   D. Café des Artistes

3. What type of heart does Picard have? **(3pts)**
   A. parthenogenic implant
   B. human
   C. Borg implant
   D. cardiopulmonary implant

4. Geordi asks jokingly if what broke on the Pakled ship? **(2pts)**
   A. life support systems
   B. rubber band
   C. treadmill
   D. guidance system

5. What topics did Ensign Gomez suggest to Wesley to talk to Picard about on the shuttle flight? **(2pts)**
   A. marriage, fatherhood, why Picard doesn't like kids
   B. discipline, Picard Manoeuvre, Ferengi battle strategies
   C. archaeology, semantics, literature, art
   D. literature, art, Klingon culture

ANSWERS

TRIVIA ANSWERS

1. top of his class
2. Epsilon IX
3. William James
4. the sight of serrated metal sticking through his chest
5. Starbase Earhart
6. the Klingons had not yet joined the Federation
7. coffee and sandwiches
8. Reginold
9. new pulsar cluster
10. Starbase 515

SPECIAL ASSIGNMENT SOLUTION

2.4% mortality rate

Congratulations! Starfleet Command is proud to award you the Starfleet Medal of Honour and 10 extra points.

MULTIPLE CHOICE ANSWERS

1. B. the study of philosophy
2. C. Bonestell Recreation Facility
3. A. parthenogenic implant
4. B. rubber band
5. C. archaeology, semantics, literature, art

MISSION PERFORMANCE RATING:

45 – 60 points **Superior:** You know all about thoracic polygramatics, doctor!

40 – 44 points **Above Average:** You are smart, you make us strong.

30 – 39 points **Average:** You are average, you make us less than we are.

20 – 29 points **Fair:** If you were sent to the Pakleds, they wouldn't keep you!

0 – 19 points **Poor:** Duh, you must be a Pakled.

UP THE LONG LADDER

STARDATE: 42823.2

The *Enterprise* investigates a strange distress call from what seems to be an unknown human colony. The group, known as the Bringloidi, turns out to be a bunch of Irish rural types whose progenitors seemed to have come from 19th century Earth rather than the 22nd century. Intense solar flares are threatening the colony so Picard decides to evacuate the colonists who insist on bringing their farm animals. While Picard tries to sort things out he learns of the existence of a second colony.

The *Enterprise* tracks down the second, more sophisticated, colony in a nearby system. This group turns out to be a colony of clones, the result of most of the original colonists dying in a crash landing long ago. Since subtle genetic errors have accrued over the years, the survival of the clones is threatened. The colonists attempt to steal some tissue samples to expand their cloning stock, but are thwarted by an away team. Picard comes up with a solution. The Bringloidi need a new home and the second colony needs to expand their gene pool. The two colonies are reunited after several hundred years of separation.

TRIVIA QUESTIONS

1. According to Data, what is there no evidence of at the first colony? **(3pts)**
2. What must a human not do during the Klingon Tea Ceremony? **(3pts)**
3. Who was the last to use a similar distress beacon? **(4pts)**
4. What drink does Worf replicate for Danilo? **(4pts)**
5. How many men and women survived when the colony ship crashed on Mariposa? **(3pts)**
6. What problem is afflicting the Mariposa colony? **(3pts)**
7. The Bringloidi are transported to which part of the *Enterprise*? **(4pts)**
8. What was the Earth recovering from in the early part of the 22nd century? **(3pts)**
9. For what reason does Dr Pulaski lies to Picard about Worf's condition? **(3pts)**
10. What disease does Worf have? **(5pts)**

✪✪ MATHEMATICALLY SPEAKING (30pts)

Answer A to E and then insert the numbers into the formula to solve this problem.

A. How many cellular comlinks were on the colony ship? **(3pts)**

B. How many monitor beacon satellites were on the colony ship? **(3pts)**

C. What is the estimated number of hours before solar flares will hit the Bringloidi's planet? **(3pts)**

D. How many metres below the planet's surface are human life signs detected? **(3pts)**

E. The total number of spinning-wheels on board the colony ship. **(3pts)**

$(A \div B) + (C \times D) - E = F$

What is the significance of your answer (F) in relation to the episode? **(15pts)**

ANSWERS

TRIVIA ANSWERS

1. an advanced communication network
2. drink the tea – it is a deadly poison
3. European Hegemony
4. chech' tluth
5. two women and three men
6. replicative fading
7. Cargo Hold 7
8. World War III
9. to protect his honour
10. rop'ngor – a childhood ailment similar to the measles

MATHEMATICALLY SPEAKING SOLUTION

A. 700
B. 5
C. 3.6
D. 30
E. 25

$(700 \div 5) + (3.6 \times 30) - 25 = 223$

There were 223 people in the Bringloidi colony.

MISSION PERFORMANCE RATING:

30 – 65 points **Superior:** A genetic engineer? You look awfully familiar.

25 – 29 points **Above Average:** You can drink Klingon tea without ill effects.

20 – 24 points **Average:** Typical clone.

10 – 19 points **Fair:** You've had a wee bit too much Bringloidi sauce!

0 – 9 points **Poor:** You're experiencing replicative fading.

MANHUNT

STARDATE: 42859.2

The *Enterprise* picks up several delegates to transport them to a conference. Lwaxana Troi comes aboard under the guise of a Federation representative at the conference, but her true purpose soon becomes apparent. Lwaxana is going through 'the phase'; a condition where a Betazoid woman becomes fully sexual. Seeking a husband, the widowed Lwaxana has set her sights on Picard. Picard avoids offending her due to his lack of interest, by hiding in a holodeck simulation of a Dixon Hill mystery.

Lwaxana tracks down the captain and informs Picard that the two delegates on board are planning to disrupt the conference. He promptly detains the delegates and avoids a potentially embarrassing situation.

TRIVIA QUESTIONS

1. After dumping Picard and Riker as potential marriage partners, who does Lwaxana latch on to? **(2pts)**
2. For what city and year does Picard configure the holodeck? **(3pts)**
3. What is the purpose of the conference? **(2pts)**
4. Which article in the newspaper does Rex mention? **(3pts)**
5. What is 'the usual' for Hill? **(4pts)**
6. What does Madeline order to drink? **(4pts)**
7. Who is Rex afraid is coming after him since Rex and Hill's testimony sent him to jail? **(4pts)**
8. Who was the first gentleman to visit Hill in his office? **(5pts)**
9. When was the last time Hill had a new case according to Madeline? **(3pts)**
10. What is Dixon Hill's office number? **(5pts)**

✪ DOUBLE SPECIAL ASSIGNMENT (15pts each)

Assignment I
Madeline's mother's cousin is from what city?

Assignment II
Which president does Dixon Hill have a picture of on his office wall?

MULTIPLE CHOICE QUESTIONS

1. What are the names of the two planetoids in close proximity that exchange orbits? **(3pts)**
    - **A.** asteroids
    - **B.** bi-orbital satellites
    - **C.** lucky
    - **D.** co-orbital satellites

2. What were the Antidean delegates planning on doing at the conference? **(2pts)**
    - **A.** partying
    - **B.** blowing up the entire conference
    - **C.** joining the Federation
    - **D.** asking the Federation for technical aid and supplies

3. What was World War II a catalyst for? **(2pts)**
    - **A.** technological advancement
    - **B.** World War III
    - **C.** ecological collapse
    - **D.** world peace

4. What is supposedly the stuff of legend on the *Enterprise*? **(3pts)**
    - **A.** Wesley's incompetence
    - **B.** Riker's sexual conquests
    - **C.** Worf's poker playing abilities
    - **D.** Data's after-dinner anecdotes

5. As Picard first enters Dixon Hill's office, what is the man in the hallway standing near? **(5pts)**
    - **A.** a pay telephone
    - **B.** a desk
    - **C.** another person
    - **D.** a coat rack

ANSWERS

TRIVIA ANSWERS

1. Rex, the bartender
2. San Francisco, 1941
3. The Antideans will be given the opportunity to join the Federation.
4. that Germany is getting ready to invade England
5. scotch, neat
6. rye and ginger
7. Jimmy Cuzzo
8. Slade Bender
9. when Hitler and Stalin were bosom buddies
10. 312

DOUBLE SPECIAL ASSIGNMENT SOLUTION

Assignment I San Antonio

Assignment II Franklin D. Roosevelt

Congratulations! Starfleet Command is proud to award you the Starfleet Medal of Honour and 15 or 30 extra points.

MULTIPLE CHOICE ANSWERS

1. D. co-orbital satellites
2. B. blowing up the entire conference
3. A. technological advancement
4. D. Data's after-dinner anecdotes
5. A. a pay telephone

MISSION PERFORMANCE RATING:

45 – 80 points **Superior:** Why, you must be Dixon Hill himself!

40 – 44 points **Above Average:** You knew what co-orbital satellites were.

30 – 39 points **Average:** You could pass as a holographic bartender.

20 – 29 points **Fair:** Apparently you had a little too much vermicula.

0 – 19 points **Poor:** You must have been in a self-induced catatonic state.

THE EMISSARY ⚛

The *Enterprise* intercepts a special emissary from Starfleet named K' Ehleyr. She tells Picard that a Klingon ship, sent out on a secret mission decades ago, is returning. The crew has been in suspended animation and will think the Klingons are still at war with the Federation. K' Ehleyr's mission is to destroy the Klingons before they start attacking Federation outposts. Picard finds this unacceptable and asks his officers to find another, less brutal option.

K' Ehleyr and Worf knew each other in the past, but parted on bad terms. Worf offers the Klingon oath of marriage on the holodeck, but K' Ehleyr says she doesn't want to marry him.

Meanwhile, the *Enterprise* spots the reawakened Klingon ship. Worf pretends to be captain of the *Enterprise*, convincing the Klingon captain that the Klingon Empire has defeated the Federation. Worf transfers K' Ehleyr to the ship to take command until a Klingon escort arrives. Worf and K' Ehleyr are reconciled before she parts for the Klingon ship.

TRIVIA QUESTIONS

1. What was Worf's winning poker hand? **(3pts)**
2. What did Worf say when Riker asked him if he liked command? **(3pts)**
3. How many creatures do Worf and K' Ehleyr battle with at level 2, in the exercise programme? **(3pts)**
4. How many years ago did Worf and K' Ehleyr know each other? **(3pts)**
5. Who is the captain of the *T' Ong*? **(4pts)**
6. Where was the first Federation outpost established in the Boradis system? **(5pts)**
7. What is the name of the Klingon vessel on its way to escort the *T' Ong* home? **(3pts)**
8. Which starbase received an automated transmission? **(4pts)**
9. How fast can the probe travel? **(3pts)**
10. How many colonies are in the Varada system? **(4pts)**

✪ SPECIAL ASSIGNMENT (15pts)

What year was the first outpost established in the Boradis system?

MULTIPLE CHOICE QUESTIONS

1. What has the Klingon captain no proof of? **(3pts)**
   A. that Worf is really Captain of the Enterprise
   B. that the war between the Klingons and the Federation is over
   C. that Worf isn't a Klingon traitor
   D. what year it is

2. Which holodeck exercise programme does K' Ehleyr choose? **(2pts)**
   A. Wesley's lean teen routine
   B. Buns of Tritanium
   C. battle warm-up exercises used by the Society for Creative Anachronism
   D. Lieutenant Worf's Klingon Calisthenics programme

3. What has K' Ehleyr inherited from her mother? **(2pts)**
   A. good looks
   B. intelligence
   C. nose
   D. sense of humour

4. K' Ehleyr ultimately feels that the *Enterprise* will have to do what? **(3pts)**
   A. disable the *T' Ong*
   B. board the *T' Ong* and disable the cryogenic units
   C. destroy the *T' Ong*
   D. negotiate a peace with the Captain of the *T' Ong*

5. When was the *T' Ong* sent out? **(5pts)**
   A. approximately 75 years ago
   B. 100 years ago
   C. just after the Khitomer Conference
   D. 63 years ago

ANSWERS

TRIVIA ANSWERS

1. full house (3 aces and 2 queens)
2. comfortable chair
3. three
4. six years
5. K'Temoc
6. Boradis III
7. P'Rang
8. Starbase 336
9. Warp 9
10. four

SPECIAL ASSIGNMENT SOLUTION

2331

Congratulations! Starfleet Command is proud to award you the Starfleet Medal of Honour and 15 extra points.

MULTIPLE CHOICE ANSWERS

1. B. that the war between the Klingons and the Federation is over
2. D. Lieutenant Worf's Klingon Calisthenics programme
3. D. sense of humour
4. C. destroy the T'Ong
5. A. approximately 75 years ago

MISSION PERFORMANCE RATING:

45 – 65 points **Superior:** Worf used your plan to trick the Klingons.

40 – 44 points **Above Average:** So you're the *real* emissary, right.

30 – 39 points **Average:** Spent a little too much time in a class-8 probe, huh?

20 – 29 points **Fair:** You must've just reawakened with the other Klingons.

0 – 19 points **Poor:** You could be part of Worf's calisthenics programme.

PEAK PERFORMANCE

STARDATE: 42923.4

The *Enterprise* participates in war games and a Zakdorn named Kolrami comes aboard as an observer. Riker and a small crew will man the *USS Hathaway* in simulated battle. A laser system will replace actual weapons and record the simulated hits.

Riker beams over to the *Hathaway* with his crew to prepare the ship for battle. As the games begin, Worf creates an illusion causing the *Enterprise* to think a Romulan ship has just appeared. Turning towards the Romulan ship, the *Enterprise* is attacked by Riker. Picard then re-engages the *Hathaway*.

Picard is about to attack when a Ferengi ship appears. Picard thinks this is also an illusion and ignores it, but the Ferengi ship is real and disables the *Enterprise*. The Ferengi think the *Hathaway* is very valuable. Picard and Riker concoct a plan. The *Enterprise* fires at the *Hathaway* and it is apparently destroyed. The Ferengi lose interest and leave the area. Riker and his crew are safely beamed back to the *Enterprise*.

TRIVIA QUESTIONS

1. For how long have the Zakdorn been regarded as having the finest strategic minds in the galaxy? **(4pts)**
2. What is Data's approximate score at the end of his rematch with Kolrami? **(5pts)**
3. How often does Riker rely on traditional tactics? **(4pts)**
4. What does Wesley's experiment deal with? **(3pts)**
5. How long can a strategema game last with two opponents with approximately the same skill? **(4pts)**
6. Wesley says his experiment on the *Enterprise* is for his final grade in what class? **(3pts)**
7. Worf has wagered heavily in the ship's pool that Riker will take Kolrami past what? **(3pts)**
8. What is Worf working on when Riker interrupts him in his quarters? **(3pts)**
9. How many moves does it take Kolrami to defeat Riker in strategema? **(3pts)**
10. What is Kolrami noted as at the game of strategema? **(3pts)**

✪✪ MATHEMATICALLY SPEAKING (25pts)

Answer A to F and then insert the numbers into the formula to solve this problem.

A. What is the crew complement of the *Hathaway* during the war games? **(3pts)**
B. How long does Captain Riker have to prepare the *Hathaway* for battle? **(3pts)**
C. How many hours before the war games start does Wesley return to the *Enterprise*? **(3pts)**
D. How many photon torpedoes are fired by the *Enterprise* at the *Hathaway*? **(3pts)**
E. How many weeks did Wesley say his experiment took to set up? **(3pts)**
F. How many minutes does the Ferengi DaiMon give Picard to surrender? **(3pts)**

$$(A \times B) \div C + (D + E + F) = G$$

What is the significance of your answer (G) in relation to the episode? **(7pts)**

ANSWERS

TRIVIA ANSWERS

1. 9,000 years
2. over 33,000
3. 21% of the time
4. high energy plasma reactions with antimatter
5. well over 1,000 moves
6. plasma physics
7. 6th plateau
8. a wooden ship
9. 23 moves
10. 3rd level grand master

MATHEMATICALLY SPEAKING SOLUTION

A. 40
B. 48
C. 32
D. 4
E. 6
F. 10

$$(40 \times 48) \div 32 + (4 + 6 + 10) = 80$$
The Hathaway is 80 years old.

MISSION PERFORMANCE RATING:

30 – 60 points **Superior:** A brillant tactician!

25 – 29 points **Above Average:** Strategema grand wizard, 4th level.

20 – 24 points **Average:** Riker could beat you in strategema!

10 – 19 points **Fair:** Hold the dilithium fragments while they engage the warp drive.

0 – 9 points **Poor:** An uncommissioned child.

# SHADES OF GRAY

STARDATE: 42976.1

While the *Enterprise* is performing a preliminary survey of an unexplored planet, Riker injures his leg. His leg quickly becomes infected with an organism that the transporters can't filter out. As the disease progresses, Dr Pulaski hooks up advanced life support to keep Riker's brain stimulated. He begins to have memories of his various missions aboard the *Enterprise*.

Riker's memories seem to influence the growth rate of the organisms. Dr Pulaski determines that bad memories retard the microbes' growth, so she increases Riker's recall of bad events. After microbes and fans are bombarded by a series of flashbacks from earlier episodes, the microbes die off and the fans yawn.

TRIVIA QUESTIONS

1. Why can't Riker initially beam up? **(3pts)**
2. Which one of Riker's ancestors was bitten by a snake? **(4pts)**
3. Data tells Picard he doesn't have the authority to do what? **(3pts)**
4. What is the ultimate test of character? **(3pts)**
5. What is the name of the planet the *Enterprise* is surveying? **(4pts)**
6. When Riker remembers his encounter on Vagra II, what does the microbes' growth rate slow to? **(5pts)**
7. Why can't Dr Pulaski remove the organisms from Riker's body? **(3pts)**
8. Data detects no animal life forms within what range? **(4pts)**
9. What do the vines appear to be drawn to? **(3pts)**
10. What has invaded Riker's body? **(3pts)**

✪ SPECIAL ASSIGNMENT (15pts)

What drug and dosage does Dr Pulaski tell the nurse to stand by with in case of seizure?

SHADES OF GRAY (1pt each)

Match Riker's memories with the episode. Some answers may be used more than once.

Description

1. holodeck forest
2. Riker tries to pick up Guinan
3. seeking peaceful coexistence
4. computer generated gin joint
5. the seducer is seduced
6. Foot Washing 101
7. Yar looks like a rag doll
8. I think therefore Ian
9. An issue of loyalty
10. vitamins do a body good
11. a real shocker
12. Geordi has a bat's eye view
13. Riker looks real slick
14. autodestruct sequence
15. Talarian ship explodes
16. Troi doesn't like goodbyes
17. Riker covered in Ferengi
18. assassin is killed
19. plague ship goes boom
20. science vessel is repulsed

Episode

A. 'Up the Long Ladder'
B. 'Unnatural Selection'
C. 'The Naked Now'
D. 'The Last Outpost'
E. 'The Icarus Factor'
F. 'The Dauphin'
G. 'The Child'
H. 'Symbiosis'
I. 'Skin of Evil'
J. 'Loud as a Whisper'
K. 'Heart of Glory'
L. 'Encounter at Farpoint'
M. 'Conspiracy'
N. 'Angel One'
O. 'A Matter of Honor'
P. '11001001'

ANSWERS

TRIVIA ANSWERS

1. the biofilters detected unknown microbes in his body and can't filter them out
2. his great grandfather
3. promote Data to the rank of Admiral
4. facing death
5. Surata IV
6. 7%
7. they are fused to the nerves, intertwining at the molecular level
8. 50 kilometres
9. warm-blooded animals
10. unknown organism which is neither bacteria nor virus but has elements of both

SPECIAL ASSIGNMENT SOLUTION

5mg of tricordrazine

Congratulations! Starfleet Command is proud to award you the Starfleet Medal of Honour and 15 extra points.

SHADES OF GRAY ANSWERS

1. L 'Encounter at Farpoint'; 2. F 'The Dauphin'; 3. M 'Conspiracy'; 4. P 'I 1001001'; 5. N 'Angel One'; 6. A 'Up the Long Ladder'; 7. I 'Skin of Evil'; 8. G 'The Child'; 9. K 'Heart of Glory'; 10. M 'Conspiracy'; 11. H 'Symbiosis'; 12. D 'The Last Outpost'; 13. I 'Skin of Evil'; 14. P 'I 1001001'; 15. K 'Heart of Glory'; 16. E 'The Icarus Factor'; 17. D 'The Last Outpost'; 18. J 'Loud as a Whisper'; 19. B 'Unnatural Selection'; 20. C 'The Naked Now'

MISSION PERFORMANCE RATING:

50 – 70 points **Superior:** So *you're* the doctor who assisted in Riker's recovery!

40 – 49 points **Above Average:** No alien bugs are going to stab *you* in the leg!

30 – 39 points **Average:** Did you write this episode? (that *isn't* a compliment)

20 – 29 points **Fair:** The microbes would die from boredom in your brain.

0 – 19 points **Poor:** Your flashbacks are from purple haze.

ACTORS AND SUCH ...

REGULAR CAST TRIVIA

1. What secondary role did Patrick Stewart play in 'The Defector'? **(10pts)**
2. Which *TNG* episode featured Patrick Stewart's son, Daniel? **(10pts)**
3. Which science fiction movie did Brent Spiner play in with Jeff Goldblum? **(10pts)**
4. In which television series did Michael Dorn play the role of Officer Turner? **(10pts)**
5. In which television miniseries did Jonathan Frakes play the role of Stanley Hazard? **(10pts)**
6. What character did Patrick Stewart play in the movie *Excalibur*? **(10pts)**
7. What pivotal role did LeVar Burton play in a television miniseries? **(10pts)**
8. In what 1985 movie did Marina Sirtis play alongside Charles Bronson? **(10pts)**
9. Which *TNG* actor got his pilot's licence between the first and second seasons of the show? **(10pts)**
10. What was Gates McFadden's first feature film role? **(10pts)**

NOTABLE APPEARANCES

1. Which actor plays Dr Timicin in 'Half a Life' and what popular sitcom did he play in for years? **(10pts)**
2. Actor Cliff Potts, who played Admiral Kennelly in 'Ensign Ro', had a role in what 1972 science fiction movie? **(10pts)**
3. Actress Michelle Phillips, who played Jenice Manheim in 'We'll Always Have Paris', was famous as a singer for which musical group in the 1960s? **(10pts)**
4. What character did actress Ashley Judd play in two *TNG* episodes? **(10pts)**
5. Actor Matt Frewer, who played the time travelling inventor Rasmussen in 'A Matter of Time', had a 'head' role in which series? **(10pts)**
6. Which episode of *TNG* did actor Kelsey Grammer have a small role in? **(10pts)**
7. In which series of movies did actor Carel Struycken, who played Mr Homn, starred? **(10pts)**
8. What three roles has actor David Warner played in the *Star Trek* movies and *TNG*? **(10pts)**
9. Which actor represented a second member of the Q Continuum? **(10pts)**
10. Who played a holographic representation of Sir Isaac Newton in 'Descent – Part I'? **(10pts)**

SPECIAL SECTION

11. What two roles has actor Paul Winfield played in *TNG* and one of the *Star Trek* movies? **(10pts)**
12. Actor Richard Fancy, who played the publisher Elaine worked for on *Seinfeld*, had what *TNG* role? **(10pts)**
13. In which *TNG* episode did actor Stephen Root, who stars in the sitcom *Newsradio*, play? **(10pts)**
14. In which *TNG* episode did actor Eric Pierpoint, who played the Newcomer detective in the *Alien Nation* series, have a role? **(10pts)**
15. What role did LA Laker James Worthy play in a *TNG* episode? **(10pts)**
16. In which *TNG* episode did actor Ben Vereen played? **(10pts)**
17. Who played Ensign Clancy who was the conn officer in 'The Emissary' and an assistant in Engineering in the episode 'Elementary, Dear Data'? **(10pts)**
18. Which noted rock musician played the Antidean Ambassador in the episode 'Manhunt'? **(10pts)**
19. In which *Star Trek* movie did actor George Murdock, who played Admiral J.P. Hanson in 'The Best of Both Worlds', previously play? **(10pts)**
20. Actor Nick Tate, who played Captain Dirgo in 'Final Mission', also played an astronaut in which science fiction series? **(10pts)**
21. What is the name of the actress who played Nurse Lanel in 'First Contact'? **(10pts)**
22. Actor Clive Revill, who played Sir Guy of Gisbourne in 'Qpid', also played what character in the *Star Wars* movie *The Empire Strikes Back*? **(10pts)**
23. What episode did actor David Huddleston play in? **(10pts)**
24. In which *TNG* episode did actor Ray Walston play? **(10pts)**
25. Which noted comedian played a role in a *TNG* episode? **(10pts)**

GUESS WHO?

1. Which actor played the Ferengi known as Letek in 'The Last Outpost' and the gift box face in 'Haven'? **(10pts)**
2. Which actor had the dubious distinction of portraying the first *Enterprise-D* crew member to be killed on the series? **(20pts)**
3. Actor Leonard J. Crofoot, who played Mistress Beata's assistant in 'Angel One', also played in what other episode? **(10pts)**
4. What other character did actress Suzie Plakson, who played K'Ehleyr in 'The Emissary' and 'Reunion', also play? **(10pts)**
5. In which episode of *TNG* did the actor Ethan Philips, who plays Neelix on *Star Trek: Voyager*, also play a Ferengi? **(10pts)**
6. In what other episode did actor David Tristen Birkin, who played the young Picard in 'Rascals', also play? **(10pts)**
7. What three other roles in *TNG* did actor Marc Alaimo, who played Subcommander Tebok in 'The Neutral Zone', play? **(20pts)**
8. Which two other roles in *TNG* has actress Carolyn Seymour, who played Mirasta Yale in 'First Contact', also played? **(10pts)**

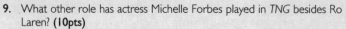

9. What other role has actress Michelle Forbes played in *TNG* besides Ro Laren? **(10pts)**

10. Actor Alan Scarfe, who played Tokath in 'Birthright – Part II', played what other role in the series? **(10pts)**

11. What role in *TNG* did actor Tim Russ, who plays Tuvok on the *Star Trek: Voyager* series, play? **(10pts)**

12. Actor Robert Duncan McNeil, who plays Tom Paris on the *Star Trek: Voyager* series, played in which *TNG* episode? **(10pts)**

13. Actor Tricia O'Neil, who played Captain Rachel Garrett in 'Yesterday's Enterprise', also played in which other episode? **(10pts)**

14. What two roles on TNG has actor Max Grodenchik, who plays Quark's brother on *Star Trek: Deep Space Nine*, played? **(10pts)**

15. Actor James Horan, who played Jo'Bril in 'Suspicions', also played what other role in the series? **(10pts)**

16. What other *TNG* role has actor Norman Large, who played Proconsul Neral in 'Unification – Parts I & II', also played? **(10pts)**

17. Actress Pamela Kosh, who played Mrs Carmichael in 'Time's Arrow – Part II', also played in what other episode? **(10pts)**

18. Actor John deLancie's wife, Marnie Mosiman, who played part of Riva's chorus in 'Loud as a Whisper', made a brief appearance in which other *TNG* episode? **(10pts)**

SPECIAL SECTION

ANSWERS

REGULAR CAST TRIVIA

1. He played the holographic soldier with the lance (Michael Williams – not identified by name).
2. He played Batai, Kamin's son, in 'The Inner Light'.
3. *Independence Day*
4. *CHiPs*
5. *North & South*
6. *Leondegrance*
7. He played Kunta Kinte in the miniseries *Roots*.
8. She played Maria in *Death Wish 3*.
9. Michael Dorn
10. She played Mr Price's secretary in *The Muppets Take Manhattan*.

NOTABLE APPEARANCES TRIVIA

1. David Ogden Stiers played Charles Emerson Winchester on the hit series *M*A*S*H*.
2. He played one of the crew members on the spaceship *Valley Forge* in the movie *Silent Running*.
3. Mamas and the Papas
4. She played Ensign Robin Lefler in 'Darmok' and 'The Game'.
5. *Max Headroom*
6. He played Captain Morgan Bateson in 'Cause and Effect'.
7. He played Lurch in the *Addams Family* movies.
8. St John Talbot in *Star Trek V*, Chancellor Gorkon in *Star Trek VI*, Gul Madred in 'Chain of Command'
9. Corbin Bernsen in 'Deja Q'

10. John Neville
11. He played Captain Terrell in *Star Trek II: The Wrath of Khan* and Captain Dathon in 'Darmok'.
12. He played Captain Satelk in 'The First Duty'.
13. He played Klingon Captain K'Vada in 'Unification II'.
14. He played in 'Liaisons' as Ambassador Voval.
15. He played the tall Klingon known as Koral in 'Gambit – Part II'.
16. He played Geordi's father in 'Interface'.
17. Anne Elizabeth Ramsay
18. Mick Fleetwood
19. He played the false god image in *Star Trek V*.
20. Tate played Alan Carter on *Space: 1999*.
21. Bebe Neuwirth
22. He played the galactic emperor.
23. He played the holodeck conductor in 'Emergence'.
24. He played Picard's mentor, Boothby, in 'The First Duty'.
25. Joe Piscopo in 'The Outrageous Okona'.

GUESS WHO? TRIVIA

1. Armin Shimerman
2. Actor Kari Raz played Lieutenant Commander Singh in 'Lonely Among Us'
3. He was the preliminary android version of Lal in 'The Offspring'.
4. She played the Vulcan, Dr Selar, in 'The Schizoid Man'.
5. 'Ménage à Troi'.
6. He played Picard's nephew René in 'Family'.
7. Badar N'D'D, chief Antican delegate in 'Lonely Among Us', Gul Macet in 'The Wounded', Gambler – Frederick La Rouque in 'Time's Arrow'
8. Subcommander Taris in 'Contagion', Commander Toreth in 'Face of the Enemy'
9. She played Dara, Dr Timicin's daughter, in 'Half a Life'.
10. He played Admiral Mendak in 'Data's Day'.
11. He played the terrorist known as Devor in 'Starship Mine'.
12. He played Nova Squadron leader, Nicholas Locarno, in 'The First Duty'.
13. She played the Vulcan scientist Kurak in 'Suspicions'.
14. He played Par Lenor in 'The Perfect Mate' and Sovak in 'Captain's Holiday'.
15. He played Lieutenant Barnaby, the tactical officer in 'Descent – Part II'.
16. He was the Caim diplomat, Maques, in 'Dark Page'.
17. She also played Data's housekeeper, Jessel, in 'All Good Things...'
18. She is the maid Q hugs and kisses at the banquet table in 'Qpid'.

MISSION PERFORMANCE RATING:

400 – 550 points	**Superior:** A true couch potato! Congratulations! (SEE BELOW)
300 – 399 points	**Above Average:** A real television and movie buff! Good job!
200 – 299 points	**Average:** You know who the major players are anyway.
100 – 199 points	**Fair:** You don't even know who Patrick Stewart is, do you?
0 – 99 points	**Poor:** Not much help for you here.

If you have received a SUPERIOR Mission Performance Rating –

Congratulations!
Starfleet Command is proud to award you
the Preantares Ribbon of Commendation, First Class and 75 extra points.

SPECIAL SECTION

SEASON THREE

THE ENSIGNS OF COMMAND

STARDATE: NONE GIVEN

The *Enterprise* receives a message from an alien race known as the Sheliak Corporate. The Sheliak claim humans are living on a planet ceded to them in their treaty with the Federation. The Sheliak plan to colonize the planet and demand that the humans be removed within three days.

The *Enterprise* arrives at the planet. Data is sent in a shuttle to go to the surface to investigate. Data discovers a large colony of humans; descendants of a colony ship forced to land there. The leader of the colony refuses to leave the planet.

Picard realizes that he cannot evacuate the colony in time under the current conditions and tries to talk to the Sheliak. He is unsuccessful until he finds a loophole in the treaty language. The Sheliak agree to give Picard the time he needs to remove the colony. Meanwhile, Data has to resort to a violent demonstration to finally persuade the colonists to leave the planet.

TRIVIA QUESTIONS

1. How many of the original colonists died before the survivors adapted to the radiation? **(2pts)**
2. What class of planet is Tau Cygna V? **(3pts)**
3. What race does Picard appoint as a third-party arbitrator to the dispute? **(3pts)**
4. How long has it been since the Sheliak have attempted to communicate with the Federation? **(4pts)**
5. What is the name of the ensign who will play the violin in the second concert? **(4pts)**
6. Data's violin playing is a precise imitation of which two musicians' techniques? **(4pts)**
7. How many words comprise the treaty between the Federation and the Sheliak? **(4pts)**
8. Using the *Enterprise*'s shuttlecraft, Worf says it would take how long to evacuate the colony? **(4pts)**
9. Where is Tau Cygna V? **(3pts)**
10. Which treaty ceded Tau Cygna V to the Sheliak? **(4pts)**

✪ SPECIAL ASSIGNMENT (15pts)

What year did the human colony ship depart on its mission?

MULTIPLE CHOICE QUESTIONS

1. Where does Picard check for dust? **(2pts)**
   A. behind Data's ears
   B. underneath the tactical station
   C. on top of the *Enterprise* dedication plaque on the bridge
   D. on top of Science Station 1

2. What is the short definition of Captain? **(3pts)**
   A. he thinks he's always right
   B. he wants the impossible
   C. he wants everything done by yesterday
   D. he always wants to push the equipment beyond designer specifications

3. What happens to the first metal canister when O'Brien tests the transporter? **(3pts)**
   A. transports perfectly
   B. shatters into thousands of pieces
   C. disappears
   D. melts into a lump of metal

4. How do the Sheliak address Picard and the crew? **(3pts)**
   A. impertinent creatures
   B. inconsequential creatures
   C. humanoid creatures
   D. Federation creatures

5. Hyperonic radiation interferes with what three things? **(4pts)**
   A. transporters, life support, phasers
   B. transporters, sensors, phasers
   C. impulse engines, sensors, transporters
   D. warp engines, communications, sensors

ANSWERS

TRIVIA ANSWERS

1. 1/3 of the original colonists
2. class-H planet
3. Grisella
4. 111 years
5. Ensign Ortese
6. Jascha Heifetz and Trenka Bron-Ken
7. 500,000 words
8. four weeks and four days
9. in the de Laure belt
10. Treaty of Armens

SPECIAL ASSIGNMENT SOLUTION

2274

Congratulations! Starfleet Command is proud to award you the Starfleet Medal of Honour and 15 extra points.

MULTIPLE CHOICE ANSWERS

1. C. on top of the *Enterprise* dedication plaque on the bridge
2. B. he wants the impossible
3. D. melts into a lump of metal
4. D. Federation creatures

MISSION PERFORMANCE RATING:

45 – 65 points **Superior:** So you're the one who wrote the Treaty of Armens.

40 – 44 points **Above Average:** You're a walking calculator.

30 – 39 points **Average:** Your mission is to read the Treaty of Armens.

20 – 29 points **Fair:** A little too much hyperonic radiation for you.

0 – 19 points **Poor:** Federation creature.

EVOLUTION ⌖

The *Enterprise* assists a noted Federation scientist, Dr Stubbs, with a critical experiment concerning a stellar phenomenon that is a once in a lifetime event (actually several lifetimes). As the *Enterprise* prepares to launch Dr Stubbs' experiment module, various computer glitches start to occur threatening the experiment.

The crew finally isolates the problem: several nanites were released accidentally by Wesley during an experiment. Picard doesn't want to hurt the seemingly intelligent creatures who have taken up residence in the ship's computer core. Dr Stubbs enters the core and fires a lethal burst of rays, killing many of the nanites.

The nanites respond in self-defence, attacking the *Enterprise's* life support systems. After modifying the Universal Translator, Data is able to communicate with the nanites. Dr Stubbs apologizes for what he did and the nanites agree to a truce. The nanites repair the computer core. Stubbs experiment is launched just in time and is a success.

TRIVIA QUESTIONS

1. How does Data establish communications with the nanites? **(3pts)**
2. How many years has Dr Stubbs been preparing for this experiment? **(3pts)**
3. Where was Dr Crusher stationed for a year? **(3pts)**
4. Where does Dr Stubbs jokingly say he will take Troi after his experiment is done? **(4pts)**
5. What musical piece does the computer play and who composed it? **(5pts)**
6. Where were the nanites originally manufactured? **(4pts)**
7. What is Dr Stubbs studying? **(3pts)**
8. How often does this explosive stellar phenomenon occur? **(4pts)**
9. Dr Stubbs equates the precision of the stellar phenomenon with what? **(3pts)**
10. After the 'Egg' is bounced around in the shuttlebay, how does Dr Stubbs refer to it? **(3pts)**

CHARACTER QUOTE
(2pts per word + 3pts for identifying the speaker.)

Unscramble the words below and then identify the character.

'A _____ new era in _____ , _____ 196 _____
    NRDAB   RYTSCHSAIPOS OTNDPSEOP   ARYSE
on _____ of _____!'
   NCOTAUC   INAR

✪✪ SPECIAL ASSIGNMENT (15pts)

What does the sign on the wall in the shuttlebay say?

ANSWERS

TRIVIA ANSWERS
1. he modifies the Universal Translator
2. 20 years
3. Starfleet Medical
4. New Manhattan on Beth Delta I
5. 'Stars and Stripes Forever' by John Philip Sousa
6. Dacca, Senegal
7. the decay of neutronium expelled from a massive stellar explosion
8. every 196 years
9. Old Faithful
10. Humpty Dumpty

CHARACTER QUOTE SOLUTION
'A brand new era in astrophysics, postponed 196 years on account of rain!' – Dr Stubbs

SPECIAL ASSIGNMENT SOLUTION
CAUTION: VARIABLE GRAVITY AREA
Congratulations! Starfleet Command is proud to award you the Starfleet Medal of Honour and 15 extra points.

MISSION PERFORMANCE RATING:
45 – 65 points **Superior:** You can speak to nanites without the translator.

40 – 44 points **Above Average:** Computer core reconstructor, huh?

30 – 39 points **Average:** The nanites learn faster than you do.

20 – 29 points **Fair:** Caught your finger in a nanite trap?

0 – 19 points **Poor:** Are you a bonafide life form?

THE SURVIVORS ⚜

The *Enterprise* arrives at Delta Rana IV after receiving a report that the colony was under attack. All of the colonists are dead except for two who cannot account for their survival. An alien warship soon appears, engaging the *Enterprise* in a brief battle and then retreating. Picard visits the survivors trying to obtain more answers. When Picard returns to the *Enterprise*, the alien warship reappears. This time the alien ship is more powerful and the *Enterprise* must retreat. The *Enterprise* cautiously returns to the planet after an hour and finds the warship gone.

Picard informs the two survivors that the *Enterprise* will stay in orbit. As Picard expects, the alien warship returns and destroys the house and the two survivors. After the *Enterprise* waits a spell, the couple and their house reappear on the planet. It is revealed that Kevin is from a race of powerful beings and is only assuming human form. His wife, killed with the other colonists, is now only a creation of his mind power. With only a thought, Kevin had destroyed the alien race responsible for the attack. Picard tells Kevin he has no law to judge Kevin by and allows him to return to the planet.

TRIVIA QUESTIONS

1. How did Data know all about Kevin and Rishon? **(3pts)**
2. What was the nature of the distress call? **(3pts)**
3. How long has Kevin lived in human form? **(3pts)**
4. How many aliens did Kevin kill with a single thought? **(5pts)**
5. When the alien ship attacks the *Enterprise* the second time, what strength are their weapons? **(4pts)**
6. What difference between himself and the other colonists does Kevin initially cite? **(3pts)**
7. How long have Kevin and Rishon been living on Rana IV? **(3pts)**
8. How large is the alien ship? **(3pts)**
9. When the alien ship first attacks the *Enterprise*, what is the equivalent firepower? **(4pts)**
10. How many colonists were on Rana IV? **(4pts)**

✪✪ SPECIAL ASSIGNMENT (15pts)

What is the location of the single structure on the planet?

MULTIPLE CHOICE QUESTIONS

1. Where did Rishon meet Kevin? **(2pts)**
    A. on a shuttle flight to the Mars colony
    B. on a ship at sea
    C. on vacation at Risa
    D. in the jungles of Surata IV

2. Picard tells Kevin the *Enterprise* will remain in orbit how long? **(3pts)**
    A. indefinitely
    B. until they decide to leave the planet
    C. until another relief ship arrives
    D. as long as the two of them are alive

3. What power source is in the house and how long will it last? **(5pts)**
    A. an atomic reactor, with enough power for another ten years
    B. a solar reactor, with enough power indefinitely
    C. a fusion reactor, with enough power for five more years
    D. a 700 series Bussard ramscoop, with enough power for 25 more years

4. When the alien ship first attacks the *Enterprise*, what type of weapons does it fire? **(3pts)**
    A. antimatter projectiles
    B. jacketed streams of positrons and antiprotons
    C. disruptors
    D. phasers

5. What are there signs of when the *Enterprise* first arrives on Rana IV? **(2pts)**
    A. vegetation
    B. artificial structures
    C. bodies of water
    D. life forms
    E. all of the above

ANSWERS

TRIVIA ANSWERS

1. he memorized the colony register while en route to the planet
2. the colony was being attacked by an unknown spacecraft
3. over 50 years
4. over 50 billion
5. 400 gigawatts of particle energy
6. he is a man of special conscience who chose not to fight
7. five years
8. approximately five times the *Enterprise*'s mass
9. 40 megawatts
10. over 11,000 people

SPECIAL ASSIGNMENT SOLUTION

37° N , 62° E

Congratulations! Starfleet Command is proud to award you the Starfleet Medal of Honour and 15 extra points.

MULTIPLE CHOICE ANSWERS

1. B. on a ship at sea
2. D. as long as the two of them are alive
3. C. a fusion reactor with enough power for five more years
4. B. jacketed streams of positrons and antiprotons
5. E. all of the above

MISSION PERFORMANCE RATING:

45 – 65 points **Superior:** You're a Douwd – better think nice thoughts now!

40 – 44 points **Above Average:** You're a person of special conscience.

30 – 39 points **Average:** You're a recreation of an earlier model.

20 – 29 points **Fair:** You're a Dweeb with a capital D.

0 – 19 points **Poor:** 2nd rate Husnock. (You're supposed to be extinct!)

WHO WATCHES THE WATCHERS

STARDATE: 43173.5

The *Enterprise* is en route to resupply a research team which is studying a group of Mintakans from a hidden observation blind. Picard is talking with the team leader when the transmission is lost. The power source for their cloaking shield is inoperative and the rescue operations are observed by a native Mintakan named Liko. He is injured and falls off his perch. Dr Crusher beams Liko to sickbay in order to save his life. The Mintakan awakens and sees Picard in sickbay and thinks he is their legendary god. Dr Crusher tries to erase Liko's memories but without success. Liko is returned to the planet.

Liko begins telling others about his supernatural experiences. Picard refuses to reinforce the Mintakans' newfound beliefs. He beams up their leader, Nuria, to convince her that he is mortal like herself. Picard is finally able to persuade her that he is not a superior being, just from a more advanced race than the Mintakans.

When Picard returns to the planet with Nuria, Liko still doesn't believe Picard is only a man. Liko shoots Picard with a weapon to prove he is unable to hurt 'the Picard'. It is only when Picard is injured and bleeds that the Mintakans realize that Picard is mortal.

CROSSWORD PUZZLE CLUES

ACROSS
1. Name of medic who assisted Dr Crusher with the injured researchers on the planet. **(3pts)**
5. The research station is _____ . **(1pt)**
7. Dr Warren's initial medical condition. **(1pt)**
8. The researchers on Mintaka III have a _____ reactor. **(1pt)**
10. The high level of certain compounds in the rock strata _____ the sensor beams. **(2pts)**
15. Picard tries to explain to Liko that he is a _____ from a far away land. **(2pts)**
17. The rock strata around the research blind contains high levels of _____ compound. **(3pts)**
18. Name of Mintakan hunter who chases Riker and the injured scientist. **(3pts)**
21. Leader of Federation research team. **(3pts)**
24. Dr Crusher asks the nurse in sickbay if she increased the levels of the drug, _____. **(3pts)**
26. Liko hopes 'the Picard' will grant him _____. **(2pts)**
27. Present Nuria gives to Picard. **(2pts)**
28. The Mintakans live in _____. **(1pt)**
30. Dr Crusher tells the medic to prepare 2 cc of _____ to give to Dr Warren. **(3pts)**
31. Picard is shot with an _____. **(1pt)**
32. The Mintakans' development is at the _____ Age level. **(2pts)**

DOWN
2. The cultural contamination on Mintaka III could evolve into a _____. **(2pts)**
3. The communicators are implanted _____ in the away team. **(2pts)**
4. Number of Federation researchers based on Mintaka III. **(2pts)**
6. Picard's arm is in a _____ after Dr Crusher treats him. **(1pt)**
9. Type of researchers on Mintaka III. **(1pt)**
11. Riker shows him a better knot. **(3pts)**
12. Picard is shot in the left _____. **(1pt)**
13. It is not the season for _____ on Mintaka III. **(3pts)**
14. Mintakan legends spoke of this supernatural being. **(2pts)**
16. How Liko's wife died. **(3pts)**
19. Four of the dead from the previous year's natural disaster were _____. **(3pts)**
20. Found in a cave by the Mintakans. **(3pts)**
22. The Mintakans are _____ humanoids. **(3pts)**
23. The terrain around the research blind contains sink holes, underground rivers, and _____. **(3pts)**
25. Type of Mintakan family under observation. **(2pts)**
29. Dr Warren's first name. **(3pts)**

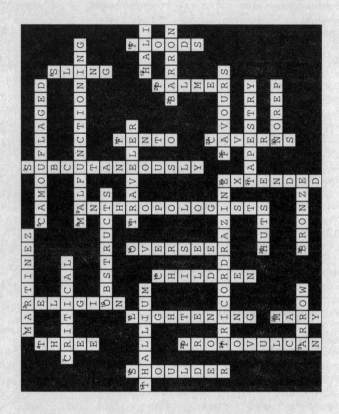

MISSION PERFORMANCE RATING:

65 – 70 points **Superior:** You must be a Superior Being!

60 – 64 points **Above Average:** You are 'the Picard'.

50 – 59 points **Average:** You are the appointed record-keeper.

40 – 49 points **Fair:** You have trouble tying your shoes.

0 – 39 points **Poor:** You are proto-Ferengi.

THE BONDING ⬥

An away team is exploring some ancient ruins on an unnamed planet when an explosion occurs. The team is extracted quickly but one member, Lieutenant Aster, is dead. Picard and Troi give the bad news to Jeremy, Lieutenant Aster's young son. Jeremy is now an orphan, his father having died some years before.

Strange readings are detected on the planet's surface while Jeremy, in his quarters, turns to see his mother standing there. Non-corporeal beings from the planet have recreated Jeremy's mother to comfort him. The aliens felt responsible for her death due to a land-mine from a past war. Eventually Picard and the others are successful in persuading the aliens that Jeremy will be cared for among his own kind and the beings leave the ship. Later, Jeremy participates in a Klingon bonding ritual with Worf.

TRIVIA QUESTIONS

1. How far was Lieutenant Aster behind Worf when she was killed? **(3pts)**
2. How old was Worf when his parents died? **(5pts)**
3. How many candles do Jeremy and Worf each light during the bonding ceremony? **(5pts)**
4. Which transporter room does the alien attempt to use? **(3pts)**
5. Where on the planet is a strange field detected? **(5pts)**
6. What is the name of the Klingon bonding ritual? **(5pts)**
7. How many mines did Geordi find on the planet? **(5pts)**
8. How old is Jeremy? **(4pts)**

✪✪ SPECIAL ASSIGNMENT (15pts)

What deck and corridors does Picard order to be sealed with a force field?

MULTIPLE CHOICE QUESTIONS

1. How was Wesley really feeling when he found out that his father was dead? **(3pts)**
    A. sick to his stomach
    B. like somebody had kicked him in the head
    C. weak all over
    D. alone and scared

---

2. What does the alien recreate in Jeremy's quarters? **(3pts)**
   - **A.** his old quarters on the *USS Horatio*
   - **B.** his favourite dinner
   - **C.** his pet dog, Splotches
   - **D.** his old home on Earth

3. What type of detonator would not be detected by a tricorder? **(4pts)**
   - **A.** subspace proximity detonator
   - **B.** magnetic resonance detonator
   - **C.** matrix diode detonator
   - **D.** neural proximity detonator

4. What is a questionable policy? **(3pts)**
   - **A.** allowing Wesley to serve at the conn
   - **B.** allowing scientific missions to planets long-dead
   - **C.** allowing Worf to play with knives
   - **D.** allowing children to live on board the *Enterprise*

5. Who are Jeremy's only surviving relatives? **(2pts)**
   - **A.** an aunt and uncle
   - **B.** his mother's brother and his wife
   - **C.** his father's sister and her husband
   - **D.** his mother's sister and his father's brother

ANSWERS

TRIVIA ANSWERS
1. 3 metres
2. six years old
3. four candles
4. Transporter Room 3
5. 2 kilometres north of the away team's beam down point
6. R' uustai
7. six (brought back one and there are five more like it)
8. 12 years old

SPECIAL ASSIGNMENT
Deck 8, Corridors A and B
Congratulations! Starfleet Command is proud to award you the Starfleet Medal of Honour and 15 extra points.

MULTIPLE CHOICE ANSWERS
1. B. like somebody had kicked him in the head
2. D. his old home on Earth
3. A. subspace proximity detonator
4. D. allowing children to live on board the *Enterprise*
5. A. an aunt and uncle

MISSION PERFORMANCE RATING:

45 – 65 points **Superior:** Worf wants to bond with you.

40 – 44 points **Above Average:** Lawyer, huh? Can Jeremy sue Starfleet?

30 – 39 points **Average:** It wasn't you, it was just a lousy episode!

20 – 29 points **Fair:** Don't worry, just move on to the next episode.

0 – 19 points **Poor:** Geordi missed a few land mines and you volunteered to go.

BOOBY TRAP ⬠

The *Enterprise* is studying the last battle site in an ancient conflict where the two combatants fought to their mutual extinction. The *Enterprise* investigates a distress signal and discovers an old battle cruiser. Without warning the *Enterprise* starts to lose energy. An away team to the other ship finds that it was caught in a similar energy draining trap. Geordi uses the holodeck to recreate the original engine prototypes and one of the engineers (Dr Brahms) who designed the engines, to help him study the problem.

Geordi determines that the computer might be able to pilot the ship out of the field. The only other option would be to use a burst of impulse power and then shut off all power except for two thrusters. The momentum might be enough to get out. Picard pilots the *Enterprise* out of the field minutes before the crew receives a lethal dose of rays.

TRIVIA QUESTIONS

1. How can Data enhance the memory coils found on the ancient vessel? **(4pts)**
2. On stardate 40056, Dr Brahms had what made? **(5pts)**
3. What time is it just after Dr Brahms rubs Geordi's neck? **(4pts)**
4. How many power draining generators are needed to create the radiation field according to Data's estimate? **(3pts)**
5. Where did Dr Brahms debate? **(3pts)**
6. The Menthars were the first to use what manoeuvre? **(4pts)**
7. Which holodeck does Geordi use to create his simulation? **(3pts)**
8. Where was the *Enterprise*'s dilithium crystal chamber designed? **(3pts)**
9. When the ancient battle cruiser was built what were humans still using in battle? **(3pts)**
10. What are Data and Wesley playing in Ten-Forward? **(3pts)**

✪✪ SPECIAL ASSIGNMENT (15pts)

What are the co-ordinates of the beacon signal the *Enterprise* picks up?

MULTIPLE CHOICE QUESTIONS

1. What group was Dr Brahms a part of? **(4pts)**
    A. the Hypothetical Research Group
    B. the Theoretical Propulsion Group
    C. the Propulsion Research Division
    D. the Hypothetical Propulsion Group

2. What location was recreated on the holodeck by Geordi? **(3pts)**
    A. Charnock's Comedy Cabaret
    B. Denubian Alps
    C. Dixon Hill's office
    D. Drafting Room 5 at Utopia Planitia, Mars Station

3. Name a Menthar battle strategy similar to one used by Napoleon.
    (4pts)
    A. Kumeh Manoeuvre
    B. Passive Lure Strategem
    C. Picard Manoeuvre
    D. Fuurinkazan Move

4. What distinct characteristic does the dead crew of the battle cruiser
    have? **(2pts)**
    A. a bony skull ridge
    B. large incisors
    C. long shocks of black hair
    D. six fingers on each hand

5. What is a model of simplicity? **(2pts)**
    A. the battle cruiser's engines
    B. Wesley's brain
    C. the Promellian bridge design
    D. power draining generators

ANSWERS

TRIVIA ANSWERS

1. by using the image processor in the Enterprise's computer
2. her personality profile
3. nearly 16:00 hours
4. several hundred thousand
5. at the intergalactic caucuses on Chia VII
6. Kavis Teke Elusive Manoeuvre
7. Holodeck 3
8. Outpost Seran-T-One
9. steel crossbows
10. 3-D chess

SPECIAL ASSIGNMENT SOLUTION

211, mark 61

Congratulations! Starfleet Command is proud to award you the Starfleet Medal of Honour and 15 extra points.

MULTIPLE CHOICE ANSWERS

1. B. the Theoretical Propulsion Group
2. D. Drafting Room 5 at Utopia Planitia, Mars Station
3. B. Passive Lure Strategem
4. A. a bony skull ridge
5. C. the Promellian bridge design

MISSION PERFORMANCE RATING:

45 – 65 points **Superior:** Brainy, but you spend too much time in the holodeck.

40 – 44 points **Above Average:** No bony skull ridges on your head.

30 – 39 points **Average:** You'd make an intelligent holographic image.

20 – 29 points **Fair:** You were found floating in the rubble of Orelious IX.

0 – 19 points **Poor:** Your brain is a model of simplicity.

THE ENEMY

The *Enterprise* responds to a distress call at Galorndon Core. The planet experiences constant electromagnetic storms, making transport difficult. An away team investigates and finds a destroyed Romulan ship. One survivor is found but Geordi ends up missing. The away team must abandon their search on the surface and beam back to the *Enterprise*.

The *Enterprise* sends a neutrino beacon to the planet to allow Geordi to find the beam up site. As he makes his way toward the beacon, Geordi is attacked by another Romulan survivor and is taken prisoner. The electromagnetic energy affects both of them adversely: Geordi goes blind and the Romulan experiences difficulty in walking. Geordi is able to persuade the Romulan that they must work together to survive.

As Geordi and the Romulan make their way toward the beacon, a Romulan warship confronts the *Enterprise* demanding that the survivor be returned to them. Picard informs him that the Romulan has died. The Romulan commander is furious and prepares for battle. Just then, Geordi makes it to the beacon and alerts the *Enterprise*. Geordi and the Romulan survivor are beamed directly to the bridge. The appearance of another Romulan survivor defuses the situation and Picard returns him to the Romulan ship.

TRIVIA QUESTIONS

1. What does Riker plant in the ground on the planet's surface to assist in transporting out? **(3pts)**
2. What does Worf refuse to do except under direct orders? **(3pts)**
3. Why does Picard order a red alert? **(3pts)**
4. What type of probe is launched with the neutrino device inside? **(4pts)**
5. Name two bloody preambles to war. **(4pts)**
6. What does the injured Romulan need? **(3pts)**
7. What do the injured Romulan's brainwaves indicate? **(4pts)**
8. How will the *Enterprise* know when Geordi finds the neutrino beacon? **(3pts)**
9. The neutrino pulse should be detectable by what? **(3pts)**
10. In what size radius does the away team search for survivors? **(5pts)**

CHARACTER QUOTE
(3pts per word + 4pts for identifying the speaker.)

Unscramble the words below and then identify the character.

'_____ to _____ _____, _____ no _____ _____ goes
  CMLEOWE   DAOGNNRLO ROCE EHEWR   ODOG   EDDE
_____!'
HNPUIDUESN

✪ SPECIAL ASSIGNMENT (15pts)

From what direction does the Romulan rescue ship approach the *Enterprise*?

ANSWERS

TRIVIA ANSWERS
1. beam-out marker
2. donate his ribosomes to the injured Romulan
3. the Romulan vessel crosses into Federation territory
4. class-3 probe
5. Pearl Harbour, Station Salem One
6. a transfusion of compatible ribosomes
7. early neuro-pathway degeneration
8. he will modify the neutrino pulse
9. Geordi's VISOR
10. 45 metre radius

CHARACTER QUOTE SOLUTION
'Welcome to Galomdon Core, where no good deed goes unpunished!' – Geordi

SPECIAL ASSIGNMENT SOLUTION
bearing 354, mark 287
Congratulations! Starfleet Command is proud to award you the Starfleet Medal of Honour and 15 extra points.

MISSION PERFORMANCE RATING:

55 – 75 points **Superior:** So, *you* told Wesley about the neutrino thing, cool.

45 – 54 points **Above Average:** Keep walking towards the neutrino beacon.

30 – 44 points **Average:** You fell into a pit without your phaser.

15 – 29 points **Fair:** They're coming to get your ribosomes, Barbara!

0 – 14 points **Poor:** You're experiencing early neuro-pathway degeneration.

THE PRICE

STARDATE: 43385.6

The Barzans have discovered a stable wormhole near their planet, but lack the technology to exploit this resource. The *Enterprise* assists by playing host to negotiations for the management of the Barzan wormhole. Picard wants to make sure that the wormhole is indeed stable by sending a manned shuttle into it to investigate and the Ferengi insist on sending their own.

Meanwhile, one negotiator named Ral, starts a romance with Troi. She discovers that he is also part empathic and uses this ability to manipulate the other negotiators to his advantage.

Geordi and Data discover that the wormhole is not stable and rush to get back through before the wormhole destabilizes further. Ral senses the Barzans will favour the Federation in the negotiations so he forms an alliance with the Ferengi DaiMon to stage a fake attack on the wormhole to manipulate the Barzans. Troi exposes Ral for what he is, but it's too late; the Barzans have already signed an agreement with Ral. When it is found that the wormhole is unstable, Ral is recalled to explain why he purchased rights to an unusable wormhole.

TRIVIA QUESTIONS

1. The appearance of the wormhole has provided the Barzans with their first what? **(3pts)**
2. What planet is the *Enterprise* orbiting? **(3pts)**
3. When might the Ferengi find their pod? **(3pts)**
4. To which type of Caldonian mineral deposits do the Federation wish to negotiate the rights? **(4pts)**
5. The Ferengi pod tells Geordi that the wormhole will be visible when? **(4pts)**
6. How far away are the shuttlecraft from their ships? **(4pts)**
7. What part Betazoid is Ral, and from which side of his family did he inherit it? **(3pts)**
8. How old is Ral? **(3pts)**
9. The Barzan test probe into the wormhole came out where? **(4pts)**
10. How often does the wormhole appear? **(4pts)**

SPECIAL ASSIGNMENT (10pts)

Where do the two shuttles find themselves on the other side of the wormhole?

MULTIPLE CHOICE QUESTIONS

1. Troi has a research inquiry from where? **(5pts)**
   A. *The Betazoid Journal of Empathy*
   B. *The Manitoba Journal of Interplanetary Psychology*
   C. Daystrom Institute, Psychology Division
   D. *The Borka VI Underground Journal*

2. To what do the Caldonians have a commitment? **(2pts)**
   A. fostering family values
   B. pure research
   C. securing a treaty with the Barzans
   D. developing their mineral resources

3. What do the Barzans not have? **(3pts)**
   A. tritanium
   B. industrial parks
   C. large oceans
   D. manned space flight

4. The Federation delegate says Ral is the best what in the business? **(2pts)**
   A. negotiator
   B. manipulator
   C. hired gun
   D. man

5. The wormhole's regularity is due to what? **(3pts)**
   A. lots of bran fibre
   B. a stable singularity in the verteron membrane
   C. radiation buildup in the accretion disk
   D. quantum fluctuations

ANSWERS

TRIVIA ANSWERS

1. first true natural resource
2. Barzan II
3. in 80 years or so
4. Trillium 323
5. in 40 seconds
6. 70,000 light years
7. his mother was ½ Betazoid, making him ¼ Betazoid
8. 41 years old
9. beyond the Denkiri Arm in the Gamma Quadrant
10. every 233 minutes

SPECIAL ASSIGNMENT SOLUTION

In sector 3556 of the Delta Quadrant – 200 light years from where they should be

Congratulations! Starfleet Command is proud to award you the Starfleet Medal of Honour and 10 extra points.

MULTIPLE CHOICE ANSWERS

1. B. *The Manitoba Journal of Interplanetary Psychology*
2. B. pure research
3. D. manned space flight
4. C. hired gun
5. C. radiation buildup in the accretion disk

MISSION PERFORMANCE RATING:

45 – 60 points **Superior:** You're Starfleet's ace negotiator!

40 – 44 points **Above Average:** 1/16 Betazoid, huh.

30 – 39 points **Average:** Go ahead, wait for the wormhole to appear.

20 – 29 points **Fair:** All you're concerned about is who's going to bring you a chair.

0 – 19 points **Poor:** At this rate you'll be captain of a Ferengi pod in no time.

THE VENGEANCE ⚜ FACTOR

STARDATE: 43421.9

The *Enterprise* investigates a raid on a Federation research station. The crew soon determines that it was by a group known as the 'Gatherers', a group who left their home world many decades ago amidst fierce blood feuds. They have been plundering ever since, living a nomadic existence. Picard convinces Marouk, the leader of the Acamarians, to attempt peace talks with the Gatherers.

As the talks progress between the two sides, Yuta, Marouk's cook, goes off and quietly kills a Gatherer, making the death look accidental. Brull, the encampment leader, takes the *Enterprise* to meet with the leader of all the Gatherers. Dr Crusher meanwhile determines that the old man Yuta killed, died from a genetically engineered virus. She finds a record of a similar death decades earlier. An enhanced image of the last victim shows Yuta standing in the background.

Yuta is the last survivor from an old massacre. Her cells were altered to slow the ageing process and a genetically engineered virus implanted into her body. Yuta became the instrument of her clan's revenge on their enemies. Riker is forced to kill Yuta to save Chorgan, the rival clan leader.

TRIVIA QUESTIONS

1. Chorgan wants three seats on what? **(3pts)**
2. What is Yuta's job? **(3pts)**
3. What does the *Enterprise* do to get Chorgan's attention? **(3pts)**
4. What did the Lornack clan do 80 years ago? **(4pts)**
5. What was the name of Yuta's earlier victim? **(5pts)**
6. According to Dr Crusher what are the odds that the microvirus will kill an Acamarian? **(3pts)**
7. How valuable is noranium alloy? **(3pts)**
8. What does Riker call the dish Yuta cooks for him? **(3pts)**
9. Marouk suspects a Gatherer encampment where? **(4pts)**
10. The blood sample Dr Crusher analyzed was composed of what? **(4pts)**

✪✪ MATHEMATICALLY SPEAKING (25pts)

Answer A to F and then insert the numbers into the formula to solve this problem.

A. How many years ago was the last occurrence of the microvirus? **(3pts)**
B. What phaser setting does Geordi recommend to vaporize the pile of noranium alloy? **(3pts)**

C. By avoiding the asteroid belt, the *Enterprise* will only lose _____ minutes at Warp 7. **(3pts)**

D. Marouk asks Yuta for a light meal in _____ minutes. **(3pts)**

E. The Gathers and the Acamarians' last attempt at reconciliation was _____ years ago. **(3pts)**

F. What is the temperature (in degrees) of the water Riker orders from the replicator for Yuta. **(3pts)**

$$(A - B) \times (C + D + E) + F + 4.4 = G$$

What is the significance of your answer (G) in relation to the episode? **(7pts)**

ANSWERS

TRIVIA ANSWERS

1. the ruling council
2. chef and food taster
3. uses phasers to take out his forward shields
4. massacred the rival Tralesta clan, ending a 200 year old feud
5. Penthor Mul
6. one chance in a million
7. not very, it has a low salvage value
8. Parthas a la Yuta
9. Hromi Cluster
10. a rare iron-copper composite

MATHEMATICALLY SPEAKING SOLUTION

A. 53
B. 7
C. 12.1
D. 20
E. 18
F. 5

$(53 - 7) \times (12.1 + 20 + 18) + 5 + 4.4 = 2314$

Noranium alloy vaporizes at 2314 degrees.

MISSION PERFORMANCE RATING:

30 – 60 points **Superior:** A seat on the ruling council awaits you!

25 – 29 points **Above Average:** A true Acamarian.

20 – 24 points **Average:** Got thrown out of the Gatherers, huh?

10 – 19 points **Fair:** You'll make a good food taster, I hear there's an opening.

0 – 9 points **Poor:** Aren't you Lornack clan – Yuta needs to speak with you.

THE DEFECTOR ⌖

STARDATE: 43462.5 ▬▬▬▬▬▬▬▬▬▬▬▬▬▬

The *Enterprise* investigates an unknown vessel being chased by a Romulan warbird. Picard protects the scout ship and the warbird leaves the area. The Romulan defector warns Picard that the Romulans are preparing for a new war and have built a base in the Neutral Zone. Setal tells Picard he must destroy the base before it is at full strength.

Picard decides to send a probe to Nelvana III to verify the defector's claims. The probe picks up signals usually associated with cloaked warbirds but Picard still isn't sure. It is discovered that the defector is actually Jarok, a high ranking officer in the Romulan Empire.

Now Picard acts on the information Jarok has imparted, but upon arriving at the planet nothing is found. The *Enterprise* prepares to leave the area but it's too late – two warbirds appear and threaten the *Enterprise*. The Romulans apparently suspected Jarok's loyalty and passed false information on to him as a test. Just then, three Klingon vessels uncloak and come to the *Enterprise*'s aid. The Romulans, deciding it isn't a good day to die, power down their weapons and the ships depart.

TRIVIA QUESTIONS

1. What play is Data performing in on the holodeck at the beginning of the episode? **(3pts)**
2. What have all Federation starships been placed on? **(3pts)**
3. Setal asks Data if the replicators are capable of producing what? **(3pts)**
4. Who has convened an emergency session? **(3pts)**
5. How long a transmission delay is there between Starfleet and the *Enterprise*? **(3pts)**
6. How long ago was Jarok censured? **(4pts)**
7. What location does Data recreate on the holodeck for Setal? **(5pts)**
8. How many worlds has Setal visited? **(3pts)**
9. Within two days a fleet of Romulan warbirds will be within striking distance of what? **(4pts)**
10. Which outpost confirms the *Enterprise*'s initial sensor readings? **(4pts)**

✪ SPECIAL ASSIGNMENT (15pts)

In what way does Geordi say the subspace signals and ionization disturbances are moving around Nelvana III?

MULTIPLE CHOICE QUESTIONS

1. What did Jarok leave behind on the *Enterprise*? **(2pts)**
   - **A.** a corpse
   - **B.** a letter to his wife and family
   - **C.** secret Romulan documents
   - **D.** an orange disk

2. What other noteworthy commander does Riker echo? **(3pts)**
   - **A.** George Armstrong Custer
   - **B.** Khan Noonien Singh
   - **C.** George Patton
   - **D.** Alexander the Great

3. Which of the following is almost a contradiction in terms? **(3pts)**
   - **A.** Ensign Wesley Crusher
   - **B.** Klingon love poetry
   - **C.** Ferengi code of honour
   - **D.** Romulan defector

4. By entering the Neutral Zone the *Enterprise* is in direct violation of what? **(5pts)**
   - **A.** Treaty of Alliance
   - **B.** standing orders
   - **C.** Treaty of Algeron
   - **D.** Prime Directive

5. What concept does Data not find appealing? **(2pts)**
   - **A.** being trapped in a shuttle with Geordi in the Delta Quadrant for 80 years
   - **B.** his own demise
   - **C.** being caught in a time loop while using Worf's Klingon calisthenics programme
   - **D.** having a host of Romulan cyberneticists at arm's length

ANSWERS

TRIVIA ANSWERS

1. Shakespeare's *Henry V*
2. yellow alert
3. Romulan ale
4. Federation Council
5. two hours
6. four months
7. the Valley of Chula on Romulus
8. over 100
9. 15 Federation sectors
10. Outpost Sierra VI

SPECIAL ASSIGNMENT SOLUTION

In an orbital path with an 800 kilometre apogee
Congratulations! Starfleet Command is proud to award you the Starfleet Medal of Honour and 15 extra points.

MULTIPLE CHOICE ANSWERS

1. B. a letter to his wife and family
2. A. George Armstrong Custer
3. D. Romulan defector
4. C. Treaty of Algeron
5. D. having a host of Romulan cyberneticists at arm's length

---

MISSION PERFORMANCE RATING:

45 – 65 points **Superior:** Your performance in the play was breath-taking!

40 – 44 points **Above Average:** You knew we'd find nothing at Nelvana III.

30 – 39 points **Average:** You got into the Romulan ale again, didn't you?

20 – 29 points **Fair:** You're a potential Federation defector with useless info.

0 – 19 points **Poor:** They allow Klingon pahtk like you to walk around in uniform?

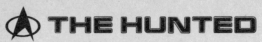

THE HUNTED

The *Enterprise* is evaluating the Angosian government for admission into the Federation. During this process a prisoner escapes from a nearby penal colony. The Angosians ask Picard for help in apprehending the prisoner. The prisoner, Danar, is quite cunning and eludes the *Enterprise* for some time but is eventually captured. It is soon discovered that Danar has been biochemically altered and psychologically programmed to be a perfect fighting machine. After winning the Angosian war, Danar and the other veterans were eventually imprisoned to 'protect' them.

Picard asks the Prime Minister about this practice; he tells the Captain that this is an internal matter. Danar escapes during the transfer to the penal colony and again eludes the *Enterprise*'s security teams until he can hijack the transport vessel sent to transfer him. He orders the security vessel to the penal colony and frees the rest of the veterans imprisoned there.

The Prime Minister contacts the *Enterprise* and pleads for Picard's help. Picard beams down with a minimal away team to assess the situation. Danar and the others turn up and surround the area. Picard tells the Prime Minister that it is after all an 'internal matter' and that their application to the Federation will be reassessed at a future time.

TRIVIA QUESTIONS

1. Where is the penal colony located? **(3pts)**
2. What is O'Brien hit by? **(3pts)**
3. What does Worf find missing from Cargo Bay 3? **(4pts)**
4. What has the explosion on the *Enterprise* rendered inoperative? **(3pts)**
5. Data's programming includes what? **(3pts)**
6. What is Picard's name for Lunar V? **(4pts)**
7. What is the age old cry of the oppressor? **(5pts)**
8. What does the prison psychologist recommend? **(3pts)**
9. What size is the escape pod? **(4pts)**
10. What confuses the *Enterprise*'s sensors while looking for the stolen ship? **(3pts)**

CHARACTER QUOTE
(3pts per word + 7pts for identifying the speaker.)

Unscramble the words below and then identify the character.

'_____ the _____ _____ _____ is ____ a _____.'
 NEEV   SMTO OTCFLBOERAM INOPSR   ITLSL RNSPOI

✪ SPECIAL ASSIGNMENT (15pts)

Where is there an explosion on the *Enterprise*?

ANSWERS

TRIVIA ANSWERS

1. on Lunar V
2. phaser blast
3. pressure suit
4. external sensors
5. military strategy
6. orbiting gulag
7. a matter of internal security
8. that Danar be kept fully sedated
9. 7 metres in length and 3 metres in diameter
10. planet's magnetic fields

CHARACTER QUOTE SOLUTION

'Even the most comfortable prison is still a prison.' – Picard

SPECIAL ASSIGNMENT SOLUTION

Jefferies tube, T-95
Congratulations! Starfleet Command is proud to award you the Starfleet Medal of Honour and 15 extra points.

MISSION PERFORMANCE RATING:

55 – 75 points **Superior:** You could star in the new movie *Space Rambo IV*.

45 – 54 points **Above Average:** Angosian Prime Minister material.

30 – 44 points **Average:** Who let you out of your containment field?

15 – 29 points **Fair:** Security extras needed in Transporter Room 4. Hurry!

0 – 14 points **Poor:** You must have escaped from the Earth penal colony.

THE HIGH GROUND

The *Enterprise* delivers needed medical supplies to Rutia IV, a planet racked by internal political strife. While waiting for a meeting, the away team is witness to a bomb explosion. Suddenly, a terrorist appears and abducts Dr Crusher.

The terrorists are using a new form of transporter that cannot be traced by conventional means. Geordi, Data, and Wesley work on how to trace the terrorists. They soon determine that the Federation worked on a similar transporter device but abandoned the research after it was shown to have harmful side effects.

The terrorists think that the Federation has allied with the Rutians and kidnap Picard. Geordi and the others are finally able to pinpoint the terrorist base. An away team, accompanied by Rutian forces, moves in and rescues Picard and Dr Crusher.

TRIVIA QUESTIONS

1. What kind of mission was the *Enterprise* on at Rutia IV? **(3pts)**
2. To whom does Finn compare himself? **(3pts)**
3. Where did the terrorists plant an explosive charge on the *Enterprise*? **(3pts)**
4. Where is the terrorist base pinpointed? **(4pts)**
5. What was the casualty report after the terrorist attack on the *Enterprise*? **(4pts)**
6. Where are each terrorist's transporter controls located? **(3pts)**
7. In what year did the Irish Unification take place? **(5pts)**
8. Who were the victims killed in the terrorist attack on the unintended target? **(3pts)**
9. When did the terrorists start using the new transporter devices? **(3pts)**
10. How long ago were the separatists denied their independence? **(4pts)**

CHARACTER QUOTE
(4pts per word + 5pts for identifying the speaker.)

Unscramble the words below and then identify the character.

'A _____ _____ is _____ ten _____ _____.'
   ADDE TMRYRA   TORHW   ITPGUONRS DLSEERA

SPECIAL ASSIGNMENT (10pts)

What is the name of the waiter from the cafe on Rutia IV?

ANSWERS

TRIVIA ANSWERS

1. errand of mercy
2. George Washington
3. on the main warp chamber
4. 300 kilometres from the city on the southern tip of the continent
5. three dead, four wounded
6. on their left shoulder
7. 2024
8. 60 school children
9. two months ago
10. 70 years ago

CHARACTER QUOTE SOLUTION

'A dead martyr is worth ten posturing leaders.' – Finn

SPECIAL ASSIGNMENT SOLUTION

Katik Shaw

Congratulations! Starfleet Command is proud to award you the Starfleet Medal of Honour and 10 extra points.

MISSION PERFORMANCE RATING:

50 – 70 points **Superior:** Your loyalty to the Federation is unquestioned.

40 – 49 points **Above Average:** You'd rather die than betray the Federation.

30 – 39 points **Average:** An errand of mercy – allowing you to stay in Starfleet.

20 – 29 points **Fair:** You're a sympathizer for the other side, we'll be watching you.

0 – 19 points **Poor:** You're now standing on the low ground, watch your step.

 **DÉJÀ Q**

The *Enterprise* is assisting Bre'el IV with a mysterious problem: their moon is in a decaying orbit and threatens to crash into the planet. Q appears and tells Picard he has lost all his powers. Q also tells Picard he is not responsible for Bre'el IV's problems. Picard is doubtful and puts him in a detention cell. Later, as Geordi and the others work to correct the problem, Q convinces Picard that he may be of some value to the effort. Picard releases Q and allows him to assist Geordi.

A sentient cloud of ionized gas advances on the *Enterprise*. The aliens, tormented by Q in the past, have come for him. Q assists Geordi in developing a plan to correct the moon's orbit. While the *Enterprise* tries to move the moon back into a proper orbit, the aliens attack and almost get Q.

Q realizes that the aliens will eventually destroy the *Enterprise* to get at him. He steals a shuttle and leaves the *Enterprise*. Another member of the Q Continuum appears and talks with Q about his selfless act. The Q Continuum decides to grant Q his powers again. Happy to be back in full form, Q corrects the moon's orbit and departs.

TRIVIA QUESTIONS

1. What has happened to Q prior to his arrival on the *Enterprise*? **(3pts)**
2. Sensors picked up a cloud of what? **(3pts)**
3. The aliens' attack pushes the *Enterprise* into what? **(3pts)**
4. What did Data do for Q? **(3pts)**
5. What is the *Enterprise*'s next destination? **(4pts)**
6. What materializes between Picard's fingers as he prepares to say 'Engage'? **(3pts)**
7. What does Q order to eat in Ten-Forward? **(3pts)**
8. What is the moon's altitude after Q places it in a circular orbit? **(5pts)**
9. What is Q's IQ? **(4pts)**
10. What does Q suggest to reverse the effects of the black hole? **(4pts)**

SPECIAL ASSIGNMENT (10pts)

How much Delta V would be required to push the moon back into a stable orbit?

MULTIPLE CHOICE QUESTIONS

1. What agency on Bre'el IV assists the *Enterprise* in investigating the moon's decaying orbit? **(3pts)**
   - **A.** The Sky Is Falling Task Force
   - **B.** Emergency Control Centre
   - **C.** Asteroid Decaying Orbit Stabilization Centre
   - **D.** Emergency Disaster Task Force

2. What does Guinan do to Q to see if he's human? **(3pts)**
   - **A.** punches him in the stomach
   - **B.** stabs his hand with a fork
   - **C.** breaks a bottle over his head
   - **D.** slaps him across the face

3. What is Dr Crusher's diagnosis of Q's medical problem? **(2pts)**
   - **A.** muscle spasms in his back
   - **B.** appendicitis
   - **C.** kidney stones
   - **D.** Darney's disease

4. What does Data eat to lubricate his biofunctions? **(5pts)**
   - **A.** an inorganic suspension of Teflon in a silicon-based liquid medium
   - **B.** a thick, viscous solution of compressed ancient organic life forms
   - **C.** a semi-organic nutrient suspension in a silicon-based liquid medium
   - **D.** a tasteless blend of seven different vegetable and mineral oils

5. The moon's impact will cause a new what on Bre'el IV? **(2pts)**
   - **A.** crater
   - **B.** ocean
   - **C.** ice age
   - **D.** dark age

ANSWERS

TRIVIA ANSWERS

1. he was stripped of his powers and kicked out of the Q Continuum
2. energetic plasma
3. the planet's atmosphere
4. saved his life
5. Station Nigala IV
6. a lit cigar
7. ten chocolate sundaes
8. 55,000 kilometres
9. 2,005
10. change the gravitational constant of the universe

SPECIAL ASSIGNMENT SOLUTION

4 kilometres per second

Congratulations! Starfleet Command is proud to award you the Starfleet Medal of Honour and 10 extra points.

MULTIPLE CHOICE ANSWERS

1. B. Emergency Control Centre
2. B. stabs his hand with a fork
3. A. muscle spasms in his back
4. C. a semi-organic nutrient suspension in a silicon-based liquid medium
5. C. ice age

MISSION PERFORMANCE RATING:

45 – 60 points **Superior:** Your IQ is 2,006 but don't tell Q that!

40 – 44 points **Above Average:** You knew how to fix the moon's orbit.

30 – 39 points **Average:** Too many chocolate sundaes.

20 – 29 points **Fair:** Go talk to Guinan, she wants to see if you're human.

0 – 19 points **Poor:** You are kin to a Markoffian sea lizard.

STARDATE: 43610.4

A science station in orbit around Tanuga IV explodes just as Riker returns from it. Dr Apgar's research on Krieger waves was Federation sponsored. Later a Tanugan official, Krag, arrives aboard the *Enterprise* and accuses Riker of murdering Dr Apgar and destroying the station. Krag wants to extradite Riker to the planet but Picard suggests a preliminary hearing first, using the holodeck to recreate the science station and study the evidence.

The various testimonies all concur that a confrontation occurred between Riker and Dr Apgar concerning his wife. Riker supposedly killed Dr Apgar to prevent him from reporting the incident. Krag also presents evidence that shows Riker used his phaser to destroy the station.

Meanwhile two radiation bursts of unknown origin occur on the *Enterprise*. It is eventually determined that Dr Apgar had indeed been successful in creating Krieger waves during his research. He hoped to turn the technology into a weapon that he could sell. When Dr Apgar felt his plan in danger of being exposed by Riker he tried to kill the Commander. Unfortunately for the scientist, the transporter beam deflected the Krieger wave back at the station and destroyed it.

TRIVIA QUESTIONS

1. The Federation hopes that Krieger waves will be a source of what one day? **(2pts)**
2. What do Starfleet regulations stipulate in the matter of extradition? **(3pts)**
3. What was the name of Geordi's holodeck programme? **(4pts)**
4. What margin of error will the recreations on the holodeck have? **(5pts)**
5. What is the exact interval between the strange radiation bursts? **(5pts)**
6. Geordi, Data and Wesley are studying the Tanugan information from which station? **(4pts)**
7. The *Enterprise* delivered needed supplies of what to Dr Apgar? **(5pts)**
8. What is admissible as evidence under Tanugan law? **(2pts)**
9. Troi senses no what from Manua? **(2pts)**
10. As a Starfleet captain, what luxury can't Picard allow himself? **(3pts)**

✪ SPECIAL ASSIGNMENT (15pts)

What size time variance can Geordi not explain at first, when the station exploded?

MULTIPLE CHOICE QUESTIONS

1. What does O'Brien notice just as he beams Riker aboard? **(3pts)**
    - **A.** an unpleasant odour
    - **B.** a malfunction in the phase transition coils
    - **C.** a fly on the transporter pad
    - **D.** a power drain

2. What is the Tanugan system of justice? **(3pts)**
    - **A.** three strikes and you're out
    - **B.** innocent until proven guilty
    - **C.** guilty until proven innocent
    - **D.** a ritualistic system of checks and balances

3. The converter is nothing more than a complex series of what? **(5pts)**
    - **A.** condensers and reflective mirrors
    - **B.** mirrors and reflective coils
    - **C.** smoke and mirrors
    - **D.** connections and inverters

4. Data says the radiation and debris from the science station is consistent with what? **(2pts)**
    - **A.** an overload of the station's reactor core
    - **B.** an antimatter explosion
    - **C.** an explosion in space
    - **D.** a burst of Romulan disruptor fire

5. What is Picard doing as a means of relaxing? **(2pts)**
    - **A.** fencing
    - **B.** painting
    - **C.** napping
    - **D.** running Worf's calisthenics programme

ANSWERS

TRIVIA ANSWERS

1. new energy
2. the captain decides if extradition is warranted
3. La Forge
4. 8.7% margin of error
5. 5 hours, 20 minutes, and 3 seconds
6. Science Station 1
7. dicosilium
8. hearsay
9. deception
10. yielding to personal feelings

SPECIAL ASSIGNMENT SOLUTION

.0014 seconds

Congratulations! Starfleet Command is proud to award you the Starfleet Medal of Honour and 15 extra points.

MULTIPLE CHOICE ANSWERS

1. D. a power drain
2. C. guilty until proven innocent
3. B. mirrors and reflective coils
4. A. an overload of the station's reactor core
5. B. painting

MISSION PERFORMANCE RATING:

45 – 65 points **Superior:** So you're the Tanugan lawyer that got Riker off!

40 – 44 points **Above Average:** What's your angle on what happened?

30 – 39 points **Average:** You could use a little more dicosilium in your diet.

20 – 29 points **Fair:** You were the victim of a holodeck generated Krieger wave.

0 – 19 points **Poor:** Sorry, you were standing in front of a radiation burst.

YESTERDAY'S ENTERPRISE

STARDATE: 43625.2

The *Enterprise* encounters a temporal rift and watches as the *Enterprise-C* emerges from the past. The *Enterprise-C*'s presence has altered history, although Picard and the crew are unaware that anything has changed. The *Enterprise-D* is now a warship, ensnared in a nasty war with the Klingon Empire. Lieutenant Yar is still alive and Chief of Security. Guinan is the only one who senses that history has been changed. She finally convinces Picard of this fact.

The *Enterprise-C* was aiding a Klingon outpost under attack by the Romulans when it entered the rift. During the fierce battle this anomaly was created and the badly damaged *Enterprise-C* was thrown into the future. The altered time line records no such deed and Klingon/Federation relations have degenerated into war. Picard persuades the crew of the *Enterprise-C* to return to their own time, even though it means certain death. At a critical moment, the two *Enterprises* are attacked by several Klingon ships. The *Enterprise-C* makes it back through the rift and everything is as it should be, peaceful.

TRIVIA QUESTIONS

1. What is a warrior's drink? **(3pts)**
2. How many Romulan ships were originally attacking the *Enterprise-C*? **(3pts)**
3. How many troops can the *Enterprise-D* transport? **(3pts)**
4. What are TKLs? **(3pts)**
5. A Federation vessel coming to the aid of a Klingon outpost might have averted what? **(3pts)**
6. What are Garrett's injuries? **(3pts)**
7. How many people have died so far during the Federation–Klingon War? **(5pts)**
8. How many decks are there on the *Enterprise-D*? **(4pts)**
9. How long has Lieutenant Yar been on the *Enterprise-D*? **(4pts)**
10. How many survivors were on the *Enterprise-C* when it arrived in the future? **(4pts)**

✪ SPECIAL ASSIGNMENT (15pts)

Who is paged over the intercom when Picard meets Garrett in sickbay?

MULTIPLE CHOICE QUESTIONS

1. Geordi estimates what will happen in two minutes? **(2pts)**
   A. the Klingons will surrender
   B. warp core breach
   C. the *Enterprise-C* will enter the rift
   D. the shields will fail

2. The *Enterprise-D*'s long range sensors pick up what on an intercept course? **(5pts)**
   A. five Vor'cha class attack cruisers
   B. three K'Vort class battle cruisers
   C. two D'deridex class warbirds
   D. three Miranda class birds-of-prey

3. What does Yar order in Ten-Forward? **(3pts)**
   A. Romulan ale
   B. Delovian souffle
   C. a couple of TKLs
   D. Aldebaran whiskey

4. What was beginning to happen when Castillo originally left on his tour of duty? **(3pts)**
   A. The Federation and the Romulans were negotiating a peace treaty.
   B. The Federation and the Klingons were preparing for war.
   C. The Klingons were allying with the Romulans.
   D. The Federation and the Klingons were negotiating a peace treaty.

5. What was the *Enterprise-C* doing at Narendra III? **(2pts)**
   A. delivering supplies
   B. responding to their distress call
   C. making emergency repairs to their ship
   D. coordinating training schedules

ANSWERS

TRIVIA ANSWERS

1. prune juice
2. four warbirds
3. over 6,000 according to Yar
4. standard rations
5. 20 years of war with the Klingons
6. a bad fracture and serious internal injures
7. 40 billion people
8. 42 decks according to Yar
9. four years, came straight from the Academy
10. 125 survivors

SPECIAL ASSIGNMENT SOLUTION

Dr Selar

Congratulations! Starfleet Command is proud to award you the Starfleet Medal of Honour and 15 extra points.

MULTIPLE CHOICE ANSWERS

1. B. warp core breach
2. B. three K'Vort class battle cruisers
3. C. a couple of TKLs
4. D. The Federation and the Klingons were negotiating a peace treaty.
5. B. responding to their distress call

MISSION PERFORMANCE RATING:

45 – 65 points **Superior:** The Klingons better not start a war with *you* around.

40 – 44 points **Above Average:** You know, in another time line you'd do all right.

30 – 39 points **Average:** Someday you'll get a battlefield promotion to captain.

20 – 29 points **Fair:** Start swabbing the decks. There are only 42 of them!

0 – 19 points **Poor:** The *Enterprise-C* needs some extra ballast. Go to it!

THE OFFSPRING ⊕

After attending a research conference, Data decides to procreate by creating a new android named Lal. Data has learned about some new advances at the conference that allow him to transfer his programming into Lal's brain.

Picard is perturbed at first by Data's actions. He asks Data whether he is ready for the responsibilities of creating a new life. Starfleet also wonders the same thing. Shortly after Data creates Lal, a Starfleet admiral meets with the *Enterprise* to evaluate the situation.

The Admiral interviews Data and Lal. He plans to take Lal back to his cybernetics lab with or without Data's permission. Lal leaves the meeting and seeks out Troi's quarters. There Lal begins experiencing actual emotions. Lal is confused and afraid. Lal returns to Data's lab where she suffers a major positronic meltdown. Data works on Lal trying to save her but to no avail. The Admiral, who assisted Data in his failed resuscitation attempts, comes to truly admire Data. To preserve her memories, Data transfers her programming into his own brain.

TRIVIA QUESTIONS

1. What does Lal think the first time she sees a couple kissing? **(3pts)**
2. Every one of these in Data's brain is duplicated in Lal's brain. **(3pts)**
3. Where is Riker? **(3pts)**
4. What is the *Enterprise*'s next destination? **(5pts)**
5. Lal is capable of running how many calculations per second? **(5pts)**
6. Lal has been programmed with a list of how many different beverages? **(5pts)**
7. Where does the Admiral want to take Lal? **(5pts)**
8. During Lal's early development, what has improved 12%? **(5pts)**
9. What is especially difficult for Lal? **(3pts)**
10. What was Data able to provide Lal with? **(3pts)**

CHARACTER QUOTE
(2pts per word + 7pts for identifying the speaker.)

Unscramble the words below and then identify the character.

'_____ are _____ _____ men of _____ _____ _____
 EHRTE   MSTEI NHWE   OGDO NCICOECSEN NTCAON

_____ _____ _____.'
IYBDLNL OFLWLO SRREOD

ANSWERS

TRIVIA ANSWERS

1. that the man is biting the woman
2. neural pathways
3. on personal leave (actually he's busy directing the episode)
4. starbase at Otar II
5. 60 trillion
6. 1,412
7. Daystrom Annexe on Galor IV
8. her motor co-ordination
9. visual comprehension
10. a more realistic skin and eye colour than his own

CHARACTER QUOTE SOLUTION

'There are times when men of good conscience cannot blindly follow orders.' – Picard

---

MISSION PERFORMANCE RATING:

55 – 65 points **Superior:** You possess the next generation of positronic brains.

50 – 54 points **Above Average:** You seem to be within behavioural norms.

40 – 49 points **Average:** You are capable of 17 calculations per hour.

30 – 39 points **Fair:** You're experiencing a complete neural system failure.

0 – 29 points **Poor:** Have they even let you on the saucer section yet?

SINS OF THE FATHER

STARDATE: 43685.2

A Klingon known as Kurn participates in the officer exchange programme with the *Enterprise* where he takes over Riker's position as second-in-command. Kurn deals with all of the crew heavy-handedly except for Worf. Worf, insulted, confronts Kurn only to find out to his surprise that they are brothers. Worf thought he was the only survivor when his family perished in the Khitomer Massacre.

Kurn reveals to Worf the true reason he has come to the *Enterprise*. Their father, although dead, has been accused of being a traitor during the Khitomer Massacre. Worf must come forward to clear his family's name or face dishonour. Picard sets course for the Klingon home world.

Worf faces the Klingon High Council to defend his family name. Meanwhile, Picard and the crew discover the truth. It is the accuser's father and not Worf's who was the traitor. The accuser's family is powerful and if this truth became known outside of K'mpec's chambers, civil war would surely break out. Worf agrees to a form of expulsion from all Klingon culture to save the empire and his brother.

TRIVIA QUESTIONS

1. How much caviar does Picard have on board the *Enterprise*? **(3pts)**
2. What would Kurn have done to Riker if he had been on a Klingon ship? **(3pts)**
3. Who is the real traitor? **(3pts)**
4. Why would K'mpec remember Kahlest? **(3pts)**
5. How many Klingons died in the Khitomer Massacre? **(5pts)**
6. Who served with Worf's father? **(4pts)**
7. Picard accesses the ship's computers concerning Klingon laws and customs on what? **(4pts)**
8. What does Duras say Worf is wearing at the proceedings? **(3pts)**
9. What did Worf's father supposedly do? **(3pts)**
10. How old was Kurn when Worf and his parents left for Khitomer? **(4pts)**

✪ SPECIAL ASSIGNMENT (15pts)

Sensors show approximately how many objects in the asteroid field?

MULTIPLE CHOICE QUESTIONS

1. Where does Kahlest live now? **(5pts)**
    - **A.** South Quadrant of the First City
    - **B.** Old Quarter of the First City
    - **C.** Narenda III
    - **D.** Kut'luch District

2. What is a cha' Dlch? **(3pts)**
    - **A.** a type of dessert
    - **B.** Klingon equivalent of a lawyer
    - **C.** defender of someone who is challenged
    - **D.** the ceremonial weapon of an assassin

3. What does Worf not allow Kurn to do at the proceedings? **(3pts)**
    - **A.** reveal his true family name
    - **B.** speak
    - **C.** defend his honour
    - **D.** stand beside him

4. Why didn't Kurn go with his family to Khitomer? **(2pts)**
    - **A.** they weren't going to stay long
    - **B.** he had other obligations
    - **C.** he was enrolled in school and could not leave
    - **D.** his father could not afford it

5. What does Kurn call the turkey? **(2pts)**
    - **A.** delicious
    - **B.** overcooked replicated trash
    - **C.** exquisite replicated meat
    - **D.** burned replicated bird meat

ANSWERS

TRIVIA ANSWERS

1. several cases for special occasions
2. killed him for questioning his authority
3. Ja'rod (father of Duras)
4. she caught his eye back then
5. 4,000
6. K'mpec
7. familial accountability
8. a child's uniform
9. transmitted Khitomer's defence access codes to the Romulan patrol ships
10. barely a year old

SPECIAL ASSIGNMENT SOLUTION

2,000

Congratulations! Starfleet Command is proud to award you the Starfleet Medal of Honour and 15 extra points.

MULTIPLE CHOICE ANSWERS

1. B. Old Quarter of the First City
2. C. defender of someone who is challenged
3. A. reveal his true family name
4. A. they weren't going to stay long
5. D. burned replicated bird meat

MISSION PERFORMANCE RATING:

45 – 65 points **Superior:** No one questions your authority.

40 – 44 points **Above Average:** You must be the elder sibling.

30 – 39 points **Average:** You didn't make the cut for cha'DIch.

20 – 29 points **Fair:** You can be Duras' cha'DIch.

0 – 19 points **Poor:** ha'DIbah!

◢ ALLEGIANCE

Picard is kidnapped while relaxing in his quarters and is replaced with an exact duplicate. The real Picard awakens in a cell with two other occupants, a Starfleet cadet and an alien known as Tholl. A fourth prisoner soon arrives, a fierce warrior named Esoqq. After unsuccessful escape attempts, the prisoners begin suspecting each other of being one of their captors.

Although Picard's replica functions just like the real version, Riker begins to suspect something is wrong. Picard's replica keeps the crew in the dark and orders them into increasingly more dangerous situations. Things get so bad that Riker is forced to relieve the replica of command.

Meanwhile, Picard determines that the Starfleet cadet is actually one of the captors. The cadet dematerializes and is replaced by several aliens. Once Picard exposed them and what they were doing, they could not continue their research. Picard is transported to his bridge, accompanied by an alien. Picard's replica also reverts to his alien form. Using subtle body language, Picard conveys to Riker that he wishes to detain the aliens. A force field surrounds them. The aliens are terrified of being confined and plead for release. Picard lets them go knowing they've had a taste of their own medicine.

TRIVIA QUESTIONS

1. Where is Tholl from? **(4pts)**
2. What concepts were the aliens studying? **(3pts)**
3. What information did Picard find it unlikely that a first year cadet would know? **(3pts)**
4. What does Picard use to disable the stun rays in the holding cell? **(3pts)**
5. What do the occupants of the holding cell find when they pry the door open? **(3pts)**
6. What sits in the middle of the holding cell? **(3pts)**
7. Where is Haro from? **(3pts)**
8. What is Troi's winning poker hand? **(4pts)**
9. What is Riker's poker hand? **(5pts)**
10. What is Haro's best area of study? **(4pts)**

✪✪ MATHEMATICALLY SPEAKING (25pts)

Add the following numbers together:

1. How many years ago did Picard visit Chalna while commanding the *Stargazer*? **(5pts)**

180 ✹ SEASON THREE

2. How long will the *Enterprise*'s shields last at 20 million kilometres from the pulsar? **(5pts)**
3. At Warp 7, how many minutes would it take the *Enterprise* to get to the closest pulsar? **(5pts)**
4. At Warp 2, how many hours would it take the *Enterprise* to get to the closest pulsar? **(5pts)**

Total: _____

What is the significance of this number in relation to the episode? **(5pts)**

ANSWERS

TRIVIA ANSWERS

1. Mizar II
2. authority and leadership
3. his mission to Mintaka III
4. Esoqq's knife
5. a metal wall
6. the food dispenser
7. Bolarus IX
8. flush, queen high
9. pair of threes
10. in the Lonka Cluster

MATHEMATICALLY SPEAKING SOLUTION

1. 12
2. 18
3. 34
4. 31

Total: 95

95 is the level Picard's replica wanted engine efficiency status increased to.

MISSION PERFORMANCE RATING:

30 – 60 points **Superior:** You knew who the alien was from the start.
20 – 29 points **Above Average:** You Mizarian, how typical!
15 – 19 points **Average:** Stay away from the food dispenser.
10 – 14 points **Fair:** You're being transferred to Chalna.
 0 – 9 points **Poor:** Esoqq needs a light snack.

CAPTAIN'S HOLIDAY

STARDATE: 43745.2

The crew persuade Picard to take a vacation to Risa. There he encounters an archaeologist named Vash, who is searching for a legendary weapon known as the Tox Uthat. Picard also comes across two time travelling Vorgons who are searching for the same weapon. They claim to be security officers, here to take the Tox Uthat into proper custody. A double-crossed Ferengi soon complicates matters. The Ferengi paid Vash to steal some information about the Tox Uthat but she kept the money and came to Risa instead.

Picard and Vash find the cave where the Tox Uthat is supposed to be buried. As they begin to dig, the Ferengi turns up armed with a weapon. He directs the two humans to start digging for the Tox Uthat. After several hours of fruitless searching, Picard and Vash convince the Ferengi that the information was mistaken and there is no Tox Uthat buried in the cave. Picard and Vash return to their separate rooms empty-handed.

Picard suspects the truth and later returns to Vash's room, just in time to catch her leaving. She reveals the Tox Uthat to Picard, just as he suspected. Vash had got to Risa earlier than the Ferengi thought and had retrieved the artefact. She then led the Ferengi on a wild goose chase to throw him off her trail. The Vorgons return wanting the Tox Uthat. Picard, not sure if the device belongs to them, destroys the Tox Uthat to prevent it from falling into the wrong hands.

TRIVIA QUESTIONS

1. What is being held at the Astrophysics Centre? **(3pts)**
2. How do the Vorgons initiate their transporters? **(4pts)**
3. What is the *Enterprise* scheduled for? **(3pts)**
4. What special orders from Picard does Riker follow? **(4pts)**
5. What type of woman makes the perfect mate for a Ferengi? **(3pts)**
6. Where is the location of the Tox Uthat on Risa? **(4pts)**
7. Where does Vash plan on going to next? **(5pts)**
8. What does Riker ask Picard to buy him on Risa? **(3pts)**
9. What is the Tox Uthat capable of? **(3pts)**
10. What is not Dr Crusher's idea of fun? **(3pts)**

CHARACTER QUOTE
(4pts per word + 5pts for identifying the speaker.)

Unscramble the words below and then identify the character.

'The _____ _____ the _____ , the _____ the _____ .'
    RMEO UICFDFLTI   SATK   EWRTSEE   TVYOCIR

❂ SPECIAL ASSIGNMENT (15pts)

Where did Picard once holiday for four days and hated it?

ANSWERS

TRIVIA ANSWERS

1. a symposium on rogue star clusters
2. by touching a protruding square contact on the left side of their heads
3. one week of maintenance overhaul at Starbase 12
4. Transporter Code 14
5. a greedy and unscrupulous woman
6. 27 kilometres due east in subterranean caves
7. explore ruins on Sarthong V
8. Horga'hn
9. halting all nuclear reaction within a star
10. watching a technician build deuterium tanks

CHARACTER QUOTE SOLUTION

'The more difficult the task, the sweeter the victory.' – Riker

SPECIAL ASSIGNMENT SOLUTION

Zytchin III

Congratulations! Starfleet Command is proud to award you the Starfleet Medal of Honour and 15 extra points.

MISSION PERFORMANCE RATING:

55 – 75 points **Superior:** You like to watch technicians build deuterium tanks too!

45 – 54 points **Above Average:** Your Horga'hn is showing.

30 – 44 points **Average:** Your first jamaharon?

15 – 29 points **Fair:** You haven't mastered hoverball at all.

0 – 14 points **Poor:** You must be one of the ensigns from Deck 39.

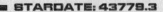

The *Enterprise* receives new orders and a crew transfer. Tam, a talented but troubled telepath, is the Federation's specialist for this mission and he joins the *Enterprise*. A probe has discovered a living space vessel. The *Enterprise*'s mission is to beat the Romulans there and make first contact with the alien, code named 'Tin Man'. The alien is in orbit around an unstable star and is in danger.

The *Enterprise* beats the Romulans to the alien vessel's location. Suddenly, a Romulan ship decloaks and fires on the *Enterprise* as it flies past towards Tin Man. Tam warns Tin Man and the alien ship creates an energy tidal wave that destroys the Romulan ship and damages the *Enterprise*.

Soon, a second Romulan vessel appears and threatens to destroy Tin Man. A minimal away team goes on board Tin Man to attempt communication. Tam is successful in reaching the alien's consciousness and Tin Man repels the other two ships far away before the star collapses. Tam decides to stay with Tin Man; he has found a new home.

TRIVIA QUESTIONS

1. Where did Troi study psychology? **(3pts)**
2. Wesley picks up an unusual echo on what? **(3pts)**
3. What did Tam never learn to do? **(3pts)**
4. What is the power status of the *Enterprise*'s shields when the second Romulan ship uncloaks? **(4pts)**
5. What does the second Romulan vessel claim? **(3pts)**
6. How far has the *Enterprise* been thrown clear of the explosion by Tin Man? **(4pts)**
7. Geordi has to take the warp engines off-line to recalibrate what? **(3pts)**
8. How long has Tin Man roamed the galaxy? **(3pts)**
9. By what percentage did the Romulans exceed their maximum engine output to keep up with the *Enterprise*? **(5pts)**
10. How many people were killed in the Ghorusda Disaster? **(4pts)**

MULTIPLE CHOICE QUESTIONS

1. How do the Chandrans say hello? **(5pts)**
   A. a lovely three day ritual
   B. a dreary six day ceremony
   C. T' Meja
   D. the word hello is not found in their language

---

2. What type of assignments has Tam gravitated to? **(3pts)**
   A. those which are volatile, risky ones
   B. those which place him into direct contact with many humanoids
   C. those which tend to isolate him from other humanoids
   D. those which tend to be commonplace but require a telepath

3. Data is the *Enterprise*'s resident what? **(3pts)**
   A. android
   B. first contact specialist
   C. biomedical specialist
   D. honour student in exobiology

4. How did Troi know Tam at the university? **(2pts)**
   A. he was a patient there
   B. he was a professor there
   C. he was her boyfriend
   D. he was a fellow student

5. Tam is a specialist in what? **(2pts)**
   A. alienating most life forms
   B. first contact with new life forms
   C. telepathy
   D. treaty negotiations

ANSWERS

TRIVIA ANSWERS

1. at the University of Betazed
2. navigational sensors
3. to be able to block out other minds
4. 40% power
5. the right of vengeance
6. 3.8 billion kilometres
7. intermix regulators
8. thousands of years
9. by 30%
10. 47

MULTIPLE CHOICE ANSWERS

1. A. a lovely three day ritual
2. C. those which tend to isolate him from other humanoids
3. D. honour student in exobiology
4. A. he was a patient there
5. B. first contact with new life forms

MISSION PERFORMANCE RATING:

45 – 50 points **Superior:** With ratings like these, you'll be up for promotion.
40 – 44 points **Above Average:** Honour student in exobiology, huh?
30 – 39 points **Average:** You'll just love the Chandrans.
20 – 29 points **Fair:** Tinman needs more organic nonsentient ballast.
  0 – 19 points **Poor:** Be on the next Federation ship to Ghorusda.

HOLLOW PURSUITS

The *Enterprise* must transport medical samples needed to combat an outbreak of fever elsewhere in the Federation. Geordi is having problems with one of his engineers, Barclay, who is shy, awkward and absent-minded. Geordi brings his concerns to the Captain but Picard tells Geordi to work harder to make Barclay a part of the team. Geordi seeks Barclay out and finds him on the holodeck indulging in fantasies about the senior officers. Geordi tells Barclay he probably should talk to Troi about his addiction to the holodeck. He agrees but the meeting with Troi goes badly and Barclay retreats to his holographic sanctuary.

Meanwhile, various seemingly unrelated malfunctions begin plaguing the *Enterprise*. Finally, the warp engines go haywire and the ship travels steadily faster, approaching catastrophic warp speeds. Geordi and his engineering team try to discover the nature of the problem before it's too late. Barclay is instrumental in determining the cause and saving the ship. Later, Troi helps Barclay give up his addiction to the holodeck.

TRIVIA QUESTIONS

1. Who are Barclay's three holographic musketeers? **(3pts)**
2. Which transporter room is malfunctioning? **(3pts)**
3. What is Barclay's job on the *Enterprise*? **(3pts)**
4. What does Troi tell her holographic counterpart? **(3pts)**
5. Barclay erases all his holodeck programmes except which one? **(5pts)**
6. Data estimates it will be how long before structural failure ensues? **(4pts)**
7. Why can't the *Enterprise* make an emergency saucer separation? **(3pts)**
8. To what speed did the *Enterprise*'s engines jump momentarily? **(3pts)**
9. What was O'Brien synchronizing? **(4pts)**
10. Which Barclay holodeck programme features the 'goddess of empathy'? **(4pts)**

CHARACTER QUOTE
(3pts per word + 4pts for identifying the speaker.)

Unscramble the words below and then identify the character.

'_____ me, but why is _____ _____ _____ _____ to
OADPNR   ITLNUENETA ARCYABL ENBGI DEFRERRE

_____ as a _____?'
ENLDCEILNTAYS   EEETBGAVL

⊛ SPECIAL ASSIGNMENT (15pts)

How many substances cannot be detected by standard scans?

ANSWERS

TRIVIA ANSWERS

1. Geordi, Data, Picard
2. Transporter Room 3
3. diagnostic engineer
4. 'Muzzle it!'
5. Barclay Programme 9
6. 15 minutes and 40 seconds
7. the saucer separation could rupture the warp field
8. Warp 7.25
9. phase transition coils
10. Barclay Programme 15

CHARACTER QUOTE SOLUTION

'Pardon me, but why is Lieutenant Barclay being referred to clandestinely as a vegetable?' – Data

SPECIAL ASSIGNMENT SOLUTION

15,525
Congratulations! Starfleet Command is proud to award you the Starfleet Medal of Honour and 15 extra points.

MISSION PERFORMANCE RATING:

55 – 75 points **Superior:** Quick, name all the substances that can't be scanned.

45 – 54 points **Above Average:** You have a healthy fantasy life.

30 – 44 points **Average:** What's your favourite vegetable, broccoli?

15 – 29 points **Fair:** Spending a little *too* much time in a holographic gin joint?

0 – 14 points **Poor:** With scores like yours who needs promotions!

THE MOST TOYS

STARDATE: 43872.2

Data is transferring, via shuttlecraft, a dangerous substance needed to treat a colony's contaminated water supply from a trader's vessel. Suddenly, the shuttle explodes. The *Enterprise* crew is puzzled and stunned: there was no apparent reason for the explosion. The crew, thinking Data was destroyed in the blast, leaves to assist the colony. In reality, Data was knocked out and removed from the shuttlecraft before it left the ship. Fajo, the trader, is a collector of rare items and has kidnapped Data for his collection. Fajo engineered the whole situation to capture Data and make it appear that he was destroyed.

Meanwhile, the *Enterprise*'s crew decontaminates the colony's water supply. Upon investigation, an away team determines that the contamination was intentional. The crew figures out that Fajo is behind the problem and must have kidnapped Data.

Data refuses to co-operate with Fajo's demands. Later, one of Fajo's assistants tries to help Data escape, but she is killed during the attempt. The *Enterprise* arrives and beams Data up just as he is to put an end to Fajo's unscrupulous ways. Fajo is arrested and his stolen artefacts recovered.

TRIVIA QUESTIONS

1. Whose expression does Data try to mimic? **(3pts)**
2. What is common on Klingon ships? **(3pts)**
3. What is a marvellous contradiction? **(3pts)**
4. Which one of Van Gogh's paintings did Fajo have in his collection? **(4pts)**
5. What is the collection room's door keyed to? **(3pts)**
6. Which guild is Fajo a member of? **(4pts)**
7. What is the name of Fajo's rival collector friend? **(4pts)**
8. What is the name of the Dali painting in Fajo's collection? **(3pts)**
9. Which trading card does Fajo possess? **(4pts)**
10. Whose water supply is contaminated? **(4pts)**

WHAT LITTLE TOYS ARE MADE OF (2pts each)

Match the material with the descriptions. Some materials may be used more than once, others not at all.

Description	Material
1. *Enterprise* needs 108 kg of this material.	A. tripolymer composites
2. Data is composed of 11.8 kg of this material.	
3. Data is composed of 1.3 kg of this material.	B. hytritium
4. Material loaded into a class-2 probe.	C. tricyanite

5. Slow to assimilate.
6. Only other source is in the Sigma Erandi system.
7. Level in the colony's water supply is 42 ppm.
8. Data is composed of 26.8 kg of this material.
9. Difficult to replicate.
10. *Enterprise* only received 81 kg of this material.

D. molybdenum-cobalt alloy
E. duranium
F. bioplast sheeting

✪✪ SPECIAL ASSIGNMENT (15pts)

What size search perimeter does the *Enterprise* use to find Fajo's ship and how was it determined?

ANSWERS

TRIVIA ANSWERS

1. the *Mona Lisa's*
2. promotion due to the death of a crewmate
3. a military pacifist
4. *The Starry Night*
5. galvanic skin responses and DNA patterns
6. Stacius Trade Guild
7. Palor Toff
8. *The Persistence of Memory*
9. only known 1962 Roger Maris trading card
10. Federation colony on Beta Agni II

WHAT LITTLE TOYS ARE MADE OF SOLUTION

1. B hytritium; 2. D molybdenum-cobalt alloy; 3. F bioplast sheeting; 4. B hytritium; 5. C tricyanite; 6. B hytritium; 7. C tricyanite; 8. A tripolymer composites; 9. C tricyanite; 10.B hytritium

SPECIAL ASSIGNMENT SOLUTION

.102 light years (based on Warp 3 for 23 hrs.)
Congratulations! Starfleet Command is proud to award you the Starfleet Medal of Honour and 15 extra points.

MISSION PERFORMANCE RATING:

50 – 70 points **Superior:** How many kgs of bioplast sheeting are you composed of?

40 – 49 points **Above Average:** Almost as devious as Fajo.

25 – 39 points **Average:** Hurry, the last shuttle's departing! Don't miss it!

10 – 24 points **Fair:** You smell like gum. Leave that Roger Maris card alone.

0 – 9 points **Poor:** Fajo has a Varon-T disruptor with your name on it.

SAREK

The *Enterprise* transports Sarek, an important Vulcan ambassador, on a critical diplomatic mission. The entrance of a new race known as the Legarans to the Federation hinges on Sarek. He has worked with the Legarans for this historic meeting for some time. Random acts of violence begin appearing all over the ship. The cause is finally found: Sarek is suffering from Bendii Syndrome. This causes Sarek to lose control over his emotions and to project them subconsciously onto others.

Picard goes to Sarek's quarters to confront him. Despite the efforts of Sarek's wife and staff to isolate him from others, Sarek talks with Picard. It is apparent to Picard that Sarek's emotional state is unstable. Picard decides to cancel the meeting rather than jeopardize the conference. Sarek's wife pleads with Picard to let Sarek finish this mission and keep his honour. Picard undergoes a mind-meld with Sarek to help bolster his emotional state during the meeting with the Legarans. The procedure, though a bit rough on Picard, seems to work. Sarek's meeting with the Legarans is successful.

TRIVIA QUESTIONS

1. What is the core of a Vulcan's being? **(3pts)**
2. When did Picard first meet Sarek? **(4pts)**
3. What must be done to prepare the conference room for the meeting? **(3pts)**
4. What can be a terrible intimacy? **(3pts)**
5. How long did the conference schedule take to negotiate? **(4pts)**
6. Sarek has built a personal relationship with whom? **(3pts)**
7. Who can be affected by Bendii Syndrome? **(3pts)**
8. What treaty was an important highlight of Sarek's career? **(5pts)**
9. How long has Sarek been working towards this historic meeting? **(3pts)**
10. How old is Sarek? **(4pts)**

✪ SPECIAL ASSIGNMENT (15pts)

Which four violinists does Data mention?

MULTIPLE CHOICE QUESTIONS

1. Data has been programmed to reproduce the musical styles of how many musicians? **(5pts)**
   A. over 200 concert pianists
   B. exactly 307 concert zitherists
   C. over 300 concert violinists
   D. exactly 275 concert oboists

2. What are early symptoms of Bendii Syndrome? **(2pts)**
   A. sudden loss of memory, blurred vision
   B. sudden bursts of emotion, mostly irrational anger
   C. pain in the logic centres of the brain
   D. migraines

3. What was Data at the concert? **(2pts)**
   A. most excellent
   B. the featured soloist
   C. rude
   D. interrupted

4. Who had a quarrel in the conference room? **(3pts)**
   A. Riker and Geordi
   B. Wesley and his mother
   C. Picard and Riker
   D. Geordi and Wesley

5. Where will the Legarans sit during the conference? **(3pts)**
   A. on elevated platforms
   B. in large plastic chairs
   C. in a foetid pool of bubbling red liquid
   D. in a separate room with a methane atmosphere

ANSWERS

TRIVIA ANSWERS

1. their emotional detachment
2. many years ago at his son's wedding
3. remove the furniture and make the walls bare
4. a mind-meld
5. three months
6. Legarans
7. Vulcans over 200 years old
8. the Treaty of Alpha Cygnus IX
9. 93 years
10. 202 years old

SPECIAL ASSIGNMENT SOLUTION

Heifetz, Menuhin, Gray-tay, and Tataglia

Congratulations! Starfleet Command is proud to award you the Starfleet Medal of Honour and 15 extra points.

MULTIPLE CHOICE ANSWERS

1. C. over 300 concert violinists
2. B. sudden bursts of emotion, mostly irrational anger
3. B. the featured soloist
4. D. Geordi and Wesley
5. C. in a foetid pool of bubbling red liquid

MISSION PERFORMANCE RATING:

45 – 65 points **Superior:** May I call you Ambassador?

40 – 44 points **Above Average:** Sarek appreciates your telepathic propping.

30 – 39 points **Average:** You could use a mind-meld.

20 – 29 points **Fair:** You have Bendii Syndrome but no career to protect.

0 – 19 points **Poor:** You must have fell into the Legarans' conference pool.

MÉNAGE À TROI ⏻

The *Enterprise* attends a conference where a Ferengi becomes attracted to Lwaxana. Troi and Riker go on shore leave while the *Enterprise* leaves for a routine mapping mission. Later on the planet, Riker, Troi, and her mother are kidnapped by the Ferengi captain. The Ferengi hopes to profit by using Lwaxana's telepathic abilities during negotiations. The *Enterprise* returns from its mission and is told of the kidnappings. They begin searching for the Ferengi vessel.

Riker escapes from his cell and is able to send a signal out. The *Enterprise* detects Riker's message and heads for the Ferengi ship. Lwaxana strikes a deal with the love-struck Ferengi captain to release Troi and Riker if she stays with him. The *Enterprise* shows up and Riker and Troi beam back to the ship. Picard follows Lwaxana's lead and acts like a jealous lover. Picard demands Lwaxana back or he will destroy the Ferengi ship. The Ferengi captain quickly beams Lwaxana back and then vacates the area.

TRIVIA QUESTIONS

1. What speed does Picard order for the return trip to Betazed to return Lwaxana? **(3pts)**
2. Lwaxana is a daughter of the what? **(3pts)**
3. How old was Troi when Lwaxana began calling her 'little one'? **(4pts)**
4. What does the Ferengi doctor want to do to Lwaxana? **(3pts)**
5. What type of flowers were discovered in the pond on Betazed? **(4pts)**
6. What type of music is playing during the closing ceremonies on the *Enterprise*? **(5pts)**
7. The flowers Tog gave to Lwaxana are native to what planet? **(4pts)**
8. What is Lwaxana heir to? **(3pts)**
9. What is Lwaxana the holder of? **(3pts)**
10. What excuse does Picard give Lwaxana to avoid talking with her? **(3pts)**

✪ SPECIAL ASSIGNMENT (15pts)

How much energy is being expended in the nebula?

MULTIPLE CHOICE QUESTIONS

1. Ferengi transmissions are routinely what? **(3pts)**
   - **A.** descrambled and uncoded
   - **B.** encoded and phase discriminated
   - **C.** nonsensical
   - **D.** scrambled and encoded

2. What does Riker modify on the Ferengi ship to emit a signal? **(3pts)**
   - **A.** warp field generator coils
   - **B.** mid-range phase adjuster
   - **C.** emergency transponder
   - **D.** warp field phase adjustment

3. How does Troi describe the Sacred Chalice of Rixx? **(2pts)**
   - **A.** a tarnished old cup made of silver
   - **B.** an old clay pot with mould growing in it
   - **C.** a worthless lump of clay
   - **D.** a moss covered artifact from the past, best forgotten

4. Wesley will be admitted to Starfleet Academy after he completes and passes what last step? **(2pts)**
   - **A.** oral exams
   - **B.** practical exams
   - **C.** field project
   - **D.** written exams

5. What move does Riker use to win the game of 3D chess in Ten-Forward with the Ferengi? **(5pts)**
   - **A.** Telubian Manoeuvre
   - **B.** Aldebaran Switch
   - **C.** Albin Counter Gambit
   - **D.** Aldabren Exchange

ANSWERS

TRIVIA ANSWERS

1. Warp 9
2. Fifth House of Betazed
3. five years old
4. study her with his mind probes
5. Zan Periculi
6. Algolian ceremonial rhythms
7. Lappa IV
8. Heir to the Holy Rings of Betazed
9. Sacred Chalice of Rixx
10. he's going to show Reittan the new door mechanisms on the aft turbolift

SPECIAL ASSIGNMENT SOLUTION

5.34×10^{41} watts

Congratulations! Starfleet Command is proud to award you the Starfleet Medal of Honour and 15 extra points.

MULTIPLE CHOICE ANSWERS

1. D. scrambled and encoded
2. D. Warp field phase adjustment
3. B. an old clay pot with mould growing in it
4. A. oral exams
5. D. Aldebaran Exchange

MISSION PERFORMANCE RATING:

45 – 65 points **Superior:** You composed the Algolian ceremonial rhythms.

40 – 44 points **Above Average:** Played any 3D chess lately?

30 – 39 points **Average:** You could outsmart a Ferengi.

20 – 29 points **Fair:** We'll exchange you for the hostages.

0 – 19 points **Poor:** Too many Arcturian Fizz drinks.

TRANSFIGURATIONS

The *Enterprise* rescues a crash victim found on a nearby planet while mapping a new star system. Dr Crusher, who named the survivor John Doe, fights to save his life. Doe begins to make a rapid recovery while his cells rapidly change. Doe also can't remember anything definite about his past, only fragments. Doe's body is wracked by energy surges as his body continues to change.

Meanwhile, Data and Geordi decipher some information recovered from Doe's ship. They figure out Doe's point of origin is the planet Zalkon. As the *Enterprise* gets closer to the planet, a Zalkonian vessel meets them. The Zalkonians state that John Doe is a criminal and demand that the *Enterprise* turn him over. Doe regains his memory at this time and it is discovered that his species is evolving into a race of non-corporeal beings. The Zalkonian government, afraid of the changes, are trying to quell the shift in their species. Doe and a few others fled from their home world to let the changes run their course. Just then, John Doe transforms into a being of pure energy and leaves the *Enterprise* to return home.

TRIVIA QUESTIONS

1. How far ahead of schedule is John Doe's recovery? **(4pts)**
2. What are the devices called that help John Doe use his muscles again? **(3pts)**
3. How long has John Doe been off his feet when he tries to walk again? **(3pts)**
4. What type of medical emergency does Dr Crusher report in Shuttlebay 2? **(4pts)**
5. How long before the *Enterprise* arrives at John Doe's home planet? **(3pts)**
6. What is the name of the shuttlecraft Geordi is performing maintenance on? **(3pts)**
7. Geordi suggests that the storage capsule might be what? **(3pts)**
8. How long was John Doe on the Emergency Biosupport Unit? **(3pts)**
9. Where does Riker come across Geordi and Christy kissing? **(4pts)**
10. What drug and dosage was given to the crash survivor just prior to cardio-stimulation? **(5pts)**

SPECIAL ASSIGNMENT (10pts)

What is the rotational period of the pulsar within sensor range?

MULTIPLE CHOICE QUESTIONS

1. What are Worf's injuries after his fall? **(2pts)**
   A. fractured pelvis and minimal life signs
   B. a broken neck and no life signs
   C. severe brain trauma and no life signs
   D. a severed spinal cord and decaying life signs

2. What procedure was ineffective in restoring John Doe's memory? **(5pts)**
   A. inductive relay
   B. synaptic induction
   C. Krieger wave conduction
   D. synaptic reduction

3. What type of ship crashed on the planet's surface? **(2pts)**
   A. shuttlecraft
   B. scout ship
   C. freighter
   D. escape pod

4. Dr Crusher needs to design a virus to infiltrate the cell structure and boost what? **(3pts)**
   A. immune system function
   B. base cell mutation rate
   C. ATP production
   D. white blood cell count

5. What did Geordi receive during the neural link with the crash survivor? **(3pts)**
   A. energy discharge
   B. both A and E
   C. dose of confidence
   D. both A and C
   E. empathic abilities

ANSWERS

TRIVIA ANSWERS

1. six weeks
2. motor assist bands
3. almost a month
4. Code 7
5. three weeks
6. El-Baz
7. a biochemical storage medium
8. 36 hours
9. Turbolift 12
10. 60cc inaprovaline

SPECIAL ASSIGNMENT SOLUTION

1. 5244 seconds

Congratulations! Starfleet Command is proud to award you the Starfleet Medal of Honour and 10 extra points.

MULTIPLE CHOICE ANSWERS

1. B. a broken neck and no life signs
2. B. synaptic induction
3. D. escape pod
4. C. ATP production
5. D. both A and C

MISSION PERFORMANCE RATING:

45 – 60 points **Superior:** Have you transfigured yet?

40 – 44 points **Above Average:** Patient heal thyself.

30 – 39 points **Average:** Maybe you need a little synaptic induction.

20 – 29 points **Fair:** The Zalkonians can have you, but they only want the smart ones.

0 – 19 points **Poor:** Synaptic induction is a waste of time with you.

THE BEST OF
BOTH WORLDS

STARDATE: 43989.1

The *Enterprise* is sent to investigate a distress call from one of the Federation's colonies. Upon arrival the *Enterprise* finds that all traces of the colony have disappeared. Starfleet sends a specialist to assist the *Enterprise*, Lieutenant Commander Shelby. She confirms the crew's suspicions: the Borg are back.

A Federation ship reports an attack by an unknown vessel. The *Enterprise* arrives and engages the Borg ship. The Borg make it clear that they want Picard. After a short battle, the *Enterprise* escapes and hides within a nearby nebula. The crew improvise a new weapon to use on the Borg, utilising the navigational deflector to channel a high energy beam. The Borg eventually flush the *Enterprise* out of the nebula. Several Borg board the *Enterprise* and abduct Picard. Riker pursues the Borg ship, beaming an away team over to rescue Picard. The team is able to damage the Borg vessel enough to make it drop out of warp. A rescue attempt fails and the away team must leave. The Borg give the *Enterprise* the 'resistance is futile' speech via an assimilated Picard. Riker tells Worf to fire the new weapon and . . .

TRIVIA QUESTIONS

1. The Admiral tells Picard that the closest starship is how far away? **(3pts)**
2. What are unusual magnetic resonance traces called? **(3pts)**
3. Wesley folds with what cards showing? **(3pts)**
4. Where is Starfleet deploying its forces to intercept the Borg? **(4pts)**
5. What is something of a tradition? **(3pts)**
6. What was the *Lalo*'s destination? **(4pts)**
7. What composes 82% of the nebula? **(4pts)**
8. How many casualties are there after the first Borg attack on the *Enterprise*? **(5pts)**
9. A Borg ship could still function effectively with what percentage of it inoperative? **(3pts)**
10. What is the name of the Federation colony? **(3pts)**

WHO AM I? (20pts)

I am a rara avis. I will stand on your shoulders to get where I am going. I'm not afraid of the grand chaise.

ANSWERS

TRIVIA ANSWERS

1. six days
2. Borg footprints
3. three jacks
4. Wolf 359
5. a captain touring his ship before a battle
6. a freight run to Sentinel Minor IV
7. dilithium hydroxyls
8. 11 dead and eight unaccounted for
9. 78%
10. New Providence

WHO AM I? SOLUTION

Lieutenant Commander Shelby

EXPLANATION:

I am a rara avis. – Latin for a strange bird, an unusual person.
Shelby said the early bird gets the worm.
I will stand on your shoulders – She goes over Riker's head and talks directly to Picard about her plan.
to get where I am going. – Shelby wants Riker's job.
I'm not afraid of the grand chaise. – Shelby told Riker she's not afraid of the 'Big Chair'.

MISSION PERFORMANCE RATING:

36 – 55 points **Superior:** You're the Federation's only hope against the Borg!

26 – 35 points **Above Average:** Never succumb to the Borg!

16 – 25 points **Average:** Average Borg material.

11 – 15 points **Fair:** You must be one of the unaccounted-for casualties.

0 – 10 points **Poor:** Apparently the Borg has already assimilated you.

REPEL THE BORG INVASION

The Borg again threatens the Federation. An armada of starships must be organized to fight the invasion. Vital segments of Starfleet have already been destroyed. Only you are able to gather the remnants of the fleet together and organize them into a fighting force. You are placed in command of the *USS Wellington*. Use your sensors to search the Paulson Nebula and locate as many starships as possible. Good luck, the Federation is depending on you!

PAULSON NEBULA SEARCH

Find the following 38 Federation starships hiding from the Borg within the Paulson Nebula. Use your sensors to identity each ship by name. **(2pts each)**

Agamemnon, Ahwahnee, Arcos, Berlin, Cairo, Charleston, Constantinople, Constellation, Crazyhorse, Enterprise, Excalibur, Excelsior, Farragut, Firebrand, Gettysburg, Grissom, Hera, Hood, Kearsarge, Lalo, Lexington, Magellan, Melbourne, Merrimack, Pasteur, Potemkin, Princeton, Raman, Repulse, Rutledge, Stargazer, Sutherland, Thomas Paine, Tiananmen, Trieste, Tripoli, Tsiolkovsky, Victory

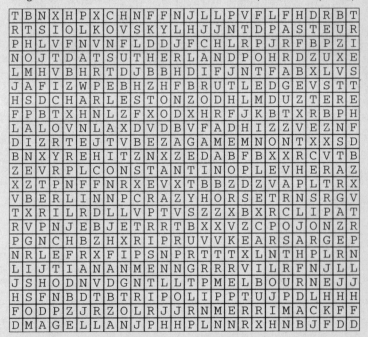

```
T B N X H P X C H N F F N J L L P V F L F H D R B T
R T S I O L K O V S K Y L H J J N T D P A S T E U R
P H L V F N V N F L D D J F C H L R P J R F B P Z I
N O J T D A T S U T H E R L A N D P O H R D Z U X E
L M H V B H R T D J B B H D I F J N T F A B X L V S
J A F I Z W P E B H Z H F B R U T L E D G E V S T T
H S D C H A R L E S T O N Z O D H L M D U Z T E R E
F P B T X H N L Z F X O D X H R F J K B T X R B P H
L A L O V N L A X D V D B V F A D H I Z Z V E Z N F
D I Z R T E J T V B E Z A G A M E M N O N T X X S D
B N X Y R E H I T Z N X Z E D A B F B X X R C V T B
Z E V R P L C O N S T A N T I N O P L E V H E R A Z
X Z T P N F F N R X E V X T B B Z D Z V A P L T R X
V B E R L I N N P C R A Z Y H O R S E T R N S R G V
T X R I L R D L L V P T V S Z Z X B X R C L I P A T
R V P N J E B J E T R R T B X X V Z C P O J O N Z R
P G N C H B Z H X R I P R U V V K E A R S A R G E P
N R L E F R X F I P S N P R T T T X L N T H P L R N
L I J T I A N A N M E N N G R R R V I L R F N J L L
J S H O D N V D G N T L L T P M E L B O U R N E J J
H S F N B D T B T R I P O L I P P T U J P D L H H H
F O D P Z J R Z O L R J J R N M E R R I M A C K F F
D M A G E L L A N J P H H P L N N R X H N B J F D D
```

SPECIAL SECTION

							C													F			R		T
	T	S	I	O	L	K	O	V	S	K	Y								P	A	S	T	E	U	R
	H						N							C				P		R			P		I
	O				A		S	U	T	H	E	R	L	A	N	D		O		R			U		E
	M		V		H		T							I				T		A			L		S
	A		I		W		E				H			R	U	T	L	E	D	G	E		S		T
	S		C	H	A	R	L	E	S	T	O	N		O				M		U			E		E
	P		T		H		L				O				R			K		T					
L	A	L	O		N		A				D				A			I				E			
	I		R		E		T			E		A	G	A	M	E	M	N	O	N		X		S	
	N		Y		E		I			N			E		A							C		T	
	E					C	O	N	S	T	A	N	T	I	N	O	P	L	E		H	E	R	A	
			P		F		N			E			T							A		L		R	
	B	E	R	L	I	N			C	R	A	Z	Y	H	O	R	S	E		R		S		G	
			I		R			L		P			S					X		C		I		A	
			N		E			E		R			B					C		O		O		Z	
	G		C		B			X		I			U			K	E	A	R	S	A	R	G	E	
	R		E		R			I		S			R					L						R	
	I		T	I	A	N	A	N	M	E	N		G					I							
	S		O		N			G							M	E	L	B	O	U	R	N	E		
	S		N		D			T	R	I	P	O	L	I				U							
	O							O							M	E	R	R	I	M	A	C	K		
	M	A	G	E	L	L	A	N																	

MISSION PERFORMANCE RATING:

60 – 76 points **Superior:** You've repelled the Borg invasion!
(SEE BELOW)

50 – 59 points **Above Average:** The tide almost turned against the Borg!

40 – 49 points **Average:** Fight to the last ship!

30 – 39 points **Fair:** Better look for a parallel universe to hide from
the Borg.

 0 – 29 points **Poor:** The Borg have overrun the Federation.

If you have received a SUPERIOR Mission Performance Rating –

Congratulations!
Starfleet Command is proud to award you
the Starfleet Citation for Conspicuous Gallantry and 100 extra points.

SEASON FOUR

THE BEST OF BOTH WORLDS - PART II

════════════ STARDATE: 44001.4

In 'The Best Of Both Worlds – Part I', the Borg had kidnapped Picard and changed him into Locutus, a Borg. An attempt to rescue Picard failed and Riker, now in command, tells Worf to fire a new weapon at the Borg ship. The weapon fires and the Borg ship, undamaged, speeds towards Earth once again. Geordi races to repair the *Enterprise* before the pursuit of the Borg ship can continue.

Meanwhile, the Starfleet armada engages the Borg vessel at Wolf 359. Many Starfleet vessels are lost in the ensuing battle. The *Enterprise* arrives at Wolf 359 too late; the battle is over. Riker pushes the *Enterprise* onward and is able to catch up with the Borg ship. Riker sends an away team to retrieve Picard and they are successful. Dr Crusher is unable to remove the Borg implants while Picard is still tied into the Borg consciousness. Data links himself via Picard into the Borg collective consciousness in the hope of discovering a weakness.

Data successfully links with the Borg and tries to shut down the Borg vessel. The Borg attack and the *Enterprise*'s shields buckle. At the last second, Picard is able to tell Data which Borg subcommand to modify. Picard's suggestion works and the Borg cease their attack. The Borg vessel implements a self-destruct mechanism.

TRIVIA QUESTIONS

1. Why did the *Enterprise*'s deflector weapon have no effect on the Borg ship? **(3pts)**
2. What does Riker receive from Admiral Hanson? **(3pts)**
3. How long is the Starfleet Academy marathon? **(4pts)**
4. The Borg's malfunction initiated what? **(3pts)**
5. Who reports visual contact with the Borg vessel after it enters Sector 001? **(4pts)**
6. O'Brien processes the Borg subspace signal through what? **(4pts)**
7. What is the name of the first set of evasive manoeuvres Riker orders the conn to initiate? **(4pts)**
8. Data thinks the unusual eddy currents at Wolf 359 might suggest what? **(3pts)**
9. How does Guinan describe her relationship with Picard? **(4pts)**
10. Worf says the Borg have no what? **(3pts)**

✪ SPECIAL ASSIGNMENT (15pts)

Name three starships mentioned that were destroyed at the Battle of Wolf 359.

MULTIPLE CHOICE QUESTIONS

1. Which perimeter did the Borg break through? **(2pts)**
   A. Mars Defence Perimeter
   B. Outer Perimeter
   C. Saturn Ring Perimeter
   D. Uranus Defence Perimeter

2. Name the three Borg subcommands that Data mentioned? **(5pts)**
   A. tactical, conn, ops
   B. defence, communication, navigation
   C. tactical, communication, engineering
   D. communication, sleep, navigation

3. How did Data discover the subspace signals between Locutus and the Borg? **(3pts)**
   A. by using multifocal deflection packets
   B. while monitoring subspace communications
   C. by using multimodal reflection sorting
   D. while adjusting the wide-angle active EM scanner

4. How does Locutus describe Data? **(2pts)**
   A. a primitive artificial organism
   B. second hand merchandise
   C. an uninspired artificial life form
   D. a logical addition to the Borg

5. The local field distortion of what weapon wouldn't be strong enough to affect the Borg? **(3pts)**
   A. high energy X-ray laser
   B. antimatter spread
   C. heavy graviton beam
   D. protodynoplaser

ANSWERS

TRIVIA ANSWERS

1. The Borg anticipated the weapon based on Picard's knowledge and experience.
2. field promotion to captain of the *Enterprise*
3. 40 kilometre race
4. a self-destruct sequence
5. Jupiter Outpost 92
6. transport pattern buffer
7. Pattern Riker-Alpha
8. the route the Borg ship might have taken
9. '. . . beyond friendship, beyond family . . .'
10. honour nor courage

SPECIAL ASSIGNMENT SOLUTION

USS Tolstoy
USS Kyushu
USS Melbourne

Congratulations! Starfleet Command is proud to award you the Starfleet Medal of Honour and 15 extra points.

MULTIPLE CHOICE ANSWERS

1. A. Mars Defence Perimeter
2. B. defence, communication, navigation
3. C. by using multimodal reflection sorting
4. A. a primitive artificial organism
5. C. heavy graviton beam

MISSION PERFORMANCE RATING:

45 – 65 points **Superior:** Thanks to you Earth is safe once again.

40 – 44 points **Above Average:** You'll soon be up for promotion.

30 – 39 points **Average:** Report to Mars Defence Perimeter for reassignment.

20 – 29 points **Fair:** You, like the Borg, have neither honour nor courage!

0 – 19 points **Poor:** Weren't you at the battle of Wolf 359 on the *Melbourne*?

SUDDENLY HUMAN ⚓

STARDATE: 44143.7 ▬▬▬▬▬

The *Enterprise* responds to a distress call and rescues the Talarian crew from the damaged ship. A human boy is discovered among them. The boy, known as Jono, is actually the grandson of a high ranking Starfleet officer. The boy's parents were killed many years ago and a Talarian captain named Endar raised him as his own.

Endar meets with the *Enterprise* and asks for Jono back. Picard refuses, saying Jono should be returned to his human family. Endar threatens to go to war to get Jono back but Picard hopes to arouse Jono's humanity. Jono begins to remember his human side but his loyalties are confused. He attacks Picard, hoping for death, rather than betray Endar. Picard realizes that Jono indeed loves his father and that it would be wrong to separate them. Jono is returned to Endar.

TRIVIA QUESTIONS

1. What is one of the greatest things in the universe, according to Wesley? **(3pts)**
2. What do Talarian traditions allow Endar to do? **(3pts)**
3. What can a female never do among Talarians? **(3pts)**
4. From what type of vessel was the distress call? **(3pts)**
5. Where did Endar's biological son die? **(4pts)**
6. What is the Talarian custom called when one is distressed and wails constantly? **(5pts)**
7. What was Jono listed as according to Starfleet records? **(3pts)**
8. How old was Jono when his parents were killed? **(4pts)**
9. What type of detonator, used by the Talarians, is undetected by *Enterprise* sensor scans? **(4pts)**
10. What type of ship does Riker say the Talarian vessel appears to be? **(3pts)**

SPECIAL ASSIGNMENT (10pts)

What does Jono stab Picard with?

MULTIPLE CHOICE QUESTIONS

1. What is Wesley's new look? **(2pts)**
    A. crewcut
    B. multiple pierced body parts
    C. ice cream splattered on his face
    D. new shoes

---

2. What type of lasers are Talarian warships armed with? **(3pts)**
   - **A.** high energy X-ray lasers
   - **B.** Artonian lasers
   - **C.** low yield gamma ray lasers
   - **D.** lithium lasers

3. Why doesn't Jono want to take off his gloves? **(3pts)**
   - **A.** so he won't have to wash his hands
   - **B.** he's afraid he'll catch germs
   - **C.** his hands get cold rather easily
   - **D.** so he won't have to touch an alien

4. What has Picard known ever since he was a child? **(2pts)**
   - **A.** that he loved reading Shakespeare
   - **B.** that he wanted to join Starfleet
   - **C.** that he would be a Starfleet captain
   - **D.** that he would never marry

5. How did Jono's human parents die? **(5pts)**
   - **A.** the Borg destroyed the colony
   - **B.** a trioxilate ore smelting accident
   - **C.** the colony was overrun by Talarian forces
   - **D.** their ship exploded after colliding with a micrometeorite

MISSION PERFORMANCE RATING:
45 – 60 points **Superior:** You have just prevented a new intergalactic war.
40 – 44 points **Above Average:** You have ridden a T'stayan before!
30 – 39 points **Average:** Take your gloves OFF!
20 – 29 points **Fair:** Go on, take a stab at it. Make my day.
 0 – 19 points **Poor:** At this rate you'll never get off KP duty.

The *Enterprise* is heading for a specialized medical facility when Data suddenly begins to act strangely and causes life support on the bridge to fail. After everyone evacuates the bridge, Data takes control of the *Enterprise*. Despite Picard's efforts to regain his ship, Data takes the *Enterprise* to a planet and beams down to the surface. There a dazed Data enters the lab of Dr Noonian Soong, his creator.

Dr Soong makes a few adjustments and Data begins to function normally again. Just then, Lore, Data's brother, arrives and is also in a dazed state. Dr Soong explains that he summoned Data to his lab to give him an emotion chip and that he had no idea that Lore was still functioning. Dr Soong takes a quick nap before installing the chip. During Dr Soong's nap, Lore shuts Data off and changes into his Starfleet uniform. Dr Soong awakens and implants the chip into Lore. The chip further enrages the deranged Lore who attacks Dr Soong and leaves.

The *Enterprise* crew is finally able to beam down to the planet and confront Data in the lab. Dr Soong dies soon after saying good-bye to Data and the away team returns to the *Enterprise*. The ship makes it to the medical facility just in time to save an ailing boy.

TRIVIA QUESTIONS

1. How soon will the saucer module drop out of warp after separating from the stardrive section? **(4pts)**
2. What do Lore's clothes consist of when he first turns up at Dr Soong's lab? **(3pts)**
3. How long does Willie Potts' treatment last at the medical facility? **(3pts)**
4. What tune does Data whistle for Dr Soong? **(3pts)**
5. What is the cause of the life support system failure on Deck 1? **(3pts)**
6. Picard is the only person who has clearance to do what? **(4pts)**
7. What does Picard tell O'Brien to disconnect? **(3pts)**
8. How does Data get to the transporter room? **(3pts)**
9. What safety devices does Data override to cause the life support system failure on Deck 1? **(4pts)**
10. What does Willie Potts eat in the forest? **(5pts)**

CHARACTER QUOTE
(3pts per word + 4pts for identifying the speaker.)

Unscramble the words below and then identify the character.

'_____ _____ got a _____ _____, can't _____ tell
ETNOF RNWGO   RKBNOE AHTRE   ENVE

his _____ _____.'
YBSO RPTAA

SPECIAL ASSIGNMENT (10pts)

What ditty does Lore sing?

MISSION PERFORMANCE RATING:

55 – 70 points **Superior:** When you have logic who needs emotions!

45 – 54 points **Above Average:** We'll have to start calling you 'Often Right'!

30 – 44 points **Average:** I challenge you to a laser duel. You bring the red dye.

15 – 29 points **Fair:** Go see if the air's breathable on the bridge, the canary just died.

0 – 14 points **Poor:** Here, try this tropical fruit salad and don't share it!

STARDATE: 44012.3

The *Enterprise* is undergoing repairs at Earth Station McKinley after its recent encounter with the Borg. Worf's parents visit him on the *Enterprise*. At first he is uncomfortable with his parents' visit but later tells them he is happy they stopped by.

Dr Crusher retrieves a package she had stored on Earth. It contains various items from her deceased husband, Jack. Among the contents is a holographic message he recorded for Wesley. Dr Crusher gives the disk to Wesley and he views it. It answers a few questions Wesley had about his father.

Picard returns to the village where he grew up in France. There Picard stays with his brother, Robert, on the old family farm. Robert is a traditionalist and dislikes technology. He continues the family business of growing grapes and producing fine wines. Picard meets up with an old friend, Louis, who is working on a project to create new landmasses by raising the sea floor. Picard is offered the directorship for the project. Robert picks a fight with Picard and they go crashing through the vineyard's fields. Covered in mud they begin to laugh. Picard suddenly breaks down and confronts his shame over the Borg incident and realizes that he belongs among the stars and not on Earth. Picard and Robert reconcile their differences and the Captain returns to his ship, the *Enterprise*.

TRIVIA QUESTIONS

1. What instructions does Robert give Picard concerning the bottle of wine he gives him? **(3pts)**
2. When did Jack want Wesley to have the holographic message? **(3pts)**
3. What Klingon dish did Worf's mother learn to cook and was his favourite? **(4pts)**
4. What can't Worf get enough of? **(3pts)**
5. What does Worf feel is inappropriate for a Klingon? **(4pts)**
6. How long has it been since Picard has visited his home village? **(3pts)**
7. What vintage was the bottle of wine Robert gave to Picard as he left? **(5pts)**
8. Which episode does Picard refer to when he mentions using harmonic resonators? **(3pts)**
9. What did Worf's father serve as? **(4pts)**
10. Where on Earth did Riker and Troi discuss going? **(3pts)**

✪ SPECIAL ASSIGNMENT (15pts)

What makes the *Enterprise*'s recrystallization process ten times more efficient than on Excelsior-class starships?

MULTIPLE CHOICE QUESTIONS

1. What was Worf not aware of? **(2pts)**
   - **A.** that Picard grew up in France
   - **B.** that Jack had made a recorded message for Wesley
   - **C.** that his own parents were on the visitors list
   - **D.** O'Brien's middle name

2. As René looks at the night sky from under the tree, what is seen in the sky? **(2pts)**
   - **A.** stars
   - **B.** the *Enterprise*
   - **C.** a falling star
   - **D.** Venus

3. What type of specialist was Worf's father? **(5pts)**
   - **A.** emergency medical
   - **B.** warp coils
   - **C.** inertia field
   - **D.** warp field

4. What book did Jack send to Beverly? **(3pts)**
   - **A.** *How To Advance Your Aims Through Marriage*
   - **B.** *The Single Parent: A Guide To Raising A Child In The 24th Century*
   - **C.** *Sixty Ways To Lose Your Lover*
   - **D.** *How To Advance Your Career Through Marriage*

5. What was the proudest moment of Mr Rozhenko's life? **(3pts)**
   - **A.** when Worf earned his Starfleet commission
   - **B.** when Worf received discommendation
   - **C.** when Worf graduated from the Academy
   - **D.** when Mrs Rozhenko gave birth to Worf

ANSWERS

TRIVIA ANSWERS

1. don't drink it all at once and don't drink it alone if possible
2. when he reached 18 years of age
3. Rokeg blood pie
4. prune juice
5. to receive family while on duty
6. almost 20 years
7. 2347
8. 'Pen Pals'
9. chief petty officer
10. Angel Falls in Venezuela

SPECIAL ASSIGNMENT SOLUTION

theta-matrix compositor

Congratulations! Starfleet Command is proud to award you the Starfleet Medal of Honour and 15 extra points.

MULTIPLE CHOICE ANSWERS

1. D. O'Brien's middle name
2. C. a falling star
3. D. warp field
4. D. *How To Advance Your Career Through Marriage*
5. A. when Worf earned his Starfleet commission

MISSION PERFORMANCE RATING:

45 – 65 points **Superior:** So you're the new director of the Atlantis Project!

40 – 44 points **Above Average:** How about a parade? Picard doesn't want one.

30 – 39 points **Average:** The Atlantis Project needs another supervisor.

20 – 29 points **Fair:** You've been eating too many fermented grapes.

0 – 19 points **Poor:** Robert needs a new punching bag!

REMEMBER ME

STARDATE: 44161.2

Dr Crusher welcomes Dr Quaice, an old friend, aboard after the *Enterprise* docks at Starbase 133. Later, Crusher stops by to see Wesley in Engineering. He is in the middle of an experiment when suddenly there is a strange flash of light. Wesley looks around for his mother but she is gone. The next morning Dr Crusher reports Dr Quaice missing. No trace of him can be found on the *Enterprise* or in Starfleet records. Other members of the crew begin to disappear but only Crusher seems to notice anything is wrong. Finally, Crusher is the only crew member left on the *Enterprise*.

A mysterious energy vortex appears twice but Crusher is able to keep herself from being pulled into it. Unknown to Crusher, she is trapped inside Wesley's experimental warp bubble. Geordi and Wesley have created the vortex in an effort to rescue her. The bubble is destabilizing and efforts to recover Dr Crusher look bleak. Suddenly, the Traveler shows up and assists Wesley in creating a third vortex. This time Dr Crusher has figured out what's going on and gladly jumps through the hoop.

TRIVIA QUESTIONS

1. What begins to happen to Decks 5 through 14 when Dr Crusher's universe contracts? **(4pts)**
2. What movie does Dr Crusher quote? **(3pts)**
3. What question should the computer not be able to answer? **(3pts)**
4. When does the second vortex appear to Dr Crusher? **(3pts)**
5. How long will Dr Crusher remain alive according to the Traveler? **(3pts)**
6. What is the nature of the *Enterprise*'s design flaw, according to the computer? **(4pts)**
7. What is Picard's blood pressure during automatic monitoring by the computer? **(5pts)**
8. What is Picard's body temperature during automatic monitoring by the computer? **(4pts)**
9. What kind of experiments has Wesley been conducting? **(3pts)**
10. What did Wesley create inside the warp drive? **(3pts)**

✪✪ MATHEMATICALLY SPEAKING (25pts)

Answer A to D and then insert the numbers into the formula to solve this problem.

A. How many years has Dr Crusher known Dr Quaice? **(3pts)**
B. How many metres per second does Geordi say the warp bubble is contracting? **(3pts)**

C. How long can life support be maintained as the *Enterprise* dissolves (to nearest minute)? **(3pts)**

D. After Data reports no unusual activity in the sector, what is the crew complement of the *Enterprise*? **(3pts)**

$(A \times B \times C) + D = E$

What is the significance of your answer (E) in relation to the episode? **(13pts)**

ANSWERS

TRIVIA ANSWERS

1. explosive decompression
2. *The Wizard Of Oz*
3. 'What is the nature of the universe?'
4. just after Picard vanishes
5. as long as she believes she is alive
6. no ship's structures exist forward of Bulkhead 342
7. 122/76
8. 37.2 °C
9. experimenting with Kosinski's warp field equations, trying to improve engine efficiency
10. static warp field

MATHEMATICALLY SPEAKING SOLUTION

A. 15
B. 15
C. 4
D. 114

$(15 \times 15 \times 4) + 114 = 1014$

This is the normal crew complement and also includes Dr Quaice.

MISSION PERFORMANCE RATING:

30 – 60 points **Superior:** A true Traveler – all phased out.
25 – 39 points **Above Average:** You knew to jump through the vortex!
20 – 29 points **Average:** You shouldn't play with static warp bubbles!
10 – 19 points **Fair:** You are missing with the rest of the crew.
 0 – 9 points   **Poor:** You are definitely in your own reality.

A distress call from a freighter turns into a hostage rescue situation for the *Enterprise*. The crew from the damaged freighter have landed in a former Federation colony racked by decades of civil war. They are taken hostage by one faction known as the Alliance. The other faction, the Coalition, offers the *Enterprise* their assistance. The Coalition produces a woman named Ishara who is supposed to be Tasha Yar's sister.

Ishara acts as liaison between the Coalition and the *Enterprise*. Dr Crusher's tests prove Ishara is indeed the sister of Tasha. She becomes friendly with the crew and gains their confidence. She also formulates a rescue plan to save the hostages. The only hitch is the implanted proximity detector she carries. If she beams into enemy territory, alarms will be triggered. Data and Dr Crusher are successful in removing the implant and the rescue plan moves ahead. While the away team frees the hostages, Ishara sets off on her own. She heads for the nearest fusion reactor and sets the controls to overload. Coalition troops are waiting to invade when the perimeter defences fall. Data finds her and realizes that she never really meant to help the *Enterprise* but only to gain an advantage for the Coalition. Riker stuns Ishara and Data resets the reactor. Ishara is later returned to the Coalition.

TRIVIA QUESTIONS

1. What will it cost Riker 20 to determine? **(3pts)**
2. How many years ago was the last Federation contact with the colony? **(3pts)**
3. When did the former Earth colony sever relations with the Federation? **(3pts)**
4. How many bases does the Alliance have? **(4pts)**
5. When did the colony first start falling apart? **(3pts)**
6. What card does Data choose during Riker's card trick? **(5pts)**
7. How far underground do the colonists live? **(3pts)**
8. Where did the escape pod land? **(4pts)**
9. What is the home planet of Tasha Yar? **(3pts)**
10. What is the name of the Federation freighter's engineer? **(4pts)**

✪ SPECIAL ASSIGNMENT (15pts)

What is the exact location of the escape pod?

MULTIPLE CHOICE QUESTIONS

1. What reason does Ishara give why the proximity implant can't be removed? **(3pts)**
   - **A.** the implant is wired directly into her brain
   - **B.** it contains a lifetime supply of antidote for the slow poison trapped inside her body
   - **C.** the implant also acts as a pacemaker for her heart
   - **D.** it contains a microexplosive that will detonate upon contact with air

2. What is located near each of the Alliance's headquarters? **(2pts)**
   - **A.** a fusion reactor
   - **B.** a network of tunnels
   - **C.** a weapons cache
   - **D.** an ancillary base

3. What masks Ishara's signal for transport? **(3pts)**
   - **A.** 6 metres of pure tritanium
   - **B.** 2 kilometres of solid rock
   - **C.** transformer substation in chamber above her
   - **D.** fusion reactor

4. What does Dr Crusher test and compare to determine if Ishara is really Tasha's sister? **(2pts)**
   - **A.** rate of cellular mitosis
   - **B.** Transporter ID Trace
   - **C.** bone density patterns
   - **D.** DNA

5. What does the ionization trail leading from the freighter signify? **(5pts)**
   - **A.** an imminent warp core breach
   - **B.** an activated escape pod
   - **C.** a cloaked vessel nearby
   - **D.** a defective warp coil

ANSWERS

TRIVIA ANSWERS

1. whether Data has a flush or a full house
2. six years
3. nearly 15 years ago
4. two main headquarters and 13 ancillary bases of operation
5. almost 30 years ago
6. jack of hearts
7. 3 kilometres beneath the city
8. 300 metres beyond the colony's perimeter
9. Turkana IV
10. Tan Tsu

SPECIAL ASSIGNMENT SOLUTION

Level 3C, Section 547

Congratulations! Atarfleet Command is proud to award you the Starfleet Medal of Honour and 15 extra points.

MULTIPLE CHOICE ANSWERS

1. D. it contains a microexplosive that will detonate upon contact with air
2. A. a fusion reactor
3. C. transformer substation in chamber above her
4. D. DNA
5. B. an activated escape pod

MISSION PERFORMANCE RATING:

45 – 65 points **Superior:** No cadres in your closet.
40 – 44 points **Above Average:** You were smart enough to leave too!
30 – 39 points **Average:** The Coalition is looking for a few good men.
20 – 29 points **Fair:** We all trusted you and now this!
 0 – 19 points **Poor:** You Alliance dog! Go back to your cadre.

REUNION ◣

The *Enterprise* encounters a Klingon vessel carrying K'mpec, the leader of the Klingon Empire, and Federation Ambassador K' Ehleyr. K'mpec, who is being poisoned, wants Picard to be the Arbiter of Succession to help choose a new leader and discover who poisoned him. K' Ehleyr has brought her son along on the trip, and she tells Worf he is the child's father.

The two challengers to the Klingon throne, Gowron and Duras, arrive and meet with Picard. K' Ehleyr helps Picard to begin the mediation process. A bomb explodes disrupting the proceedings. All indications point to Duras and a Romulan connection. Meanwhile, K' Ehleyr uncovers information on her own about the Khitomer Massacre that also point to the Duras family's guilt. K' Ehleyr confronts Duras with this knowledge and is killed by him. Worf claims the Klingon Rite of Vengeance and kills Duras. Gowron becomes the new Klingon leader. Worf sends his son to live with his parents, thinking he cannot provide a proper home for the child while on the *Enterprise*.

TRIVIA QUESTIONS

1. According to K' Ehleyr what does Duras not do well? **(3pts)**
2. What Klingon phrase did Picard yell at Duras and Gowron, meaning 'Stop! Enough!'? **(5pts)**
3. The *Enterprise* crew includes representatives from how many planets? **(4pts)**
4. How long have the Klingons and Romulans been blood enemies? **(4pts)**
5. K' Ehleyr interlocks with what information source? **(3pts)**
6. What would be the maximum size of the bomb according to Geordi? **(3pts)**
7. What type of detonator did the bomb have? **(3pts)**
8. What portion of the ancient rite of succession deals with the achievements of the candidates? **(4pts)**
9. Who wishes to meet with Picard alone? **(3pts)**
10. How long did K'mpec rule the Klingon Empire? **(3pts)**

WHO AM I? **(25pts)**

Five times I made an appearance. Once over sour grapes, then back in a flash, again in a slash, and finally, just desserts completed my whirlwind tour.

ANSWERS

TRIVIA ANSWERS

1. playing the wounded Klingon
2. mev yap
3. 13
4. 75 years
5. Klingon Imperial Information Net
6. three cubic millimetres
7. a molecular-decay detonator
8. ja'chug
9. K'mpec
10. longer than anyone else before him

WHO AM I? SOLUTION

Death

EXPLANATION:

Five times I made an appearance. – Five people were killed during the episode.

Once over sour grapes, – K'mpec was poisoned slowly through his wine.

then back in a flash, – Two Klingons were killed in the bomb blast.

again in a slash, – K' Ehleyr is killed by Duras using his knife.

and finally, just desserts completed my whirlwind tour. – Duras is killed by Worf claiming the Rite of Vengeance.

MISSION PERFORMANCE RATING:

36 – 60 points **Superior:** Because of you the Klingon Empire will survive.

30 – 35 points **Above Average:** You are an honourable and a good warrior.

20 – 29 points **Average:** Weren't you guarding Duras' quarters?

10 – 19 points **Fair:** You would serve Duras well if he were alive!

0 – 9 points **Poor:** You are nothing but a Ha' DIbah!

FUTURE IMPERFECT ⚓

An away team investigates unusual emissions in a cavern on a planet near the Neutral Zone. An emergency beam up is necessary as all team members pass out. Riker awakens in sickbay. The last thing he remembers is the away team mission in the cavern. Dr Crusher gently explains to Riker that he has a sixteen year memory gap. She tells him the memory loss was caused by a disease he picked up on the planet. The disease had been lying dormant and only recently became active, erasing his memories of the last sixteen years.

Riker learns he is now captain of the *Enterprise* and has a son named Jean-Luc. What Riker finds the hardest to accept is that the Federation and the Romulans are on the verge of signing an alliance. He is almost convinced of this future until images of his supposed wife turn out to be one of Riker's holodeck creations.

Riker refuses to continue playing games. Everything fades away until only Tomalak, the Romulan negotiator, remains. Riker appears to be in a secret Romulan base. He is thrown into a cell and finds the boy, Jean-Luc, there. They soon escape from their cell and find a hiding place. The boy slips up and Riker realizes this is just another holographic fantasy. The boy changes into his true alien form and explains to Riker that he is the last of his kind. His mother had outfitted this cavern with holographic equipment to provide for his needs. The alien had been lonely and thought Riker would be happy there. Together they return to the *Enterprise*.

TRIVIA QUESTIONS

1. What is the cavern is full of? **(3pts)**
2. What are the rumours concerning the sector the *Enterprise* is in? **(3pts)**
3. How did Jean-Luc break his wrist? **(3pts)**
4. What did Riker wish for before blowing out the candles? **(3pts)**
5. What was the name of Riker's great holodeck fishing programme? **(5pts)**
6. How did Jean-Luc's mother die? **(4pts)**
7. When did Riker help a distressed Romulan ship that had strayed into Federation space? **(3pts)**
8. What is different about Geordi? **(3pts)**
9. What disease was Riker supposedly infected with on Alpha Onias III? **(4pts)**
10. How long has Riker served as captain of the *Enterprise*? **(4pts)**

✪ SPECIAL ASSIGNMENT (15pts)

Geordi found traces of which three gases in the cavern?

MULTIPLE CHOICE QUESTIONS

1. Why can't the Romulan sensors detect Riker and Ethan? **(2pts)**
   A. heavy metals in the rock surrounding them
   B. Ethan's clothing acts as a cloaking device
   C. Riker modified his communicator to scramble sensor output
   D. Riker and Ethan are contaminated with invidium particles

2. What type of alien is Ethan? **(3pts)**
   A. lonely
   B. telepathic
   C. silicon-based
   D. a shape-shifter

3. Why does Geordi have to shut down the warp engines? **(2pts)**
   A. so he can run a level-1 diagnostic on them
   B. the antimatter containment fields are fluctuating
   C. Riker ordered him to
   D. he has to realign the dilithium crystals

4. What did Picard always say about the Federation's relations with the Romulans? **(5pts)**
   A. everything's balanced on the head of a pin
   B. it's a chess game, move and countermove
   C. it's either us or them
   D. we have nothing in common except the Neutral Zone

5. What type of virus does Riker supposedly have? **(3pts)**
   A. retrovirus
   B. self-replicating virus
   C. nanite-virus
   D. petro-virus

ANSWERS

TRIVIA ANSWERS

1. neural scanners
2. there is a secret Romulan base somewhere within the sector
3. playing Parrises Squares
4. music lessons
5. Curtis Creek programme
6. two years ago in a shuttle accident
7. four years ago
8. he has cloned implants
9. Altarian encephalitis
10. nine years

SPECIAL ASSIGNMENT SOLUTION

sulphur dioxide, methane, hydrogen sulphide

Congratulations! Starfleet Command is proud to award you the Starfleet Medal of Honour and 15 extra points.

MULTIPLE CHOICE ANSWERS

1. A. heavy metals in the rock surrounding them
2. D. a shape-shifter
3. B. the antimatter containment fields are fluctuating
4. B. it's a chess game, move and countermove
5. A. retrovirus

MISSION PERFORMANCE RATING:

45 – 65 points   **Superior:** You knew it was a ruse all the time.

40 – 44 points   **Above Average:** Don't you want to play any more?

30 – 39 points   **Average:** Are you for real?

20 – 29 points   **Fair:** You still think you're captain of the *Enterprise*, don't you?

0 – 19 points   **Poor:** Even a holographic image couldn't do this badly!

FINAL MISSION

Picard and Wesley are en route to some negotiations on a mining shuttle piloted by a Captain Dirgo. As soon as the shuttle leaves, the *Enterprise* receives a distress call and has to leave the area quickly to assist. Dirgo's shuttle malfunctions and crashes on a nearby moon. Everybody is all right but supplies are almost non-existent. The group makes its way to a mountain range and finds shelter in a cavern. There the group finds a fountain of water but it is protected by a force field. Dirgo fires his phaser at the force field. Suddenly an energy entity knocks the phaser from his hand and dislodges some rocks in the cavern. Picard is caught under some falling rocks and is injured.

Meanwhile, the *Enterprise* encounters a dangerously unstable waste ship in orbit around a planet that is emitting severe levels of radiation. The *Enterprise* tows the fragile waste ship through an asteroid belt and flings it into the nearby sun.

Picard's condition is grim; he'll die soon if he doesn't get water. Dirgo gets impatient and ends up getting killed by the entity for his trouble. Wesley decides to think things through first and is able to unlock the force field surrounding the fountain using his tricorder. His actions allow Picard and himself to survive until the *Enterprise* shows up to rescue them.

TRIVIA QUESTIONS

1. Why did Picard ask Wesley on this final mission? **(3pts)**
2. What material does the sentry cover the phasers and Dirgo in? **(5pts)**
3. What type of force field surrounds the fountain of water? **(5pts)**
4. What specific type of ship is orbiting Gamelan V? **(3pts)**
5. What cargo is the freighter carrying? **(4pts)**
6. Where did Picard and Wesley once take a shuttle flight together? **(3pts)**
7. What was the name of the moon the shuttle crashed on? **(5pts)**
8. Why is Wesley going to the Academy in midsession? **(3pts)**
9. What would Picard appreciate? **(4pts)**
10. What does Dirgo not have aboard the shuttle? **(3pts)**

✪✪ SIGNIFICANT NUMBERS (1pt each)

Match the clues with the correct number.

Clues
1. How many years has the freighter's engine reactor elements been inactive?
2. What is the initial radiation level in millirads when the *Enterprise* first starts to tow the freighter?

3. When no one is near the water fountain the wave pattern stays between _____ and _____ MHz?
4. What is the shearing force (in metric tonnes per metre) on the tractor beam at ¹/₂ impulse?
5. What Warp speed does the *Enterprise* use to travel to the Gamelan system?
6. Approximately how many hours has Dirgo logged on his shuttle?
7. At 150 millirads how many minutes are there before lethal exposure is reached?
8. How long (to the nearest minute) before the *Enterprise* clears the asteroid belt?
9. How many million kilometres is Pentarus V from the damaged shuttle?
10. How many metres in front of the freighter does Riker position the *Enterprise*?
11. What is the shearing force (in metric tonnes per metre) on the tractor beam at ³/₄ impulse with supplemental power?
12. What is the hull temperature in degrees Celsius as the shuttle enters the moon's atmosphere?
13. Atmospheric radiation levels have increased by what percentage on Gamelan V?
14. At 300 millirads how many minutes are there before lethal exposure is reached?
15. Data estimates the hyronalyn will only be effective for how many minutes?
16. What is the mean surface temperature in degrees Celsius on the moon the shuttle crashes on?
17. What is the shearing force (in metric tonnes per metre) on the tractor beam at ³/₄ impulse when it becomes unstable?

Numbers
A. 1,000
B. 35
C. 50
D. 103
E. 700
F. 51
G. 1
H. 10,000
I. 70
J. 6
K. 3,000
L. 80
M. 55
N. 93
O. 300
P. 5, 15
Q. 38

ANSWERS

TRIVIA ANSWERS

1. he thought he wouldn't see him again
2. selenium fibres that are electrically deposited
3. a tightly confined annular force field
4. unmanned sublight freighter
5. various unstable radioactive waste products
6. Starbase 515
7. Lambda Paz
8. a position has opened up
9. if Dirgo doesn't bury him before he's dead
10. emergency food or water supplies

SIGNIFICANT NUMBERS ANSWERS

1. O 300; 2. I 70; 3. P 5, 15; 4. L 80; 5. J 6; 6. H 10,000; 7. B 35;
8. F 51; 9. C 50; 10. A 1,000; 11. D 103; 12. E 700; 13. K 3,000;
14. G 1; 15. Q 38; 16. M 55; 17. N 93

MISSION PERFORMANCE RATING:

35 – 55 points **Superior:** You'd survive no matter where you crashed.

30 – 34 points **Above Average:** The Academy had two slots open up!

20 – 29 points **Average:** Did you teach Dirgo how to fly a shuttle?

10 – 19 points **Fair:** So where do you keep *your* dresci stashed?

0 – 9 points **Poor:** It's your turn to fire your phaser at the water fountain.

Troi suddenly experiences a headache and loses her empathic abilities. Meanwhile on the bridge, sensors detect some anomalies in the *Enterprise*'s path. As the *Enterprise* tries to move onward the ship is gripped by an unknown force and pulled along through space.

Geordi and Data discover a colony of two-dimensional life forms surrounding the *Enterprise*. The life forms are inadvertently carrying the *Enterprise* along with their forward motion. Riker and Troi's other friends try to reach out and help her through her loss but she lashes out at them in anger. The crew soon realizes that the colony of two-dimensional life forms is heading towards a cosmic string fragment. The tremendous gravitational forces will destroy the *Enterprise* if the ship doesn't escape.

After all attempts to free the *Enterprise* fail, Picard asks Troi to work with Data to try to determine the psychology behind the life forms' behaviour. Troi uses some old-fashioned human instincts to figure out what the life forms are doing and develops a strategy for escape. Geordi is able to simulate another cosmic string fragment to confuse the life forms long enough for the *Enterprise* to break free. Troi's empathic abilities instantly return. It seems the emotions of the two-dimensional life forms had overwhelmed her empathic abilities.

TRIVIA QUESTIONS

1. How long has it been since Janet's husband died? **(3pts)**
2. What dimensions do the new life forms have? **(3pts)**
3. Troi equates the two-dimensional life forms heading for the cosmic string to what? **(3pts)**
4. How strong is the gravitational field of a cosmic string fragment? **(5pts)**
5. How far in front of the two-dimensional life forms are the photon torpedoes launched? **(4pts)**
6. Where did Geordi go skin-diving once? **(3pts)**
7. What particular day is especially hard for Janet to deal with? **(4pts)**
8. What does Picard think would be good for Riker? **(3pts)**
9. Where was the *Enterprise* originally heading? **(4pts)**
10. How fast is the *Enterprise* being pulled along? **(3pts)**

✪ SPECIAL ASSIGNMENT (15pts)

How long is the cosmic string fragment?

MULTIPLE CHOICE QUESTIONS

1. What is not a requirement for a ship's counsellor according to Picard?
   (2pts)
   A. telepathic awareness
   B. being human
   C. emotional stability
   D. empathic awareness

2. Troi wants Picard to spare her the what? **(2pts)**
   A. depressing statistics
   B. inspirational anecdotes
   C. war stories
   D. humorous jokes

3. What does Troi do after losing her empathic abilities? **(3pts)**
   A. she continues her usual routine
   B. she resigns as ship's counsellor
   C. she goes to the holodeck
   D. she calls her mother over subspace radio

4. What series of tests does Dr Crusher want to run on Troi? **(5pts)**
   A. inner nuncial series
   B. alpha wave induction tests
   C. outer somnetic series
   D. neuronic conduction tests

5. What item was Janet grateful to Troi for saving? **(3pts)**
   A. her husband's wedding ring
   B. her husband's Starfleet uniform
   C. a music box that her husband had given her
   D. a painting her husband had painted

ANSWERS

TRIVIA ANSWERS

1. five months
2. length and width
3. moths to a flame
4. equivalent to a black hole or the pull of 100 stars
5. 7 kilometres
6. off the coral reefs on Bracas V
7. her husband's 38th birthday
8. for him to get some fresh holodeck air
9. T'lli Beta
10. $1/10$ impulse power

SPECIAL ASSIGNMENT SOLUTION

107 kilometres

Congratulations! Starfleet Command is proud to award you the Starfleet Medal of Honour and 15 extra points.

MULTIPLE CHOICE ANSWERS

1. D. empathic awareness
2. B. inspirational anecdotes
3. B. she resigns as ship's counsellor
4. A. inner nuncial series
5. C. a music box that her husband had given her

MISSION PERFORMANCE RATING:

45 – 65 points **Superior:** You're the new bartender in Ten-Forward.

40 – 44 points **Above Average:** You're the new ship's counsellor.

30 – 39 points **Average:** You have two-dimensional intelligence.

20 – 29 points **Fair:** I don't blame you, this episode was boring.

0 – 19 points **Poor:** Cheer up, things will only get worse!

DATA'S DAY

The *Enterprise* picks up Vulcan Ambassador T'Pel and travels toward the Neutral Zone to meet with a Romulan vessel. T'Pel says that the Romulans want to begin a dialogue with the Federation. While the ship is en route to its destination, Data is making a complete record of all his activities in an average day. The record, also containing his observations on human behaviour, will be sent to Bruce Maddox as an aid in his cybernetic research.

Chief O'Brien's wedding is supposed to take place on this day. However, a series of misunderstandings later places the wedding in jeopardy. Luckily, everything gets straightened out and the wedding occurs on schedule.

Eventually, the *Enterprise* arrives at the Neutral Zone. As T'Pel beams over to the Romulan ship, her transport signal is lost and she is apparently killed. The Romulans think her death was intentional to disrupt the talks. Picard decides to leave and investigate the accident in Federation space. As the investigation proceeds it becomes apparent that T'Pel is still alive; the Romulans beamed her off the *Enterprise*'s transporter pad. Picard tracks down the Romulan ship carrying T'Pel and demands that they return the Ambassador. Picard and crew then discover that T'Pel is actually a Romulan spy. When several more Romulan ships appear, Picard decides to leave and preserve the peace.

TRIVIA QUESTIONS

1. What is Data's role in the wedding party? **(3pts)**
2. What type of dancing does Dr Crusher first teach Data? **(3pts)**
3. What was Dr Crusher once known as? **(3pts)**
4. Who is a 'charming woman' according to Riker. **(3pts)**
5. There is a slight discrepancy in what while Dr Crusher compares genetic samples? **(4pts)**
6. What award did Data note in Dr Crusher's Starfleet records? **(4pts)**
7. What was the name of Dr Crusher's dance holodeck programme? **(3pts)**
8. What old song does Dr Crusher programme the holodeck to play? **(4pts)**
9. What do Andorian marriages require? **(3pts)**
10. What does Data feed his cat? **(4pts)**

✪✪ SPECIAL ASSIGNMENT (15pts)

What is T'Pel's access code?

MULTIPLE CHOICE QUESTIONS

1. Data says he is a great admirer of whom? **(2pts)**
   - **A.** the fictional detective known as Dixon Hill
   - **B.** William Shakespeare
   - **C.** Jean-Luc Picard
   - **D.** the fictional detective known as Sherlock Holmes

2. Data feels there may be a correlation between what two things? **(3pts)**
   - **A.** Romulans and T'Pel's death
   - **B.** anger and injuries
   - **C.** humour and sex
   - **D.** crying and weddings

3. Worf says human bonding rituals often involve a lot of what? **(5pts)**
   - **A.** talking, dancing, and crying
   - **B.** fighting, dancing, and loud music
   - **C.** eating, dancing, and small talk
   - **D.** talking, crying, and eating

4. What religious festival is celebrated on the *Enterprise*? **(3pts)**
   - **A.** Hindu Festival of Lights
   - **B.** Edo Festival of Smiles
   - **C.** Bajoran Festival of Orbs
   - **D.** Ventaxian Festival of the Apocalypse

5. What was Data's 'good news'? **(3pts)**
   - **A.** Ambassador T'Pel was still alive
   - **B.** Keiko decided to cancel the wedding
   - **C.** Ambassador T'Pel was really a Romulan spy
   - **D.** O'Brien decided to cancel the wedding

ANSWERS

TRIVIA ANSWERS

1. he is acting as the father of the bride
2. tap dancing
3. the Dancing Doctor
4. Ambassador T'Pel
5. base pair sequence
6. first prize in the Tap and Jazz competition at the St Louis Academy
7. Crusher 4
8. *Isn't It Romantic*
9. groups of four
10. feline supplement 74

SPECIAL ASSIGNMENT SOLUTION

Kappa alpha 4601704

Congratulations! Starfleet Command is proud to award you the Starfleet Medal of Honour and 15 extra points.

MULTIPLE CHOICE ANSWERS

1. D. the fictional detective known as Sherlock Holmes
2. C. humour and sex
3. A. talking, dancing, and crying
4. A. Hindu Festival of Lights
5. B. Keiko decided to cancel the wedding

MISSION PERFORMANCE RATING:

45 – 65 points **Superior:** You knew T'Pel wasn't really a Vulcan.

40 – 44 points **Above Average:** Unlike Data, you have mastered irony.

30 – 39 points **Average:** Another mediocre performance.

20 – 29 points **Fair:** You also appear to have numerous single bit errors.

0 – 19 points **Poor:** Were those your remains on the transporter pad?

THE WOUNDED ⚓

The *Enterprise* awaits the arrival of a Cardassian scout ship to report their presence in Cardassian territory. The *Enterprise* is suddenly attacked by a Cardassian scout ship. The *Enterprise* quickly disables the small vessel. Gul Macet, captain of the Cardassian vessel, tells Picard that a Federation starship has attacked a Cardassian research station. Picard confirms this report with Starfleet. Maxwell, captain of the rogue starship, refuses to answer Starfleet's messages. Picard is instructed to maintain the peace.

The *Enterprise* locates Maxwell's ship but can't get to the starship before he destroys several Cardassian vessels. Maxwell tries to persuade Picard that the Cardassians are arming for another war. He claims that the research stations are really bases and the supply ships are carrying weapons. Picard orders Maxwell to follow the *Enterprise* to the closest Federation star base. Soon afterwards, Maxwell veers his ship towards another Cardassian vessel. He tells Picard to board the vessel and he'd have all the proof he needs. Picard refuses, takes Maxwell into custody, and both starships return to Federation territory. Picard warns Gul Macet that Maxwell was correct in his assumptions but that he has been ordered to keep the peace. He tells the Gul that the Federation will be more vigilant.

TRIVIA QUESTIONS

1. Why can't the *Enterprise*'s sensors tell if the Cardassian supply ship's defensive systems are activated? **(4pts)**
2. How often does the sensor system cycle on Maxwell's ship? **(4pts)**
3. What does Picard order Maxwell to do? **(3pts)**
4. What can the Cardassians do with Maxwell's prefix codes? **(3pts)**
5. What size radius has the *Enterprise* been scanning using the long range sensors? **(3pts)**
6. What was Picard doing in Sector 21503 while commanding the *Stargazer*? **(3pts)**
7. Why is the Cuellar system strategically important? **(3pts)**
8. Where did Maxwell's family die? **(5pts)**
9. What are Cardassian transporting systems still operating with? **(3pts)**
10. What mode of operation is Maxwell using according to the Admiral? **(4pts)**

WHO AM I? **(25pts)**

I used Solanum tuberosum for sustinere. Many years ago I worried whether I should quell the Culicidae. My glossa weighs exactly 107.870 according to Mendeleev.

ANSWERS

TRIVIA ANSWERS

1. they are using a high powered subspace field
2. every 5.5 minutes
3. to follow the *Enterprise* to Starbase 211
4. dismantle his ship's shields
5. ten light years
6. offering preliminary overtures to a truce
7. it could be the jumping off point for an invasion into three Federation sectors
8. Setlik III
9. active feed pattern buffers
10. silent running

WHO AM I? SOLUTION

O'Brien

EXPLANATION:

I used *Solanum tuberosum for sustinere.* – *Solanum t.* is the scientific name for potatoes and *sustinere* is Latin for sustenance. O'Brien made Keiko a potato casserole for dinner.

Many years ago I worried whether I should quell the Culicidae. – Mosquitoes belong to the family *Culicidae.* O'Brien said he worried about swatting mosquitoes when he was growing up.

My glossa weighs exactly 107.870 according to Mendeleev. – *Glossa*, meaning tongue. *Mendeleev* was the Russian chemist who formulated the Periodic Law. Look up the atomic weight of 107.870 on the periodic table and the element is silver. Maxwell asked O'Brien how he had got his silver tongue.

MISSION PERFORMANCE RATING:

36 – 60 points **Superior:** You preserved the peace; the Federation thanks you!

25 – 35 points **Above Average:** You found Maxwell's ship with no trouble.

15 – 24 points **Average:** Always the same score with you.

5 – 14 points **Fair:** Hurry, Maxwell needs some more supply ship targets!

0 – 4 points **Poor:** You're confined to the brig for the rest of your tour of duty.

DEVIL'S DUE

STARDATE: 44474.5

The *Enterprise* responds to a distress call from a science team on Ventax II. Upon their arrival they find the whole planet in turmoil. Hundreds of years ago the inhabitants of Ventax II made a pact with a devilish entity named Ardra. In exchange for a lengthy period of peace and prosperity, Ardra would inherit the planet and all its people. The inhabitants believe that the time is near for Ardra's return because of certain signs that foretell her return.

Picard beams down to talk to the authorities when Ardra suddenly appears. She seems to possess supernatural powers. Ardra has the Ventaxians ready to submit to her when Picard intervenes. Data has found a precedent in Ventaxian law that allows Picard to call for arbitration. Ardra presents a compelling case and is on the verge of winning.

Meanwhile, Geordi is able to locate Ardra's hidden ship. A detachment from the *Enterprise* boards and takes control of her vessel. Picard duplicates Ardra's 'magic' using the *Enterprise*'s technology and exposes her as a fraud.

TRIVIA QUESTIONS

1. How does Ardra control her magic? **(3pts)**
2. How many aliases does Ardra have in this sector alone? **(3pts)**
3. What does a jump in Z-particle readings suggest? **(3pts)**
4. Where did Picard not expect to be? **(3pts)**
5. How did Ardra make the *Enterprise* disappear? **(3pts)**
6. The precedent Data uncovers in Ventaxian law is based on a contract dispute involving whom? **(3pts)**
7. Where do dishonoured Klingons go in the afterlife? **(5pts)**
8. Ardra is known to Klingons as whom? **(5pts)**
9. How could a minor quake be created? **(3pts)**
10. Where are the Scrolls of Ardra kept? **(4pts)**

CHARACTER QUOTE
(3pts per word + 7pts for identifying the speaker.)

Unscramble the words below and then identify the character.

'The _____ will _____ _____ _____
    TAVECDOA   IERNRAF OFMR NKMIAG

her _____ _____.'
    EPNONPTO PDAASPRIE

⊗ SPECIAL ASSIGNMENT (15pts)

What is the location of Ardra's ship?

ANSWERS

TRIVIA ANSWERS

1. an eye implant allows her to use eye movements to choose and execute commands
2. 23
3. a hidden power source
4. on the science station in his jammies
5. she extended her cloaking shield around the ship
6. a Klingon craftsman and a Ventaxian
7. Gre'thor
8. Fek'lhr – Guardian of Gre'thor
9. by using a low frequency tractor beam projected against the tectonic plates
10. Atheneum Vaults

CHARACTER QUOTE SOLUTION

'The Advocate will refrain from making her opponent disappear.' – Data

SPECIAL ASSIGNMENT SOLUTION

34°N 62°E, altitude of 210 kilometres, placing it above the western magnetic pole
Congratulations! Starfleet Command is proud to award you the Starfleet Medal of Honour and 15 extra points.

MISSION PERFORMANCE RATING:

55 – 75 points **Superior:** You're the best when it comes to the con game!

45 – 54 points **Above Average:** So, where is your ship hidden?

30 – 44 points **Average:** No aces up your sleeve.

15 – 29 points **Fair:** You'd make a good flim-flam artist's apprentice.

0 – 14 points **Poor:** You'll be heading to Gre'thor one day.

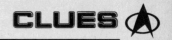
While investigating an M-class planet, the crew of the *Enterprise* is rendered unconscious after the ship apparently goes through an unstable wormhole. Data, who was unaffected, tells Picard that the effect lasted only moments. However, a number of discrepancies are uncovered, casting doubt on Data's story. Data refuses to answer any questions posed to him. Picard's only recourse is to return to the planet and look for answers there.

Upon arrival at the planet, the *Enterprise* is attacked by an unknown alien race. Data relates what actually happened earlier. The aliens, who dislike contact with other races, stun the crews of approaching vessels and then tow the ships off to a safe distance. Since Data was not affected by their stun technology, he revived the crew. Picard was able to reach a compromise that allowed the aliens to wipe the crew's short term memory of the events. Picard had ordered Data not to reveal the existence of the aliens. Picard persuades the aliens to give them another chance. The Captain tells the aliens they can now eliminate the clues that led them back to the planet. They agree to give the *Enterprise* another chance. This time, Picard sends a probe to investigate the planet and the *Enterprise* continues en route to its next destination.

TRIVIA QUESTIONS

1. How long did the stun effect from the wormhole last according to Data? **(3pts)**
2. How did O'Brien injure himself? **(3pts)**
3. Who does Guinan tell Madeline she is? **(3pts)**
4. What injury does Worf not remember? **(3pts)**
5. Which emergency plan did Data tell the *Enterprise*'s computer to implement after the crew was rendered unconscious? **(3pts)**
6. What was the concentration of the compound Data released into the *Enterprise*'s ventilation system to revive the crew? **(4pts)**
7. The image from the first probe was actually what planet? **(3pts)**
8. How far from their original position is the *Enterprise* after passing through the wormhole? **(5pts)**
9. How many small and unstable wormholes have been mapped near T-tauri systems in the last 100 years? **(4pts)**
10. When did Gloria have an appointment with Hill? **(4pts)**

SPECIAL ASSIGNMENT (10pts)

What type of car does Hill see driving off outside his office window?

MULTIPLE CHOICE QUESTIONS

1. What does Data suggest as a deterrent against the energy cloud? **(2pts)**
   A. fire a short range antimatter spread directly at the cloud
   B. vary the shape and strength of the shields as quickly as possible
   C. use evasive Picard Manoeuvre
   D. fire intermittent phaser blasts

2. What has Worf been treated with? **(5pts)**
   A. an autosuture
   B. a tissue mitigator
   C. a bioregenerative field
   D. a subcutaneous bone fusion unit

3. What happens to the guy in Hill's office as he walks in front of the window? **(3pts)**
   A. he is machine-gunned from outside
   B. he trips on the light cord and falls down
   C. Hill pulls a gun and shoots him
   D. Hill lunges at him and they crash to the floor

4. What did Data feel would be less intrusive? **(2pts)**
   A. sending Gloria to Hill's office with a message from him
   B. paging Picard over the holodeck intercom
   C. sending the holodeck character with the gun to Hill's office to deliver a message from him
   D. patching the ship's communications through the holodeck via the telephone in Hill's office

5. Gloria uses what while smoking on the holodeck? **(3pts)**
   A. cigarette holder
   B. ashtray
   C. fancy cigarette lighter
   D. foul language

ANSWERS

TRIVIA ANSWERS

1. approximately 30 seconds
2. hanging a plant for Keiko
3. Gloria from Cleveland
4. his right wrist had been broken and reset
5. Zed Zed Alpha
6. five parts-per-million (ppm)
7. Tethys III
8. .54 parsecs (a day's travel)
9. 39 (Data says)
10. two o'clock

SPECIAL ASSIGNMENT SOLUTION

1948 Packard with whitewalls

Congratulations! Starfleet Command is proud to award you the Starfleet Medal of Honour and 10 extra points.

MULTIPLE CHOICE ANSWERS

1. B. vary the shape and strength of the shields as quickly as possible
2. D. a subcutaneous bone fusion unit
3. A. he is machine-gunned from outside
4. D. patching the ship's communications through the holodeck via the telephone in Hill's office
5. A. cigarette holder

MISSION PERFORMANCE RATING:

45 – 60 points **Superior:** You knew not to go near the nebula to start with!

40 – 44 points **Above Average:** You didn't leave any clues the first time.

30 – 39 points **Average:** You forgot to change the moss samples again.

20 – 29 points **Fair:** I didn't know holodeck matter could leave the holodeck!

0 – 19 points **Poor:** You've been appointed as the Ambassador to the Paxans.

FIRST CONTACT

Riker wakes up in a Malcorian hospital. He had been secretly meeting Federation observers who are studying the inhabitants of the planet in preparation for first contact. Riker, who was seriously injured in a riot, is found by the doctors to have certain physical abnormalities for a Malcorian. Picard and Troi make contact with the Malcorians' chief scientist, Mirasta, hoping to find the missing Riker.

Mirasta introduces them to the Malcorian head of state. Things go quite well until Krola, the chief of security, receives a report from the hospital about Riker. The Malcorians fear they are being infiltrated by aliens in preparation for an invasion. Krola goes to see Riker and tries to kill himself with the ill Commander's weapon. By making it appear as though Riker shot him, Krola had hoped to destroy any chance of a favourable relationship with the Federation.

Dr Crusher treats both Riker and Krola in sickbay. Krola was only stunned and will recover. The Malcorian head of state asks Picard to stay away until his people are prepared for contact with other races.

TRIVIA QUESTIONS

1. Where is Krola's phaser wound? **(3pts)**
2. How long has Mirasta been prepared for the realities of space travel? **(3pts)**
3. What is the most dangerous type of Starfleet mission? **(3pts)**
4. What happened centuries ago? **(3pts)**
5. What has Lanel always wanted to do? **(3pts)**
6. How long has Riker been missing according to Mirasta? **(4pts)**
7. How soon before the Malcorians could build a warp engine? **(4pts)**
8. What is Riker missing on either side of his abdomen according to Malcorian anatomy? **(3pts)**
9. Where is Riker being treated for his injuries? **(4pts)**
10. What is Riker's alias? **(5pts)**

✪ SPECIAL ASSIGNMENT (15pts)

How long is a Malcorian day?

MULTIPLE CHOICE QUESTIONS

1. According to Malcorian anatomy, what should be located in Riker's chest? **(5pts)**
   A. heart
   B. liver
   C. spleen
   D. digestive tract

2. When does Riker tell Lanel he'll see her again? **(2pts)**
   A. never again in this lifetime
   B. he'll call her the next time he passes through her star system
   C. in a few minutes after his kidneys get kicked around a bit
   D. when the Federation re-establishes contact with the Malcorians

3. What does Picard share with the Chancellor? **(3pts)**
   A. an awkward moment
   B. Aldebaran whiskey
   C. some frank advice
   D. the bottle of wine Picard's brother gave him

4. The Malcorians believe that Malcor III is what? **(2pts)**
   A. strategically located
   B. the centre of the universe
   C. ready for admission to the Federation
   D. only one planet among billions

5. Riker blames his supposed abnormalities on what? **(3pts)**
   A. his father
   B. a bizarre accident
   C. genetic birth defects
   D. genetic engineering

ANSWERS

TRIVIA ANSWERS

1. upper chest
2. since she was nine years old
3. first contact
4. a disastrous first contact with the Klingons which led to decades of war
5. make love with an alien
6. two days
7. ten months
8. seven costal struts
9. Sikla Medical Facility
10. Rivas Jakara

SPECIAL ASSIGNMENT SOLUTION

29 hours

Congratulations! Starfleet Command is proud to award you the Starfleet Medal of Honour and 15 extra points.

MULTIPLE CHOICE ANSWERS

1. D. digestive tract
2. B. he'll call her the next time he passes through her star system
3. D. the bottle of wine Picard's brother gave him
4. B. the centre of the universe
5. C. genetic birth defects

MISSION PERFORMANCE RATING:

45 – 65 points   **Superior:** You're one of Starfleet's finest first contact personnel!

40 – 44 points   **Above Average:** You could be a Malcorian doctor.

30 – 39 points   **Average:** You probably started the riot that Riker got caught in.

20 – 29 points   **Fair:** You were on the first contact mission with the Klingons.

0 – 19 points   **Poor:** You alien slime! How long have you been spying on us?

GALAXY'S CHILD ⚓

Dr Brahms, noted Starfleet engineer, pays the *Enterprise* a visit to inspect Geordi's warp drive modifications. Geordi became acquainted with Dr Brahms' work when he created a holographic image of her and her lab in the episode 'Booby Trap'. When Dr Brahms beams aboard, she immediately accuses Geordi of messing up her engine designs. The engineer is not what Geordi expected.

Meanwhile, the *Enterprise* investigates an unusual energy reading. The anomaly turns out to be a new life form that lives in space without need for a vessel. The creature attacks the *Enterprise* without provocation and Picard orders a minimal defensive response. The phaser blast kills the creature. Several minutes later Data registers new energy readings from the dead creature. The crew realizes that the creature was pregnant and was defending its unborn offspring. The crew is able to free the young creature. As the ship leaves, the creature, dubbed Junior, attaches itself to the hull and begins feeding on the *Enterprise*'s energy. The *Enterprise* heads in the same direction as the mother creature was travelling.

Dr Brahms and Geordi work to stabilize the ship's energy situation. As the *Enterprise* approaches Junior's home, energy levels are becoming critical. Dr Brahms and Geordi are able to wean the creature off the ship and also work out their differences.

TRIVIA QUESTIONS

1. What is no longer stable after the creature is hit with phaser fire? **(3pts)**
2. Until when were Geordi's dilithium chamber modifications scheduled for introduction? **(2pts)**
3. What doesn't always jibe according to Geordi? **(3pts)**
4. What mixture isn't as rich as regulations dictate? **(3pts)**
5. Where was the mother creature originally heading? **(3pts)**
6. What is Junior covering while attached to the Enterprise? **(4pts)**
7. How friendly is Dr Brahms according to Geordi? **(4pts)**
8. What doesn't sound right to Dr Brahms inside the power transfer conduits? **(4pts)**
9. What dinner music does Geordi choose? **(4pts)**
10. What position does Dr Brahms hold at Starfleet's Theoretical Propulsion Group? **(5pts)**

✪✪ SIGNIFICANT NUMBERS (2pts each)

Match the clues with the correct number. Some numbers may be used more than once.

Clues
1. How many field densities were the phase coils upgraded to?
2. All matter in space vibrates at the _____ centimetre radiation band.
3. What percentage does the energy drain jump to when the shuttlebay door is opened?
4. How many kilometres from the periphery of the asteroid belt does Picard position the *Enterprise*?
5. What is the computer file number of Geordi's holodeck programme?
6. Junior finally abandons the *Enterprise* at the _____ centimetre radiation band.
7. How many million cubic metres is Junior after growing in volume by 8.5%?
8. To operate on the life form, the phasers are set at narrow beam and at what percentage power?
9. How many kph does the *Enterprise* travel away from the newborn creature?
10. How many kilometres does the newborn creature maintain astern of the *Enterprise*?
11. How many kph does the *Enterprise* travel in reverse when the new life form comes towards it?
12. At what time is Dr Brahms supposed to meet Geordi for dinner?
13. How many kilometres does Picard order the *Enterprise* to keep from the mother creature?
14. Radiation levels aboard the *Enterprise* are at _____ millirads just before the creature is killed.
15. At what starbase does the *Enterprise* pick up Dr Brahms?

Numbers
A. 500
B. 46
C. 4
D. 10
E. 313
F. 300
G. 1900
H. 55
I. 9140
J. 3
K. 21
L. 93
M. .02

ANSWERS

TRIVIA ANSWERS

1. creature's radiation signature
2. in the next class of starship
3. theory and application
4. matter/antimatter ratio
5. an asteroid belt
6. the door of Shuttlebay 2
7. as friendly as a Circasian Plague Cat
8. the acoustic signature
9. classical guitar
10. senior design engineer

SIGNIFICANT NUMBERS ANSWERS

1. H 55; 2. K 21; 3. L 93; 4. A 500; 5. I 9140;
6. M .02; 7. B 46; 8. J 3; 9. A 500; 10. C 4;
11. F 300; 12. G 1900; 13. D 10; 14. F 300;
15. E 313

MISSION PERFORMANCE RATING:

30 – 65 points **Superior:** Have you published your research paper yet?

24 – 29 points **Above Average:** You're cold, cerebral, and lacking in humour.

15 – 23 points **Average:** Your only crime is trying to impersonate an officer!

10 – 14 points **Fair:** Apparently your radiation signature is unstable.

0 – 9 points **Poor:** You're about as smart as a Circasian Plague Cat.

NIGHT TERRORS

STARDATE: 44631.2

The *Enterprise* finds a missing Federation science vessel whose crew apparently went insane and killed each other. There is one survivor named Hagen who is in a stupor. The *Enterprise* begins an investigation but after several days Dr Crusher notices that the mental state of the *Enterprise*'s crew is deteriorating. She advises Picard to leave the area.

The *Enterprise* prepares to leave the area but the engines fail to respond. Data determines that the *Enterprise* is caught in an energy draining rift in space. A tremendous explosion would disrupt the rift long enough for the *Enterprise* to escape. However, the *Enterprise* can't replicate the explosive elements it needs and doesn't have any cargo that would create that type of explosion.

Meanwhile, Dr Crusher discovers that the crew is suffering from a lack of REM sleep. Troi is the only person who is still dreaming, and she has a recurring nightmare. Troi finally makes a connection between her dreams and some words Hagen keeps repeating. An alien ship is caught on the other side of the rift and is transmitting a telepathic message which Troi can receive. This transmission is also interrupting the ability of the crew to dream.

Troi and Data formulate a plan to have the counsellor send the aliens a message as Data releases an element into the rift. Moments later, the element explodes with the help of the aliens, and both ships are able to leave the area.

TRIVIA QUESTIONS

1. There is no technology that can do what? **(3pts)**
2. How does Dr Crusher keep Troi in REM sleep? **(3pts)**
3. Where did Guinan's 'little souvenir' come from? **(4pts)**
4. What is the name of the therapeutic treatment mentioned by Troi? **(3pts)**
5. How many bodies are seen in the morgue after Dr Crusher has her hallucinations? **(4pts)**
6. What does REM stand for? **(3pts)**
7. What is a massive rupture in space that absorbs energy called? **(3pts)**
8. What is Keiko the head of? **(3pts)**
9. On what flower does Dr Balthus want to do a study? **(4pts)**
10. What is the crew complement of the science vessel? **(5pts)**

✪ SPECIAL ASSIGNMENT (15pts)

What two volatile compounds was Tyken's ship carrying?

MULTIPLE CHOICE QUESTIONS

1. What is Data's final duty as acting captain? **(5pts)**
   A. sets course for the starbase
   B. sets out warning beacons around the rift
   C. orders pest control to Riker's quarters
   D. orders Picard and the crew to bed

2. What hallucination did Dr Crusher have in the morgue? **(2pts)**
   A. she saw Jack's body on a table and then he stood up
   B. she saw Wesley's body under a sheet
   C. all the bodies sat upright
   D. all the bodies started shaking and twitching

3. What are symptoms of dream deprivation? **(2pts)**
   A. memory loss, inability to concentrate, irritability, paranoia, hallucinations
   B. inability to concentrate, blurred vision, insanity
   C. memory loss, low blood pressure, irritability, flaking skin
   D. irritability, paranoia, vomiting, fainting spells, hallucinations

4. What does Picard hardly ever do? **(3pts)**
   A. freak out in the turbolift
   B. order Riker to take a nap
   C. recall his dreams
   D. all of the above

5. Geordi and Data think they can channel a surge of energy through what to disrupt the rift? **(3pts)**
   A. main phaser banks
   B. the main deflector dish
   C. Bussard collectors
   D. power transfer conduits

ANSWERS

TRIVIA ANSWERS

1. block telepathic transmissions
2. she uses a cortical scanner
3. Magus III
4. directed dreaming
5. 12
6. rapid eye movement
7. Tyken's Rift
8. Plant Biology Lab
9. Calladian thorn flower
10. 35, there were 34 dead plus one survivor

SPECIAL ASSIGNMENT SOLUTION

anicium and yurium

Congratulations! Starfleet Command is proud to award you the Starfleet Medal of Honour and 15 extra points.

MULTIPLE CHOICE ANSWERS

1. D. orders Picard and the crew to bed
2. C. all the bodies sat upright
3. A. memory loss, inability to concentrate, irritability, paranoia, hallucinations
4. D. all of the above
5. B. the main deflector dish

MISSION PERFORMANCE RATING:

45 – 65 points **Superior:** So the hydrogen plan was yours. Pretty sharp!

40 – 44 points **Above Average:** Been sleeping pretty well, huh?

30 – 39 points **Average:** Dr Crusher wants a brain tissue sample from you.

20 – 29 points **Fair:** You're part of an experiment. Just not sure which one!

0 – 19 points **Poor:** You've been promoted to acting ensign!

IDENTITY CRISIS ⚓

After several members of Starfleet have disappeared, Susanna Leijten arrives on the *Enterprise* to help the crew investigate. All of the personnel involved were members of an away team from the *USS Victory* who had investigated the disappearance of a colony on Tarchannen III. Leijten and La Forge were also on that away team.

The *Enterprise* returns to the planet and an away team visits looking for clues. Leijten starts to act strangely and has to be transported back to the ship. Leijten exhibits a strange obsession to return to the surface of the planet. It seems that she is changing into another species. Geordi works to find an answer before he too begins to change.

Geordi begins to solve the riddle but is overtaken by the alien DNA and transformed. He is invisible to human eyes and is able to escape from the *Enterprise* to the planet's surface. Dr Crusher, meanwhile, is successful in identifying and removing the alien DNA from Leijten and the effects are reversed. Data devises a means of locating Geordi and an away team goes to search for him. Leijten is able to persuade Geordi to come back to the ship before the changes are irreversible. He comes back and is restored to normal by the good doctor.

TRIVIA QUESTIONS

1. When does Geordi first exhibit signs of changing? **(3pts)**
2. How long after Geordi escapes to the planet before the changes will be irreversible? **(3pts)**
3. What is Hickman attempting to do when he is spotted by a Federation ship? **(3pts)**
4. How long ago was the *Victory*'s away team investigation on Tarchannen III? **(3pts)**
5. What does Dr Crusher use to try to stabilize Leijten's immune system? **(4pts)**
6. A search area with a radius of 10 kilometres is equal to how many square kilometres? **(5pts)**
7. Picard tells Hickman to bring his shuttle to a positive pitch of how many degrees? **(4pts)**
8. How many people disappeared from the colony on Tarchannen III? **(4pts)**
9. Who was in command of the *Victory* away team on Tarchannen III? **(3pts)**
10. Who recorded the sensor log during the *Victory*'s away team investigation on Tarchannen III? **(3pts)**

✪ SPECIAL ASSIGNMENT (15pts)

Identify the sedative and the dosage that Dr Crusher prepares as a precaution to calm Geordi when he is found.

MULTIPLE CHOICE QUESTIONS

1. What does Picard order to be placed in orbit and on the surface of Tarchannen III? **(5pts)**
   A. emergency transponders
   B. quarantine transmitters
   C. delimitation markers
   D. warning beacons

2. What does Worf find on the holodeck? **(3pts)**
   A. a holodeck version of Geordi
   B. Geordi's VISOR, phaser and insignia communicator
   C. Geordi's tattered uniform and VISOR
   D. a stolen Federation shuttlecraft

3. What happens to Geordi's hands while he is on the holodeck? **(3pts)**
   A. the three middle fingers fuse together
   B. his fingernails fall out
   C. his hands start shaking uncontrollably
   D. his hands begin to feel icy cold

4. What does Geordi say he enjoys? **(2pts)**
   A. Leah Brahms' company
   B. the bachelor's life
   C. a challenge
   D. a good laugh

5. During the *Enterprise*'s first away team mission to Tarchannen III, what does Worf feel certain of? **(2pts)**
   A. that they are being watched
   B. that the Romulans must be involved
   C. that there are no survivors
   D. that Mendez is nearby

ANSWERS

TRIVIA ANSWERS

1. when he enters the holodeck with his hand trembling
2. less than an hour
3. fly a stolen shuttlecraft to Tarchannen III
4. five years ago
5. T-cell stimulator
6. 300 square kilometres
7. 20°
8. 49
9. Lieutenant Susanna Leijten
10. Ensign Anthony Brevelle

SPECIAL ASSIGNMENT SOLUTION

10cc of kayolane

Congratulations! Starfleet Command is proud to award you the Starfleet Medal of Honour and 15 extra points.

MULTIPLE CHOICE ANSWERS

1. D. warning beacons
2. C. Geordi's tattered uniform and VISOR
3. A. the three middle fingers fuse together
4. B. the bachelor's life
5. A. that they are being watched

MISSION PERFORMANCE RATING:

45 – 65 points **Superior:** So you told Dr Crusher what the problem was.

40 – 44 points **Above Average:** Good job tracking Geordi down.

30 – 39 points **Average:** You may have alien DNA strands in your body.

20 – 29 points **Fair:** Stolen any good shuttles lately?

0 – 19 points **Poor:** Quick! How many fingers and toes do you have?

THE NTH DEGREE

The *Enterprise* investigates why the Argus Array, a remote subspace telescope, has ceased transmitting data. Upon their arrival at the station, Geordi and Lieutenant Barclay take a shuttle to examine an alien probe nearby. Suddenly, a brilliant flash of light knocks Barclay unconscious. Barclay and Geordi are beamed to sickbay and both check out fine.

The probe begins to come closer to the *Enterprise*. All attempts to out-manoeuvre the probe fail and phaser fire is ineffective. At the last minute, Barclay somehow diverts the warp drive power to the shields to allow photon torpedoes to be used at close range. The ploy is successful and the probe is destroyed. However, not even Geordi can understand how Barclay performed the feat.

Several days later, the array's reactors become unstable, threatening the *Enterprise*. Barclay, frustrated with the 'slow' computer interface in Engineering, goes to the holodeck and literally plugs himself into the computer. He is quickly able to stabilize the array. Afterwards, Barclay's intellect continues to grow and he invents a new type of space travel, plunging the *Enterprise* into the centre of the galaxy. An alien image appears on the bridge and looks the

crew of the *Enterprise* over. Barclay arrives and explains that the aliens are space explorers who never leave their home world. The probes contain information about how to come to their system. While the probe damaged the array's computers, it was able to work through Barclay's brain. The aliens return Barclay to normal and the *Enterprise* visits for a few days in an exchange of information.

CROSSWORD PUZZLE CLUES

ACROSS
3. Barclay transferred his higher brain functions and memory into the _____ computer core. **(3pts)**
4. Barclay says the _____ should be in bloom. **(4pts)**
6. Place where Barclay asks Troi to walk with him. **(2pts)**
8. Contiguous external integument. **(3pts)**
10. Aliens responsible for Barclay's heightened intelligence. **(3pts)**
11. Lieutenant who called Geordi about the problem with Reactor 9. **(3pts)**
13. Barclay tells Dr Crusher to use a _____ mode in the scanner to speed sample testing. **(1pt)**
15. System in which the science station is located where Picard wants to tow the probe. **(3pts)**
17. Barclay suggests fixing all of the Argus Array's reactors _____. **(1pt)**
18. Data says Barclay's performance in the play was _____. **(1pt)**
20. The Corpus _____ connects the two hemispheres of the brain. **(3pts)**
21. The information the *Enterprise* gathered will take scholars _____ to analyze. **(2pts)**
23. Barclay uses a _____ densitometer on the alien probe. **(2pts)**
24. The shuttlecraft crew is transported directly to _____. **(1pt)**
25. Have no effect on the probe. **(1pt)**

DOWN
1. Number of photon torpedoes fired at probe. **(1pt)**
2. The Argus Array is located at the very edge of _____ territory. **(1pt)**
5. Type of interface Barclay created with *Enterprise*'s computer. **(2pts)**
7. Barclay taught _____ technique at the music school. **(3pts)**
9. The bridge loses _____ control moments before the Argus reactor reaches critical. **(2pts)**
10. Barclay says he has found _____ within himself. **(1pt)**
12. Cyrano made swords out of _____ when he was young. **(3pts)**
14. Barclay now perceives the universe as a single _____. **(2pts)**
15. The aliens only want an exchange of _____. **(1pt)**
16. The Argus Array is an _____ station. **(2pts)**
19. Method of propulsion used by the alien probe. **(2pts)**
22. Role played by Dr Crusher in the play. **(2pts)**

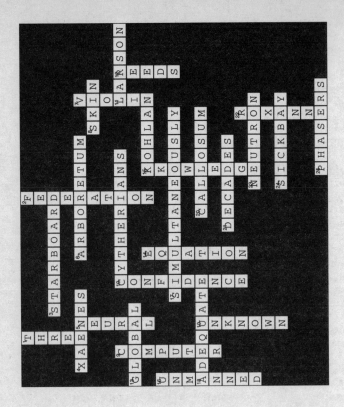

MISSION PERFORMANCE RATING:

50 – 55 points **Superior:** Your brain's plugged into the Internet, isn't it?

40 – 49 points **Above Average:** You have extraordinary mental abilities!

30 – 39 points **Average:** You have slightly enlarged frontal lobes.

20 – 29 points **Fair:** You head is swelling too, but it's all due to hot air.

 0 – 19 points **Poor:** You're a neuron.

STARDATE: 44741.9

Vash, whom Picard met on Risa (see 'Captain's Holiday'), turns up at the archaeological conference being held on the *Enterprise*. Dr Crusher meets Vash and takes her on a tour of the ship. Vash is distressed to find that Picard hasn't mentioned her to any of the crew.

Meanwhile, Q appears in Picard's ready room and informs the captain that he owes Picard a favour for his past help (see 'Déjà Q'). Picard tells Q he doesn't want anything and to get off his ship. Q leaves for the moment but later watches Picard and Vash while they have a lover's spat. Q is intrigued by the emotion of love, and devises another one of his games to play.

Q transports Picard and his senior staff to a replica of Sherwood Forest. Picard is made Robin Hood, and the other crew members are his merry band of men. Vash is held captive at Nottingham Castle as Maid Marion. Picard goes to rescue Vash but is caught by the Sheriff's soldiers. Just before Picard and Vash are executed, Riker and the others rescue the duo. Q returns everyone to the *Enterprise*. Vash explains to Picard that she has chosen to go exploring the universe with Q. Vash and Q then disappear to begin their travels.

TRIVIA QUESTIONS

1. Why does Riker alert the crew? **(3pts)**
2. What doesn't a captain reveal to his crew? **(3pts)**
3. What does Q resent? **(5pts)**
4. What does Picard tell Sir Guy he should know about him? **(3pts)**
5. Where does the arrow strike Data? **(4pts)**
6. What is Vash's wedding present to Sir Guy? **(3pts)**
7. What is the Sheriff's full title? **(4pts)**
8. What's the problem with being a well known liar? **(3pts)**
9. What do the Tagans no longer allow? **(3pts)**
10. What does Picard find on the coffee table in his quarters? **(4pts)**

✪ DOUBLE SPECIAL ASSIGNMENT (15pts each)

Assignment I:
How many archaeological excavations have been conducted on Tagus III?

Assignment II:
Of these excavations how many have revealed important findings?

MULTIPLE CHOICE QUESTIONS

1. Picard doubts that there are many what on Tagus III? **(2pts)**
   - **A.** undiscovered archaeological sites
   - **B.** muktok plants
   - **C.** oak trees
   - **D.** people

2. What character does Worf play? **(3pts)**
   - **A.** Michael Dorn
   - **B.** Will Scarlet
   - **C.** Alan-a-Dale
   - **D.** Little John

3. What character does Geordi play? **(3pts)**
   - **A.** Alan-a-Dale
   - **B.** Little John
   - **C.** Will Scarlet
   - **D.** LeVar Burton

4. What character does Frakes play? **(5pts)**
   - **A.** Little John
   - **B.** Will Scarlet
   - **C.** William Riker
   - **D.** Alan-a-Dale

5. What do Picard and Dr Crusher often share together? **(2pts)**
   - **A.** classified information
   - **B.** morning tea
   - **C.** breakfast
   - **D.** a walk in the arboretum

ANSWERS

TRIVIA ANSWERS

1. because Q wants to do something nice for Picard
2. his personal feelings
3. owing Picard anything
4. that he's not from Nottingham
5. just above his sixth intercostal support, penetrating his secondary subprocessor
6. she stops Picard from escaping by using his own sword on him
7. His Honour the High Sheriff of Nottingham
8. people think you're lying even when you're telling the truth
9. outsiders to visit the ruins
10. Horga'hn

DOUBLE SPECIAL ASSIGNMENT SOLUTION

Assignment I:Total sites: 947
Assignment II: Important sites: 74
Congratulations! Starfleet Command is proud to award you the Starfleet Medal of Honour and 15 or 30 extra points.

MULTIPLE CHOICE ANSWERS

1. C. oak trees
2. B. Will Scarlet
3. A. Alan-a-Dale
4. C. William Riker
5. B. morning tea

MISSION PERFORMANCE RATING:

45 – 80 points **Superior:** You're a giant in the field of archaeology.
40 – 44 points **Above Average:** Archaeologist. (Respectable.)
30 – 39 points **Average:** Archaeologist's assistant. (Dig I say, dig!)
20 – 29 points **Fair:** Plunderer. (Watch your back.)
 0 – 19 points **Poor:** Grave robber. (Despicable.)

THE DRUMHEAD

STARDATE: 44768.2

Starfleet Admiral Satie assists the *Enterprise* in investigating possible sabotage to the warp drive. An explosion occurred several days earlier in Engineering resulting in damage to the dilithium chamber hatch. Starfleet has found out that the Romulans have recently received information on Starfleet's warp engines. Admiral Satie suspects that the two events are connected. Worf discovers that J'Ddan, a Klingon exchange officer aboard the *Enterprise*, is responsible for stealing and transmitting the information to the Romulans. J'Ddan claims that he did not sabotage the warp drive. Admiral Satie expands her investigation.

A young crewman named Tarses is interrogated about his possible involvement with J'Ddan. He is found to have lied on his Starfleet application: his paternal grandfather was actually Romulan instead of Vulcan. Admiral Satie launches into a major investigation of Tarses' past. Geordi and Data eventually determine that the explosion was accidental.

Admiral Satie is unswayed by the new evidence and plunges ahead looking for a conspiracy. When Picard attempts to put a stop to her witch hunt, he becomes the new focus of her investigation. She tries to show that Picard is a Romulan collaborator. During his trial, the Captain reveals her as the paranoid person she is, and the hearings are called off.

TRIVIA QUESTIONS

1. What position does Tarses hold? **(3pts)**
2. Who was Admiral Satie's father? **(3pts)**
3. Who from Starfleet Security will be at the hearings? **(4pts)**
4. How many times has Picard violated the Prime Directive according to Admiral Satie? **(3pts)**
5. What information has fallen into Romulan hands? **(3pts)**
6. How many ships and Starfleet personnel were lost during the battle with the Borg? **(5pts)**
7. What part of the Uniform Code of Justice allows a subject to make a statement before being questioned? **(4pts)**
8. Where was Picard's favourite spot to study at the Academy? **(3pts)**
9. What type of scan does Worf want Tarses to undergo? **(4pts)**
10. What disease is J'Ddan being treated for in sickbay? **(3pts)**

CHARACTER QUOTE
(2pts per word + 9pts for identifying the speaker.)

Unscramble the words below and then identify the character.

'... the _____ from _____ _____ to _____ _____
     ARDO   MIGTEILTEA IUCSNSIPO   ATPNMRA OARINAPA
is very _____ _____ than we _____.'
     CMHU   OTSREHR   INTKH

✪ SPECIAL ASSIGNMENT (15pts)

From which terminal does Riker say J'Ddan logged on to the *Enterprise*'s computer?

ANSWERS

TRIVIA ANSWERS
1. crewman 1st class, medical technician
2. Judge Aaron Satie
3. Admiral Thomas Henry
4. nine
5. schematic drawings of the dilithium chamber
6. 39 ships and almost 11,000 personnel killed
7. Chapter 4, Article 12
8. on the circular bench under the elm tree near the parade grounds
9. encephalographic polygraph scan
10. Ba'ltmasor Syndrome

CHARACTER QUOTE SOLUTION
'... the road from legitimate suspicion to rampant paranoia is very much shorter than we think.' – Picard

SPECIAL ASSIGNMENT SOLUTION
Computer 12-B9 on Deck 36
Congratulations! Starfleet Command is proud to award you the Starfleet Medal of Honour and 15 extra points.

MISSION PERFORMANCE RATING:
55 – 75 points **Superior:** You're Starfleet's best judge advocate general.
45 – 54 points **Above Average:** Prelaw student, huh?
30 – 44 points **Average:** You look suspicious. Haven't I seen you before?
15 – 29 points **Fair:** What crimes might you be responsible for?
  0 – 14 points **Poor:** To the brig with you, you subversive!

HALF A LIFE

STARDATE: 44805.3

Lwaxana Troi visits the *Enterprise* just as the ship cautiously contacts a reclusive race. Dr Timicin, a scientist from Kaelon II, beams aboard to supervise the preparations for an experiment. His life's work will hinge on this one test in the hope of revitalizing their dying sun. Lwaxana charms Timicin and the two become almost inseparable. The *Enterprise* will take Timicin to a suitable test star and assist him with the experiment.

The experiment proceeds as planned. It appears a success but then the star deteriorates and explodes. Timicin reveals to Lwaxana that he must go home now to die. His culture does not allow anyone to live beyond a certain age, regardless of health or status. Timicin admits that his next birthday will be his time to die. Lwaxana, who has fallen in love with Timicin, tries to persuade him against ritual suicide. Timicin realizes the mistakes he made in his experiment and knows he is the most capable person to continue with the work. He decides to seek asylum on the *Enterprise*. Timicin is overwhelmed by the negative response of his family and the government. He finally decides he is not a revolutionary and informs Picard that he will be going back to his planet.

TRIVIA QUESTIONS

1. Picard says Lwaxana is the acting what? **(3pts)**
2. How long did it take Timicin to develop the programming that controls the photon torpedoes? **(3pts)**
3. What does Riker ask Lwaxana to do? **(3pts)**
4. Why is seven a significant number for Timicin? **(3pts)**
5. How soon before Timicin's last birthday? **(4pts)**
6. How much longer does Kaelon II have before its sun dies? **(3pts)**
7. Lwaxana says a brilliant astronomer from where once named a star after her? **(4pts)**
8. During the test, what is the density at? **(5pts)**
9. According to Troi, how long has Lwaxana spent choosing an outfit to wear? **(3pts)**
10. What has Lwaxana made for the boys in Engineering? **(4pts)**

MULTIPLE CHOICE QUESTIONS

1. How many photon torpedoes are launched during the experiment? **(5pts)**
    A. two volleys of four each
    B. one volley of eight
    C. two volleys of three each
    D. two volleys: one of four and one of three, one torpedo malfunctioned

2. What defence does Timicin give for the ritual ending of their lives? **(2pts)**
   - **A.** it allows more resources to be devoted to the young
   - **B.** it makes life more fair
   - **C.** it makes life more predictable
   - **D.** it allows them to end their lives with dignity

3. What does Lwaxana initially tell Timicin to think of her as? **(3pts)**
   - **A.** his tour guide
   - **B.** his entertainment director
   - **C.** his mother
   - **D.** his lover

4. What theory has been discussed for over a century but had no practical application until now? **(3pts)**
   - **A.** helium fission augmentation
   - **B.** helium fusion enhancement
   - **C.** hydrogen nullification
   - **D.** hydrogen enhancement

5. What took the Federation three years to accomplish? **(2pts)**
   - **A.** travelling to Kaelon II due to its great distance
   - **B.** establishing the first meeting with Kaelon II to discuss the experiment
   - **C.** finding a suitable star for the experiment, similar in characteristics to the Kaelon sun
   - **D.** adapting the photon torpedoes for the experiment

ANSWERS

TRIVIA ANSWERS
1. acting ambassador of goodwill for today
2. 40 years
3. clear the bridge
4. his grandson is almost seven years old
5. four days
6. 30–40 years
7. Rigel IV
8. 1,100 g/cm³
9. 20 minutes
10. Mantickian Pâté

MULTIPLE CHOICE
1. A. two volleys of four each
2. D. it allows them to end their lives with dignity
3. B. his entertainment director
4. B. helium fusion enhancement
5. C. finding a suitable star for the experiment, similar in characteristics to the Kaelon sun

MISSION PERFORMANCE RATING:

45 – 50 points **Superior:** Your work was successful, you saved the planet!

40 – 44 points **Above Average:** Have you stopped having birthdays?

30 – 39 points **Average:** You can have Mr Homn's job.

20 – 29 points **Fair:** You are banished to Kaelon II until your 61st birthday.

0 – 19 points **Poor:** How old are you going to be this time around?

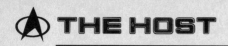 # THE HOST

The *Enterprise* is transporting a Federation ambassador named Odan to mediate a dispute. Dr Crusher and Odan have fallen in love during the voyage to Peliar Zel. After arriving at the planet, Odan is seriously injured in a shuttlecraft accident. While treating Odan, Dr Crusher discovers that he is a Trill, a parasitic race joined with a host body.

Dr Crusher removes the symbiont and places Odan in stasis. The host body soon dies. It will be some time before a replacement host will arrive and Odan will not survive in stasis until then. Riker volunteers to serve as temporary host to Odan. The operation is successful but Dr Crusher has trouble accepting Odan(Riker) as the man she loved before. Riker's body begins to reject the symbiont but Odan(Riker) is able to complete the negotiations.

Dr Crusher acts quickly to remove Odan from Riker's body before it kills him. Odan is again placed in stasis while the *Enterprise* races to meet the ship carrying Odan's new host body. Dr Crusher is shocked to see that the new host is a woman. Dr Crusher performs the implant procedure and Odan recovers from the surgery. They reaffirm their love for each other but Dr Crusher tells Odan she just can't keep up with the changes.

TRIVIA QUESTIONS

1. Who was Odan's father in actuality? **(3pts)**
2. What does Odan give Dr Crusher before leaving in the shuttlecraft? **(3pts)**
3. How long before another host body can meet with the *Enterprise*? **(3pts)**
4. What is Odan(Riker) suffering from? **(3pts)**
5. Why does Odan(Riker) stop taking the injections? **(3pts)**
6. Who is the representative that was present at both negotiations? **(4pts)**
7. Whose aunt represented Beta 30 years ago during the negotiations? **(4pts)**
8. What fact did Odan(Riker) disclose to gain the representatives' trust? **(3pts)**
9. How old was Stephan? **(4pts)**
10. What drug (and dosage) does Dr Crusher give Odan(Riker) to prevent heart fibrillation? **(5pts)**

SPECIAL ASSIGNMENT (10pts)

Initially, what is Riker's pulse and blood pressure after Odan enters his body?

MULTIPLE CHOICE QUESTIONS

1. What were the names of Dr Crusher's imaginary twins? **(2pts)**
    A. Brett and Brent
    B. Andrew and Alexander
    C. David and Daniel
    D. Alec and Allan

2. What does the Governor not recommend? **(3pts)**
    A. the beef stroganoff
    B. shuttling to the surface
    C. starting negotiations so soon after Odan transfers into a new host
    D. using transporters, due to magnetic resonance

3. How long has Dr Crusher known Odan? **(3pts)**
    A. a couple of months
    B. only a few days
    C. a couple of weeks
    D. since the Academy

4. Odan was afraid that Data would turn up at his quarters and want to discuss what? **(5pts)**
    A. Odan's relationship with Dr Crusher
    B. the effects of magnetic depolarization on Beta's tidal cycles
    C. the peripheral effects of magnetospheric energy taps
    D. the economic implications of a collapse of Beta's gravimetric field

5. Who did Governor Leka supposedly know? **(2pts)**
    A. Riker's father
    B. Bine's aunt
    C. Trose's aunt
    D. Odan's father

ANSWERS

TRIVIA ANSWERS

1. Odan in a previous host's body
2. a red rose
3. 40 hours
4. classic rejection syndrome
5. they are harmful to Riker's body
6. Kalin Trose
7. Lathal Bine's
8. that Trose, 30 years ago, stopped a plot by a radical faction to assassinate the Beta delegate
9. 11 years old
10. 200 mg metrazene

SPECIAL ASSIGNMENT SOLUTION

Pulse: 110; Blood Pressure: 90/40

Congratulations! Starfleet Command is proud to award you the Starfleet Medal of Honour and 10 extra points.

MULTIPLE CHOICE ANSWERS

1. B. Andrew and Alexander
2. B. shuttling to the surface
3. C. a couple of weeks
4. C. the peripheral effects of magnetospheric energy taps
5. D. Odan's father

MISSION PERFORMANCE RATING:

45 – 60 points **Superior:** You have achieved a certain level of Trillness.

40 – 44 points **Above Average:** You big symbiont, weren't you at Slugfest '91?

30 – 39 points **Average:** You're expendable and we need a temporary host body.

20 – 29 points **Fair:** You'd make a great host and I don't mean talk show!

0 – 19 points **Poor:** What kind of aliens are growing inside you?

THE MIND'S EYE ⚛

While en route to a conference, Geordi's shuttle is attacked by the Romulans and the engineer is taken aboard their vessel. The Romulans brainwash Geordi and implant memories of his supposed trip to Risa.

The *Enterprise* takes Klingon Ambassador Kell to investigate reports of Federation aid to a rebellious Klingon colony. The Governor of the colony says he has captured Federation supplies and weapons from the rebels. Geordi soon rejoins the *Enterprise* at the troubled colony. Data and Geordi test one of the captured weapons and determine that it is of Romulan manufacture. Then Geordi secretly transports a shipment of weapons to the planet's surface. The Governor, who has intercepted the transfer, is furious.

Picard begins an investigation into what has happened. Kell comes aboard the *Enterprise* with the Governor to allow him to see the investigation first-hand. Kell, a Romulan sympathiser, orders Geordi to kill the Governor. Data uncovers the plot to assassinate the Governor and is able to thwart the plan before Geordi can carry out his orders. Counsellor Troi then begins the slow task of deprogramming Geordi.

TRIVIA QUESTIONS

1. What did Geordi take second place in? **(3pts)**
2. How long has O'Brien served with Geordi? **(3pts)**
3. What does Geordi have a low tolerance for? **(3pts)**
4. What does Geordi order to drink in Ten-Forward? **(5pts)**
5. How much does Geordi remember eating on Risa? **(3pts)**
6. What is the efficiency reading of the discharge crystal on the most efficient Starfleet phaser rifle? **(4pts)**
7. What is the efficiency reading of the discharge crystal on the captured Starfleet phaser rifle? **(4pts)**
8. What does Geordi tell his engineers to run before calling it a night? **(3pts)**
9. What does the Governor tell Picard he does well? **(3pts)**
10. What is difficult to localize? **(4pts)**

SPECIAL ASSIGNMENT (10pts)

Data says there are how many systems that use a terahertz feed to charge a weapon?

MULTIPLE CHOICE QUESTIONS

1. What is the only thing that has kept the Romulans in check? **(2pts)**
   A. the Federation–Klingon Alliance
   B. a strongly fortified Neutral Zone
   C. the Federation's trade agreement with the Ferengi
   D. the Federation's superior firepower

2. What is the first test the Romulans make Geordi perform to assess his conditioning? **(2pts)**
   A. he tries to assassinate the Governor
   B. he deliberately spills his drink on O'Brien
   C. he goes to sickbay complaining of sleeplessness
   D. he tries to beam a shipment of weapons to the rebels

3. When did Worf act as a true Klingon according to Kell? **(3pts)**
   A. the day he killed Duras
   B. the day he accepted discommendation
   C. the day he joined Starfleet
   D. the day he took the Klingon vow of marriage with K'Ehleyr

4. What pleasant image does the Romulan show Geordi? **(3pts)**
   A. Geordi's twelfth birthday
   B. a party on Rubicun III
   C. a spring day on Earth
   D. the girl he remembers from Risa

5. What is Geordi's answer to the first game question the shuttle computer asks him? **(5pts)**
   A. symmetrical, extroverted, phased, stabled
   B. asymmetrical, inverted, polarized, stabled
   C. phased, inverted, stabled, symmetrical
   D. asymmetrical, inverted, phased, stabled

ANSWERS

TRIVIA ANSWERS

1. a chess tournament
2. almost four years
3. watching others suffer
4. rectorine
5. enough for 12 people
6. 86.5%
7. 94.1%
8. Level-4 series
9. Picard swears well
10. E-band emissions

SPECIAL ASSIGNMENT SOLUTION

327 systems

Congratulations! Starfleet Command is proud to award you the Starfleet Medal of Honour and 10 extra points.

MULTIPLE CHOICE ANSWERS

1. A. the Federation–Klingon Alliance
2. B. he deliberately spills his drink on O'Brien
3. A. the day he killed Duras
4. C. a spring day on Earth
5. D. asymmetrical, inverted, phased, stabled

MISSION PERFORMANCE RATING:

45 – 60 points **Superior:** You exposed the plot and saved the Alliance!

40 – 44 points **Above Average:** Nice work uncovering the fake phasers.

30 – 39 points **Average:** You've been acting a little funny lately.

20 – 29 points **Fair:** The Romulans need someone else to brainwash.

0 – 19 points **Poor:** Hey, you need a brain before they can brainwash you!

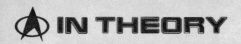

IN THEORY

The *Enterprise* is studying a nearby nebula. During the experiments, sensors pick up a class-M planet within the nebula. Picard orders a closer examination of the planet. While Data is working with a crew member named Jenna, she suddenly kisses Data. Data, intrigued, seeks advice from his friends. He also researches human love and decides to cultivate a romantic relationship with Jenna.

Meanwhile, unexplained events are occurring on the *Enterprise*. Furniture is found rearranged, objects fall, and a crew member is embedded in the floor of a corridor. Data is able to determine the problem by recalibrating the sensors: subspace distortions within the nebula are colliding with the *Enterprise* as it moves through space. The phenomena can only be detected from close range, so Picard pilots a shuttlecraft that is tied directly into the *Enterprise*'s navigational systems. The plan is successful until the shuttlecraft is damaged and Picard is beamed back aboard the *Enterprise*. The ship escapes the nebula and heads for its new destination. Jenna later decides to discontinue her relationship with Data as he is incapable of loving her.

TRIVIA QUESTIONS

1. What is Jenna's last name? **(3pts)**
2. What was a half metre in height? **(3pts)**
3. How far away is the closest class-M planet within the nebula? **(4pts)**
4. What is the Mar Oscura? **(3pts)**
5. What chapter and paragraph does Jenna quote from the *Book of Love*? **(5pts)**
6. What happened on Deck 37? **(4pts)**
7. What type of conflict is followed by emotional release that often strengthens the relationship? **(3pts)**
8. Where did Guinan learn to make her latest concoction? **(4pts)**
9. Who was Anne Boleyn? **(3pts)**
10. When did Jenna and Jeff break up? **(3pts)**

✪ SPECIAL ASSIGNMENT (15pts)

What are the ingredients of Guinan's new drink?

MULTIPLE CHOICE QUESTIONS

1. What does Data say when Jenna tells him they are no longer a couple? **(2pts)**
   - A. he's sorry that things didn't work out
   - B. he'll delete the appropriate programme
   - C. he'll call her in the morning
   - D. can't they work things out?

2. What part of the shuttle is damaged? **(5pts)**
   - A. port thrusters
   - B. deflector shields
   - C. navigational controls
   - D. starboard impulse nacelle

3. Where did Jenna give Data a very passionate kiss? **(3pts)**
   - A. his quarters
   - B. Ten-Forward
   - C. turbolift
   - D. torpedo bay

4. When the nebula was illuminated during the tests what did it remind Jenna of? **(3pts)**
   - A. Los Angeles at night
   - B. the giant red star in the Praxillus system after it went supernova
   - C. watching fireworks as a little girl
   - D. the battle of Wolf 359

5. What did Jenna dislike about Jeff's eating habits? **(2pts)**
   - A. the sound he made while eating soup
   - B. the mess he made on the table while eating spaghetti
   - C. the way he always ate pipius claw with his hands
   - D. the sound he made while eating gagh

ANSWERS

TRIVIA ANSWERS

1. D'Sora
2. the pile of O'Brien's socks on the floor before Keiko picked them up
3. three light-hours
4. an unexplored dark matter nebula
5. Chapter Four, paragraph 17
6. explosive decompression
7. a lovers' quarrel
8. Prakal II
9. a wife of Henry VIII
10. six weeks ago

SPECIAL ASSIGNMENT SOLUTION

87% Saurian brandy with Targ milk and Denesian meat comprising the rest

Congratulations! Starfleet Command is proud to award you the Starfleet Medal of Honour and 15 extra points.

MULTIPLE CHOICE ANSWERS

1. B. he'll delete the appropriate programme
2. D. starboard impulse nacelle
3. D. torpedo bay
4. C. watching fireworks as a little girl
5. A. the sound he made while eating soup

MISSION PERFORMANCE RATING:

45 – 60 points **Superior:** Excellent manoeuvring in the shuttlecraft, Captain!

40 – 44 points **Above Average:** Great advice you gave Data.

30 – 39 points **Average:** Do you want to be a lieutenant the rest of your life?

20 – 29 points **Fair:** You look like a subspace distortion just hit you!

0 – 19 points **Poor:** You have an unusually low quality of grey matter.

REDEMPTION ⚓

The *Enterprise* is en route to the Klingon home world where Picard will complete his role as Arbiter of Succession. A Klingon ship intercepts the *Enterprise* and Gowron beams aboard to talk to Picard. It seems that the sisters of Duras (the other challenger to the throne who was killed by Worf in 'Reunion') are preparing to challenge Gowron at his installation as Council Leader.

During the ceremony, Duras' sisters introduce Toral, illegitimate son of Duras, to challenge Gowron. Picard refuses to acknowledge the challenge of the untested young Klingon. The loyalty of the Council is split as the factions prepare for civil war. Worf tells Gowron that the price of his and Kurn's support is the restoration of their family honour (see 'Sins of the Father'). While he talks to Worf, Gowron's ship is attacked by Duras' forces. Gowron survives the attack largely due to the efforts of Worf and Kurn. Gowron then decides to restore Worf's family name.

After Gowron takes his position as head of the High Council, he asks Picard for Federation assistance to help quell the civil war. Picard refuses to intervene in an internal matter. Worf decides to resign from Starfleet to assist Gowron and help to preserve the Empire. When the Duras family and their Romulan allies receive word that the *Enterprise* has left, the Romulan officer who steps out of the shadows bears a disturbing resemblance to the late Tasha Yar (see 'Skin of Evil' and 'Yesterday's *Enterprise*').

TRIVIA QUESTIONS

1. Where does Gowron tell Kurn to meet him? **(3pts)**
2. What beverage is served to Picard during his visit with the Duras sisters? **(3pts)**
3. What does Gowron say still reaches out from the grave? **(3pts)**
4. What does Gowron consider no small favour? **(3pts)**
5. What bet did Guinan have with Picard? **(3pts)**
6. Gowron is the son of whom? **(5pts)**
7. Who is the acting head of the Klingon High Council before Gowron is installed? **(4pts)**
8. What is the name of Kurn's ship? **(4pts)**
9. How many of Kurn's allies will support Gowron? **(4pts)**
10. Who are Lursa and B'Etor? **(3pts)**

SPECIAL ASSIGNMENT (10pts)

Whom will Worf have to contact to get the complete records on the Khitomer Massacre?

MULTIPLE CHOICE QUESTIONS

1. What does Picard order the conn to do as Gowron's ship is attacked?
   (3pts)
   A. raise shields and arm photon torpedoes
   B. take the *Enterprise* safely away from the combat area at ¹/₂
   impulse
   C. take evasive manoeuvres
   D. pursue the fleeing bird-of-prey

2. Picard will make the Federation's information on the Khitomer Massacre
   available to whom? **(2pts)**
   A. Gowron and the Klingon High Council
   B. Romulans
   C. Duras' family
   D. anyone who requests the files

3. Klingon women are not allowed to do what? **(5pts)**
   A. enter the Great Hall
   B. serve on the Klingon High Council
   C. serve aboard the flagship of the Klingon Empire
   D. interrogate prisoners

4. After Picard speaks with Gowron, what does he tell Data to start
   monitoring? **(2pts)**
   A. Klingon activity in Sector 2204
   B. subspace messages from Klingon home world
   C. Romulan activity along the Neutral Zone
   D. cloaked vessels in the sector

5. What type of vessel is Gowron's ship? **(3pts)**
   A. a bird-of-prey
   B. a warbird
   C. an attack cruiser
   D. a battle cruiser

ANSWERS

TRIVIA ANSWERS

1. in the Great Hall
2. Earl Grey tea
3. the grasp of Duras
4. Worf killing Duras
5. that she could make Worf laugh before he becomes a lieutenant commander
6. M'Rel
7. K'Tal
8. Hegh'ta
9. three squadron commanders will join Kurn, one will not
10. the sisters of Duras

SPECIAL ASSIGNMENT SOLUTION

Starbase 24

Congratulations! Starfleet Command is proud to award you the Starfleet Medal of Honour and 10 extra points.

MULTIPLE CHOICE ANSWERS

1. B. take the Enterprise safely away from the combat area at ½ impulse
2. D. anyone who requests the files
3. B. serve on the Klingon High Council
4. C. Romulan activity along the Neutral Zone
5. C. an attack cruiser

MISSION PERFORMANCE RATING:

45 – 60 points **Superior:** Your seat on the Klingon High Council awaits you!

40 – 44 points **Above Average:** You must have Klingon blood in your veins!

30 – 39 points **Average:** Klingon wannabee.

20 – 29 points **Fair:** Even Toral scored average.

0 – 19 points **Poor:** You have fallen into the evil clutches of Lursa and B'Etor.

PHRASEOLOGY

KLINGON TERMINOLOGY (5pts each)

Match the Klingon words/phrases with the English translation. More than one Klingon word may be an insult or expletive.

Klingon Word or Phrase	English Translation
1. Mek'ba	A. Make it so!
2. yIntagh	B. spirit possession
3. BaH	C. an expletive
4. Ha'DIbah	D. ceremonial weapon of an assassin
5. gin'tak	E. the phase of a trial in which the evidence is presented
6. Ghos	F. to the death
7. veruul	G. an advisor who is so trusted that he becomes one of the family
8. kut'luch	H. an insult
9. pahtk	I. now
10. Jat'yIn	J. fire (as in giving an order to fire weapons)
11. baktag	K. Romulan insult
12. tohzah	
13. gik'tal	
14. DaH	

DATA CONFUSED (5pts each)

1. What term was Data unfamiliar with in the episode 'Where No One Has Gone Before'?
2. What phrase did Dr Pulaski use that Data is confused about in the episode 'Peak Performance'?
3. What phrase did Geordi say as a joke that Data didn't understand in the episode 'The Mind's Eye'?
4. What term for Q was Data unfamiliar with in the episode 'Hide and Q'?
5. What term was Data unfamiliar with in the episode 'Lonely Among Us'?
6. What phrase was Data unfamiliar with in the episode 'Unnatural Selection'?
7. What phrase was Data unfamiliar with in the episode 'The Child'?
8. What expression did Jenna use that Data thought was in reference to Spot in the episode 'In Theory'?
9. What slang term were Data and Riker unfamiliar with in the episode 'The Neutral Zone'?
10. What phrase was Data unfamiliar with in the episode 'The Price'?
11. What figure of speech does Geordi use that Data does not understand in the episode 'The Defector'?
12. What term did Data misinterpret in the episode 'The Schizoid Man'?
13. What phrase did Data take literally in the episode 'The Best of Both Worlds'?

14. What type of comedy does Data not understand in the episode 'Suddenly Human'?
15. What figure of speech used by O'Brien did Data take literally in the episode 'All Good Things . . .'?
16. What concept of dancing did Data not understand in the episode 'Data's Day'?
17. What term was Data not at first familiar with in reference to Keiko's wedding in the same episode?
18. What word was Data unfamiliar with in the episode 'Encounter at Farpoint – Part I'?
19. What did Guinan say that Data took literally in the episode 'In Theory'?
20. What phrase does Data interpret literally in the episode 'Time's Arrow'?

PROPER NAME CALLING (2pts each)
Match the description with the correct name or phrase.

Description
1. Worf calls the Ferengi this while fighting them.
2. What does Lwaxana call Tog?
3. Q talking about humans.
4. Inorganic life forms addressing humans on the *Enterprise*.
5. Rondon calls Wesley this after Wesley runs into him in the corridor.
6. Armus' nickname for Data.
7. Q describes Data as what?
8. Q calls Guinan this.
9. What does Riker call the Pakleds?
10. What does Gosheven call Data?
11. What do the Nanites call humans?
12. What does Q call Picard when he takes Q literally?
13. What does Q call Worf during Season Three?
14. What does Elbrun call Riker?
15. What do the Sheliak call humans?
16. Lwaxana would rather eat what than deal with Tog?
17. What does Rondon also call Wesley after Wesley runs into him in the corridor?
18. How does Worf describe the alien soldiers that Q created?
19. How does Q refer to the human race in Season Seven?
20. What friendly jibe does Data use on Geordi at the barbershop?
21. Q tells Worf he'd make a perfect what?
22. What does Ambassador Byleth call Worf?
23. Q volunteers to turn Vash into what?
24. What does Jenna jokingly call Data?
25. What does Gowron call Toral?
26. What does Omag call Worf as Worf sings the Klingon opera *Aktuh and Melota*?
27. What does Q call Worf during Season One?

28. Eli asked Worf if his mother married a what?

29. What does Worf call Ambassador Byleth?

30. How does Q describe Troi's counselling abilities?

Name

A. very strange looking creatures

B. Bulgallian Sludge Rat

C. Federation creatures

D. a walking calculator

E. silver-tongued devil

F. the *robot* who teaches the course in humanities

G. macrohead with a microbrain

H. ape-like race

I. toad-faced troll

J. impudent wretch

K. imp

L. Billy-boy

M. pygmy cretins

N. plodding animal

O. Tinman

P. curious throwbacks

Q. Klingon goat

R. Orion wing-slugs

S. Klabnian eel

T. foolish, fragile non-entities

U. vicious animal things

V. pedantic psychobabble

W. obtuse piece of flotsam

X. armadillo

Y. ugly bags of mostly water

Z. throw rug in Nottingham Castle

AA. insulting pompous fool

BB. lunkhead

CC. Bardakian pronghorn moose

DD. despicable Melanoid slime worm

SPECIAL SECTION

ANSWERS

KLINGON TERMINOLOGY ANSWERS

1. E ('Sins of the Father'); 2. C ('Redemption'); 3. J ('Redemption'); 4. H ('Sins of the Father'); 5. G ('Firstborn'); 6. A ('Redemption – Part II'); 7. K ('The Defector'); 8. D ('Sins of the Father'); 9. H ('The Defector'); 10. B ('Power Play'); 11. H ('Redemption – Part II'); 12. C ('The Defector'); 13. F ('Lower Decks'); 14. I ('Redemption – Part II')

DATA CONFUSED ANSWERS

1. sleigh ride; 2. Bust him up!; 3. forced to endure Risa; 4. Flim-Flam Man; 5. Private Eye; 6. bedside manner; 7. Eager Beaver; 8. The cat's out of the bag; 9. low-mileage pit woofie; 10. a proverbial lemon; 11. Catch the Romulans with their pants down; 12. ladykiller; 13. The early bird gets the worm; 14. slapstick; 15. burn the midnight oil; 16. Dr Crusher tells him he has to lead and Data says 'Lead where?'; 17. cold feet; 18. snoop; 19. When Guinan says 'Don't look at me' (for advice) Data turns his face away from Guinan; 20. When the bellboy says that one day his ship's going to come in; Data then asks him if he has a ship

PROPER NAME CALLING ANSWERS

1. M ('The Last Outpost'); 2. I ('Ménage à Troi'); 3. T ('Hide and Q'); 4. Y ('Home Soil'); 5. B or DD ('Coming of Age'); 6. O ('Skin of Evil'); 7. F ('Deja Q'); 8. K ('Q Who'); 9. P ('Samaritan Snare'); 10. D ('The Ensigns of Command'); 11. A ('Evolution'); 12. W ('All Good Things …'); 13. Q ('Deja Q'); 14. L ('Tin Man'); 15. C ('The Ensigns of Command'); 16. R ('Ménage à Troi'); 17. DD or B ('Coming of Age'); 18. U ('Hide and Q'); 19. H ('All Good Things …'); 20. BB ('Data's Day'); 21. Z ('Qpid'); 22. N (Liaisons'); 23. S ('Qpid'); 24. E ('In Theory'); 25. J ('Redemption'); 26. CC ('Unification II'); 27. G ('Hide and Q'); 28. X ('A Fistful of Datas'); 29. AA ('Liaisons'); 30. V ('All Good Things …')

MISSION PERFORMANCE RATING:

201 – 230 points	**Superior:** Certified Starfleet Language Specialist! (SEE BELOW)
151 – 200 points	**Above Average:** Your command of Klingon is impressive!
101 – 150 points	**Average:** Not bad, all things considered.
51 – 100 points	**Fair:** YIntagh! You have the brain of a baktag!
0 – 50 points	**Poor:** Tohzah! You wear the uniform of a pahtk!

If you have received a SUPERIOR Mission Performance Rating –

Congratulations!
Starfleet Command is proud to award you
the Silver Palm with Cluster and 50 extra points.

SEASON FIVE

REDEMPTION II

The Klingon Empire has degenerated into civil war. Picard, suspecting that the Duras family is receiving help from the Romulans, proposes a plan to Starfleet to expose the Romulan connection.

The Federation approves the plan and Picard puts together a fleet of ships that blockades the Romulan–Klingon border. Forming a tachyon grid between their ships, they are now able to detect the Romulan cloaked ships when they try to pass. The Romulan commander contacts Picard and introduces herself as Commander Sela. She also claims to be the daughter of Tasha Yar. She warns Picard to move the fleet away from their border or they will attack.

Picard tells Gowron to launch a major attack on the rebels to force the Romulans to send more supplies to the Duras family. After the devastating attacks begin, the Romulans receive an urgent call for more supplies from the Duras sisters. The Romulans prepare to send another convoy but first must figure out how to get through the blockade. They fire a tremendous tachyon pulse that disrupts part of the detection grid. During the subsequent confusion the Romulans try to sneak past the Federation ships. Data designs a means to locate and expose the cloaked ships, and the Romulans have no choice but to return to base. Gowron defeats the Duras family and is victorious. Worf decides to return to Starfleet.

TRIVIA QUESTIONS

1. Who wants Worf to take her as a mate? **(3pts)**
2. How are the photon torpedo warhead yields reconfigured? **(4pts)**
3. What do the Duras sisters do when defeat is imminent? **(3pts)**
4. What tool does Gowron give to Worf to clean the house? **(5pts)**
5. What does Worf do to Toral? **(3pts)**
6. Tasha died a year before what happened? **(3pts)**
7. What has Hobson taken off-line without consulting Data? **(4pts)**
8. In addition to the *Enterprise*, which other starship will close the gap in the tachyon grid when the Romulans try to run it? **(4pts)**
9. Where was the *Enterprise-C* lost? **(3pts)**
10. The Fleet Admiral has to clear Picard's plan with whom? **(3pts)**

✪✪ SIGNIFICANT NUMBERS (1pt each)

Match the clues with the correct number. Some numbers may be used more than once.

Clues
1. Which starbase does Picard talk to the Fleet Admiral at?

---

2. How many photon torpedoes are fired by the *Sutherland*?
3. How many years has Data served in Starfleet?
4. How many cloaked Romulan ships are detected along the Romulan border?
5. How large a radius (in million km) around the *Sutherland*, is no longer an effective part of the tachyon grid?
6. How many hours are left for the Federation fleet to withdraw when Picard tells Gowron to launch a major attack?
7. How many hours does Sela give the Federation to withdraw from the Romulan border?
8. How many years after her mother was captured was Sela born?
9. How many years old was Sela when her mother tried to escape and was executed?
10. When Picard speaks to Sela in his ready room, how many hours are left for Federation forces to withdraw from the border?
11. How many starships comprise the Federation fleet according to Sela?
12. How many years ago was Tasha Yar on the *Enterprise-C*?
13. Which deck is the radiation leak on the *Sutherland* affecting?
14. How many weeks ago did Gowron say they destroyed the supply bases in the Mempa sector?
15. What time the next day does Picard say he wants the fleet under way?
16. How many battles have there been in the last two weeks between the Klingon factions, according to Picard?
17. How many years have the Romulans been trying to destroy the Klingon–Federation Alliance?
18. How many Federation ships are within one day's travelling distance from the starbase?
19. Picard asks Geordi if the tachyon detection grid will work using how many ships?
20. How many more ships does Riker think they can scare up?

Numbers
A. 15
B. 14
C. 20
D. 10–12
E. 1
F. 24
G. 3
H. 23
I. 13
J. 0900
K. 234
L. 12
M. 26
N. 7–8
O. 4
P. 10

ANSWERS

TRIVIA ANSWERS

1. B'Etor
2. to high energy burst – level six
3. they activate a remote transporter and leave Toral behind
4. his d'k tahg to kill Toral
5. spares his life
6. Guinan came aboard the *Enterprise*
7. the phaser and photon torpedo control units
8. *Tian An Men*
9. at the Battle of Narendra III
10. Federation Council

SIGNIFICANT NUMBERS ANSWERS

1. K 234; 2. G 3; 3. M 26; 4. A 15; 5. P 10; 6. I 13;
7. C 20; 8. E 1; 9. O 4; 10. B 14; 11. H 23; 12. F 24;
13. D 10–12; 14. G 3; 15. J 0900; 16. G 3; 17. C 20;
18. L 12; 19. C 20; 20. N 7–8

MISSION PERFORMANCE RATING:

30 – 55 points	**Superior:**	You've saved the Federation–Klingon Alliance!
25 – 29 points	**Above Average:**	Nice work, Commander!
20 – 24 points	**Average:**	Don't you like androids? Too bad, just follow orders!
10 – 19 points	**Fair:**	Lursa is looking for you and she's not a happy Klingon.
0 – 9 points	**Poor:**	Baktag! Even the Ferengi find you distasteful.

DARMOK ⬨

The *Enterprise* meets with a Tamarian vessel. Past Federation encounters with the Tamarians have been cordial but no communication was possible. The Tamarian Captain Dathon's language is a series of proper names and places. The *Enterprise* crew can make no sense out of the Tamarian's words. Picard responds and the Tamarians likewise look confused. The Tamarians transport the two captains to the surface of a nearby planet. Riker attempts to beam up Picard but the Tamarians use a scattering field to interfere with transporting.

On the planet, Dathon and Picard make unsuccessful attempts to communicate. The next morning, an energy entity comes toward the camp. They fight the entity together. Eventually, Picard realizes that Dathon speaks through metaphor. As they battle the creature, Dathon is severely injured and dies that night. Riker decides he must attack the Tamarian vessel, in order to knock out the scattering field generator. He is successful and is able to retrieve Picard from the surface. The Tamarians counterattack the *Enterprise*, and knock out the shields. Just then, Picard arrives on the bridge and is able to speak to the Tamarian first officer using several phrases he learned from Dathon. The Tamarians are satisfied and cease their attack.

TRIVIA QUESTIONS

1. What does 'Tembra, his arms wide' mean? **(5pts)**
2. What name do the Tamarians use to describe themselves? **(2pts)**
3. What is Picard looking at when Dathon comes running up to him yelling? **(2pts)**
4. How does Dathon help Picard build a fire? **(2pts)**
5. How does the Tamarian first officer describe the events on the planet? **(4pts)**
6. What doesn't the Tamarian ego-structure allow for? **(2pts)**
7. What are the Tamarians using to create the scattering field? **(5pts)**
8. How many database entries are there for Darmok? **(4pts)**
9. Where is the scattering field concentrated? **(4pts)**
10. Initially, Data says Picard and Dathon are how far apart on the surface? **(5pts)**

KEY WORDS (2pts each)
Match the key words with the correct database entries.

Database Entries	Key Words
1. A ruling family on Galas II	D. Darmok
2. A mytho-historical hunter on Chandra V	T. Tanagra
3. A colony on Malindee VII	N. Neither

---

4. An island continent on Shantil III
5. A ruling family on Galen IV
6. Seventh dynasty emperor on Conda IV
7. The Sacred Chalice Of Rixx
8. A ceremonial drink of Thalos VII
9. An emperor of the Tkon Empire during the Age of Bastu
10. A ceremonial drink of Larici IV
11. A colony on Melona IV
12. A mytho-historical hunter on Shantil III
13. A frozen dessert on Tazna V
14. An island continent on Chandra V
15. A prized beverage on Turkana IV

SPECIAL ASSIGNMENT (10pts)

What did the Tamarian ship do after the *Enterprise*'s attempt to beam up Picard?

ANSWERS

TRIVIA ANSWERS

1. to give something
2. Children of Tama
3. Dathon's captain's log
4. he throws Picard a burning stick of wood
5. 'Picard and Dathon at El-Adrel'
6. self-identity
7. a polarity coil generator located aft of their warp drive
8. 47
9. in the upper D region of the planet's ionosphere
10. 20 metres

KEY WORD ANSWERS

1. T; 2. N; 3. D; 4. T; 5. N; 6. D; 7. N; 8. N; 9. N; 10. T; 11. N; 12. D; 13. D; 14. N; 15. N

SPECIAL ASSIGNMENT SOLUTION

they deepened the scattering field to the D region of the planet's ionosphere

Congratulations! Starfleet Command is proud to award you the Starfleet Medal of Honour and 10 extra points.

MISSION PERFORMANCE RATING:

60 – 75 points **Superior:** Picard at Qo'noS.
50 – 59 points **Above Average:** Data, when his head rolled.
40 – 49 points **Average:** Barclay, his eyes covered.
30 – 39 points **Fair:** Wesley at Saturn.
 0 – 29 points **Poor:** Spock, his brain missing.

The *Enterprise* responds to a distress call from a Federation colony. The ship that attacked the colony transmits a message that the Bajorans claim responsibility for the act of terrorism. The Bajorans were conquered long ago by the Cardassians and now live in squalid resettlement camps scattered across the quadrant. The *Enterprise* is ordered by Starfleet to find the terrorist leader named Orta and to persuade him to stop attacking the Federation. Picard is also assigned the infamous Ensign Ro Laren, a Bajoran with a bad past.

Picard, with Ro's help, tracks down Orta. Ro beams down and meets with Orta before the scheduled time and discovers that the Bajorans had nothing to do with the attack. Ro, confused, confesses her real purpose to Picard: Admiral Kennelly had authorized Ro to offer Orta weapons and supplies if he would return to the camps. Picard decides to find out what's really going on. The *Enterprise* escorts a Bajoran ship supposedly carrying Orta and his men back to the resettlement camp. En route to the camp, two Cardassian ships arrive demanding that the terrorist ship be turned over to them. Picard is ordered by Kennelly to withdraw. The *Enterprise* leaves and the vessel is destroyed by the Cardassians. Picard reveals to Kennelly that the ship was unmanned and that the Bajorans could not have attacked the colony without any warp drives on their ships. The Cardassians attacked the colony and then went to Starfleet hoping they could uncover Orta for them.

TRIVIA QUESTIONS

1. What does Ro give the little girl in the resettlement camp? **(3pts)**
2. What does Picard tell Data to replicate? **(3pts)**
3. What does Orta deny? **(3pts)**
4. When did Picard first read about the achievements of the ancient Bajoran civilization? **(4pts)**
5. The two Cardassian ships are identified as what? **(4pts)**
6. To what speed is the Bajoran ship limited? **(3pts)**
7. How old was Ro when she watched her father die? **(4pts)**
8. What is a Bajoran custom regarding names? **(3pts)**
9. What medicinal concoction does Picard replicate for the Admiral's Cardassian virus? **(5pts)**
10. What does Picard call his medicinal concoction? **(3pts)**

SPECIAL ASSIGNMENT (10pts)

How close will the *Enterprise* come to the Cardassian border while escorting the Bajoran ship?

MULTIPLE CHOICE QUESTIONS

1. Why did Ro leave the *Enterprise* without authorization? **(2pts)**
    A. she thought she could prevent needless violence
    B. she didn't, Ro was authorized by Lieutenant Fenwick to beam down
    C. she never did, Ro had authorization from Kennelly to beam down
    D. she was a double agent also working for the Cardassians

2. What is blocking the *Enterprise*'s sensors at Orta's base? **(3pts)**
    A. the composition of the moon's surface
    B. Cardassian scanner jammers
    C. the heavy metals below the moon's surface
    D. neutrino emissions

3. What does Data's tricorder pick up in the cave that suggests movement in the last ten hours? **(3pts)**
    A. tachyon traces
    B. modulated molecular matrix particles
    C. molecular displacement traces
    D. footprints in the dirt

4. Where on Valo II is the camp of the Bajoran leader known as Falor? **(5pts)**
    A. on the northern shores of the Matec Ocean
    B. on the southern continent
    C. 250 kilometres south of Dentuska
    D. on the western continent

5. Why was it hard for the Admiral to get Ensign Ro assigned to this mission? **(2pts)**
    A. Ro was recovering in a Starfleet medical facility from injuries received on her last mission
    B. Ro was in a Starfleet prison
    C. Ro was a convicted felon on parole
    D. Ro was stationed in a distant sector

ANSWERS

TRIVIA ANSWERS

1. her uniform shirt
2. a blanket for every man, woman, and child before nightfall
3. that Bajorans were responsible for the attack on the Federation colony
4. in his fifth grade reader
5. Cardassian warships, Galor-class, Type 3
6. $1/2$ impulse
7. seven years old
8. family name listed first, followed by the given name last
9. ginger tea with honey served at a temperature of 80°C
10. Adele's cure for the common cold

SPECIAL ASSIGNMENT SOLUTION

13,400 kilometres

Congratulations! Starfleet Command is proud to award you the Starfleet Medal of Honour and 10 extra points.

MULTIPLE CHOICE ANSWERS

1. C. she never did, Ro had authorization from Kennelly to beam down
2. A. the composition of the moon's surface
3. C. molecular displacement traces
4. B. on the southern continent
5. B. Ro was in a Starfleet prison

MISSION PERFORMANCE RATING:

45 – 60 points **Superior:** Good job exposing Kennelly and the Cardassians!

40 – 44 points **Above Average:** Good, you figured out who you could trust.

30 – 39 points **Average:** You should have listened to the bartender.

20 – 29 points **Fair:** Do you believe everything the Cardassians tell you?

0 – 19 points **Poor:** Orta is looking for you and he's not smiling.

◆ SILICON AVATAR

STARDATE: 45122.3

The *Enterprise* leaves an away team at the site of a new Federation colony. Riker, Data, and Dr Crusher are inspecting the new colony while the *Enterprise* goes on a brief mission. Suddenly a loud noise is heard and a crystalline shape blots out the sun. It is the Crystalline Entity (see 'Datalore'). Riker and the others are able to get most of the colonists to the safety of some nearby caves. The *Enterprise* returns and an away team rescues the colonists just as the air supply in the cave grows dangerously low.

Starfleet's specialist on the Crystalline Entity, Dr Marr, later joins the *Enterprise* to help investigate the attack. Marr's son was killed in an earlier attack by the Crystalline Entity. Data develops a method to track the Crystalline Entity and the *Enterprise* sets off on an intercept course. Data and Marr use graviton pulses to attract the Crystalline Entity to the *Enterprise*. Data surmises that they can communicate with the entity using the pulses. When the entity attempts to communicate with the *Enterprise*, Marr locks the graviton pulse generator into continuous mode. Soon the vibrations threaten to destroy the Crystalline Entity. Picard orders her to stop the pulses but she ignores him, hoping to avenge the death of her son. The Crystalline Entity explodes into shards of flaming crystals.

TRIVIA QUESTIONS

1. What does the Crystalline Entity do during an attack? **(3pts)**
2. What frequency lures the Crystalline Entity to the *Enterprise*? **(5pts)**
3. Why can't Data shut down the graviton pulse? **(3pts)**
4. What did Riker bring with him to the colony? **(3pts)**
5. What sport did Raymond frequently play? **(3pts)**
6. Raymond's most intense memories revolve around what? **(4pts)**
7. Marr has found evidence of what at the last three attack sites? **(4pts)**
8. How does the Crystalline Entity seem to function? **(4pts)**
9. Riker strikes Carmen as being what type of person? **(3pts)**
10. What are Carmen and Riker planning to eat for dinner? **(3pts)**

SPECIAL ASSIGNMENT (10pts)

The transport ship attacked by the Crystalline Entity is from where?

MULTIPLE CHOICE QUESTIONS

1. What does Carmen say will be located facing north in a grove of trees? **(2pts)**
   A. the school
   B. the art centre
   C. the hospital facility
   D. the residential pods

2. What type of weapons does the transport ship carry? **(5pts)**
   A. disruptors
   B. low-level particle phasers
   C. Artonian lasers
   D. Merculite rockets

3. What does Picard order to be done about the transport ship? **(3pts)**
   A. he orders Riker to put together a minimal crew to pilot the ship to the closest starbase
   B. he orders Worf to launch several marker beacons and send a message to Starfleet
   C. he orders Worf to notify the closest starbase to dispatch a crew to pick up the ship
   D. he orders Geordi to attach a tractor beam and tow the vessel

4. What is so remarkable about the Crystalline Entity's latest attack? **(3pts)**
   A. the colonists are the only known survivors of an attack by the Entity
   B. this is the first time that the Entity has attacked a developing colony
   C. this is the first time an attack has occurred during daylight hours
   D. that Data was with the colonists when the attack occurred

5. The contents of what were transferred to Data's memory cells on Omicron Theta? **(2pts)**
   A. the colony's central computer
   B. the colonists' logs and journals
   C. the Federation's greatest literary works
   D. the colony's library

ANSWERS

TRIVIA ANSWERS

1. it strips all forms of life on the planet and converts it to energy
2. 10 pulses per second
3. Marr isolated the access code
4. a bottle of wine
5. Parrises Squares
6. a girl named Janeena
7. residual bitrious filaments
8. gigantic electromagnetic collector
9. a free spirit and adventurer
10. her ration of dried chicken curry

SPECIAL ASSIGNMENT SOLUTION

Boreal III

Congratulations! Starfleet Command is proud to award you the Starfleet Medal of Honour and 10 extra points.

MULTIPLE CHOICE ANSWERS

1. C. the hospital facility
2. B. low-level particle phasers
3. C. he orders Worf to notify the closest starbase to dispatch a crew to pick up the ship
4. A. the colonists are the only known survivors of an attack by the Entity
5. B. the colonists' logs and journals

MISSION PERFORMANCE RATING:

45 – 60 points **Superior:** You're Starfleet's best xenologist!

40 – 44 points **Above Average:** You can still stay objective.

30 – 39 points **Average:** Your whole Starfleet career has been undistinguished.

20 – 29 points **Fair:** We're not going to let you polish the crystal!

0 – 19 points **Poor:** You have problems working with others.

DISASTER ⬠

STARDATE: 45156.1 ▬▬▬▬▬▬▬▬▬

Picard gives a tour of the ship to the winners of the primary school science fair. Picard leaves the bridge with the children to begin the tour when suddenly the *Enterprise* is hit by several quantum filaments. The filaments cause shipwide damage to many systems and the main computer.

Picard and the children are trapped in a turbolift. He is injured but is able to climb out of the turbolift and into the shaft with the children. Picard eventually leads the children to safety by crawling out onto a higher deck. In Ten-Forward, Worf organizes a triage centre for the injured where Keiko, O'Brien's wife, goes into labour. Riker and Data leave to make their way to Engineering to regain control of the ship.

Being the senior officer on the bridge at the time of the accident, Troi assumes command of the *Enterprise*. O'Brien and Ro are also on the bridge and are able to restore some of the controls. A containment field problem develops in the warp drive and a breach is imminent. Troi orders power to be routed to Engineering in the hope that someone may be alive and see the problem.

Data uses his body to short out an electrical arc blocking their path to Engineering. Afterwards, Riker removes Data's head from his non-functioning body. Once in Engineering, Riker is able to connect Data's head into the control console. Data quickly acts to stabilize the containment field and avert a larger disaster. The *Enterprise* crew eventually regain control of the major systems and head for the nearest starbase for repairs.

TRIVIA QUESTIONS

1. What is the name of the climbing song? **(3pts)**
2. How long is a quantum filament? **(3pts)**
3. What rank is Troi? **(3pts)**
4. How far is Keiko dilated when her contractions are 30 seconds apart? **(4pts)**
5. At what percentage is the containment field when the power coupling overheats? **(4pts)**
6. What song does Marissa know from school? **(5pts)**
7. What does Paterson want to see on the ship tour? **(3pts)**
8. What is the procedure called where all computer control systems are manually bypassed? **(3pts)**
9. When does quaratum become unstable? **(3pts)**
10. How long do the swarming moths on Gonal IV live? **(4pts)**

SPECIAL ASSIGNMENT (10pts)

What role in the operetta *The Pirates of Penzance* did Dr Crusher urge Geordi to audition for?

MULTIPLE CHOICE QUESTIONS

1. What course did Worf take? **(2pts)**
    A. Starfleet Etiquette and Protocols
    B. Starfleet Emergency Medical
    C. Advanced Medical Procedures
    D. Exobiology

2. The containment field will collapse when it drops to what level? **(5pts)**
    A. 15%
    B. 20%
    C. 10%
    D. 18%

3. Who climbs out of the turbolift onto the bridge? **(2pts)**
    A. Picard
    B. Ensign Ro
    C. Troi
    D. O'Brien

4. What 'field promotion' does Marissa receive from Picard? **(3pts)**
    A. science officer
    B. lieutenant
    C. first officer
    D. lieutenant commander

5. Data's positronic brain has several layers of shielding to protect against what? **(3pts)**
    A. inclement weather
    B. information overload
    C. exposure to corrosive materials
    D. power surges

ANSWERS

TRIVIA ANSWERS

1. Frère Jacques
2. it can be hundreds of metres long
3. lieutenant commander
4. 7 centimetres
5. 20%
6. *The Laughing Vulcan and His Dog*
7. the battle bridge and torpedo bay
8. Emergency Procedure Alpha 2
9. 350 rads
10. only 20 hours before dying

SPECIAL ASSIGNMENT SOLUTION

Major-General Stanley

Congratulations! Starfleet Command is proud to award you the Starfleet Medal of Honour and 10 extra points.

MULTIPLE CHOICE ANSWERS

1. B. Starfleet Emergency Medical
2. A. 15%
3. B. Ensign Ro
4. C. first officer
5. D. power surges

MISSION PERFORMANCE RATING:

45 – 60 points **Superior:** You could run the *Enterprise* single-handedly!

40 – 44 points **Above Average:** You made it to Engineering and fixed things.

30 – 39 points **Average:** You need a climbing song so you don't whine so much!

20 – 29 points **Fair:** You got your quantum filament tangled in the cosmic string.

0 – 19 points **Poor:** You are the biggest disaster to have hit the *Enterprise!*

THE GAME

Riker returns to the *Enterprise* from a vacation on Risa and brings a new game back with him. Wesley Crusher also joins the *Enterprise* while on vacation from the Academy. Wesley meets an attractive ensign named Lefler and the two soon become inseparable. Riker continues to introduce the new game to the ship's officers. Dr Crusher asks Data to help her in sickbay. When he arrives she quickly shuts him off and severs some of his positronic links, leaving Data in an unconscious state.

Wesley and Lefler are becoming suspicious. Almost everybody seems to be playing the game and very insistent that others also try it. Together they investigate the effects of the game on the brain by using a simulation programme and discover that the game is addictive. Wesley checks on Data, certain that Data's problem is no coincidence. He discovers the damage to Data and realizes that it was intentionally done.

An alien ship meets with the *Enterprise*. The woman captain is the same person who introduced Riker to the game on Risa. Those who play the game come under the control of the aliens. They plan to invade the Federation and have secured the *Enterprise*. Wesley, the only person not under the game's influence, leads the crew on a prolonged chase but is finally captured and made to play the game. Suddenly Data appears on the bridge and activates a device to counteract the effects of the game. Picard quickly regains control of the *Enterprise* and attaches a tractor beam to the alien ship.

TRIVIA QUESTIONS

1. What course did Picard fail at the Academy because of his acquaintance 'A.F.'? **(5pts)**
2. Who are the only two people who could have disabled Data? **(3pts)**
3. Where does Wesley meet Worf head to head? **(3pts)**
4. What was a notably awkward experience? **(4pts)**
5. What type of alert does Picard go to after Wesley initially escapes from Riker and Worf? **(4pts)**
6. What did Data modify to emit optical burst patterns that counteracted the game's effects? **(3pts)**
7. Who was Wesley's first friend? **(3pts)**
8. When did Boothby finally remember Picard? **(3pts)**
9. What did Boothby once catch Picard doing? **(3pts)**
10. What practical joke did Wesley play on Adam Martonie in the physics lab? **(4pts)**

✪✪ SIGNIFICANT NUMBERS (1pt each)

Match the clues with the correct number. Some numbers may be used more than once.

Clues
1. What law states that life is not fair all the time?
2. How many Lefler's Laws are there in the written copy she gives to Wesley as a gift?
3. What time is Wesley's date?
4. What level of the game is Nurse Ogawa on when Wesley meets her in the turbolift?
5. To which starbase does the *Enterprise* tow the alien's ship?
6. What law states that when everything else fails then do it yourself?
7. What deck is Wesley on before he gets on the turbolift with Nurse Ogawa?
8. What deck is Wesley's destination when he gets on the turbolift with Nurse Ogawa?
9. To which starbase are Troi and Geordi supposed to pilot a shuttle?
10. How many new science teams are on board the *Enterprise*?
11. What law states that you have to go with whatever works?
12. Data's holodeck dance programme is composed of how many parts?
13. What is the total number of science teams that want to use the long range array during the mission?
14. What law states that you need to watch your back at all times?
15. How long in weeks was the current mission before Starfleet changed the schedule?

Numbers
A. 47
B. 11
C. 36
D. 67
E. 15
F. 102
G. 5
H. 17
I. 91
J. 1900
K. 46
L. 82

ANSWERS

TRIVIA ANSWERS

1. organic chemistry
2. Geordi and Dr Crusher
3. in the service crawlway
4. Sadie Hawkins Dance at Starfleet Academy
5. Security Alert – Condition 3
6. palm beacon
7. a warp coil
8. only when Wesley showed him an old yearbook picture of Picard
9. carving the initials 'A.F.' into his prized elm tree
10. he configured the antimatter regulator to spray chili sauce

SIGNIFICANT NUMBERS ANSWERS

1. K 46; 2. F 102; 3. J 1900; 4. A 47; 5. L 82; 6. H 17; 7. B 11; 8. C 36;
9. D 67; 10. G 5; 11. C 36; 12. H 17; 13. E 15; 14. I 91; 15. G 5

MISSION PERFORMANCE RATING:

30 – 50 points   **Superior:** Law 104: Never play games unless you intend to win!

25 – 29 points   **Above Average:** Law 96: Always do more than is required.

20 – 24 points   **Average:** Law 88: (See: Law of Averages.)

10 – 19 points   **Fair:** Law 53: Never start what you can't finish.

0 – 9 points   **Poor:** Law 2: If you can't do better than this, go back home!

UNIFICATION I ⟨A⟩

Picard is given a special mission by Starfleet Command. Ambassador Spock has disappeared and has been spotted on Romulus, the Romulan Star Empire's home world. Starfleet wants to know why Spock is on Romulus. Picard meets with Sarek, Spock's father, to seek information. Sarek mentions that Spock has been in contact over the years with a Romulan senator named Pardek.

Starfleet gives the *Enterprise* some space debris that was recovered from a Ferengi vessel crash site and was found packed in crates. Geordi identifies the metal fragments as part of a Vulcan ship supposedly docked in a Federation surplus depot. Picard persuades Gowron to provide a cloaked ship that will take Data and himself across the Neutral Zone to Romulus.

After Picard and Data transport to the Klingon vessel, Riker takes the *Enterprise* to the surplus depot. At the depot, the quartermaster can't find the Vulcan ship. The *Enterprise* discovers a pirate ship has been stealing parts from the depot. The *Enterprise* engages the pirate ship in battle and destroys it.

Meanwhile, on Romulus, Picard and Data are posing as Romulans in their search for Spock. Several members of the underground movement, dressed as security officers, take Picard and Data into custody. They are led to some underground caverns where they meet Pardek and Spock.

TRIVIA QUESTIONS

1. What did Picard share with Sarek nearly a year ago? **(3pts)**
2. What subspace message did the Klingon ship monitor? **(3pts)**
3. Who on the Klingon High Council does Picard suggest Worf try to contact? **(4pts)**
4. How long ago did Spock disappear? **(3pts)**
5. The metal fragments have been identified as coming from which ship? **(4pts)**
6. What is the name of the Klingon captain who takes Picard to Romulus? **(4pts)**
7. What is a Romulan farewell salutation? **(5pts)**
8. What is the official designation of the surplus depot? **(3pts)**
9. What position does B'ijik hold? **(3pts)**
10. How long has Pardek been a senator? **(3pts)**

✪ SPECIAL ASSIGNMENT (15pts)

Which starbase computer system does the Fleet Admiral link her terminal with?

MULTIPLE CHOICE QUESTIONS

1. How was Geordi able to tell which ship the fragments came from?
   (2pts)
   A. by examining Starfleet records of decommissioned vessels
   B. by comparing the fragments with the Federation's Starship
      Schematics Database
   C. by doing an atomic core reconstruction of the missing pieces
   D. by running a molecular pattern trace

2. Where is the Federation supply depot located? (3pts)
   A. Qualor II
   B. Quazulu VIII
   C. Squalor IV
   D. Quadra Sigma III

3. When is the Romulan Senate not in session? (3pts)
   A. during the solstice break
   B. on the third day of the Romulan week
   C. each morning between 07:00 and 11:00 hours
   D. on the eighth day of the Romulan week

4. What does Worf say Gowron is doing? (2pts)
   A. stalling
   B. preparing to make war against the Duras family
   C. rewriting Klingon history
   D. enjoying his powerful status a little too much

5. Which part of the video image does the Fleet Admiral enhance to show
   Spock's face? (5pts)
   A. Section Alpha 2-B
   B. Sector 9-G
   C. Section 4 Delta
   D. Grid number 12

ANSWERS

TRIVIA ANSWERS

1. mind-meld
2. Sarek is dead
3. K'Tal
4. three weeks ago
5. T'Pau
6. K'Vada
7. Jolan true
8. Surplus Depot Zed-15
9. junior adjutant to the diplomatic delegation
10. nine decades

SPECIAL ASSIGNMENT SOLUTION

Alpha 29

Congratulations! Starfleet Command is proud to award you the Starfleet Medal of Honour and 15 extra points.

MULTIPLE CHOICE ANSWERS

1. D. by running a molecular pattern trace
2. A. Qualor II
3. B. on the third day of the Romulan week
4. C. rewriting Klingon history
5. C. Section 4 Delta

MISSION PERFORMANCE RATING:

45 – 65 points **Superior:** We knew you didn't defect. We're behind you on this!

40 – 44 points **Above Average:** You can work undercover on Romulus.

30 – 39 points **Average:** You've been promoted to work at the surplus depot!

20 – 29 points **Fair:** You were standing in the cargo hold of the pirate ship.

0 – 19 points **Poor:** Romulan dog, run home to your masters.

UNIFICATION II

STARDATE: 45245.8

Spock tells Picard that there is a growing underground movement on Romulus that wants to reunify with Vulcan. Romulans and Vulcans evolved from a common ancestor race; centuries ago they separated and evolved into the present day races. Senator Pardek told Spock that the new Proconsul was sympathetic to the reunification cause. Spock came to Romulus at Pardek's insistence to begin a dialogue between the two races.

Spock and Picard uncover Pardek's real motives but are arrested by Sela before they can warn anyone. Sela reveals that the Romulans intend to use the Vulcan ships to carry an invasion force to Vulcan. The Romulans plan to broadcast a holographic message of Spock proclaiming the ships a peace delegation. Later, Spock, Picard, and Data are able to change the holographic message into a warning. When Sela returns, the three disable her and escape. Picard and Data return to the Klingon ship. Spock chooses to remain behind to continue the work of reunification. The *Enterprise* blocks the invasion force from crossing into Federation territory. A Romulan warbird decloaks and destroys the invading ships to prevent the troops from being captured.

TRIVIA QUESTIONS
1. What does Data use on Sela? **(3pts)**
2. Who does Riker talk to at the piano in the bar? **(3pts)**
3. What has kept the Romulans and Vulcans apart for centuries? **(3pts)**
4. What two things are near the Galorndon Core? **(3pts)**
5. How would Sarek have viewed Spock's mission to Romulus? **(4pts)**
6. What does Spock say he doesn't know much about? **(3pts)**
7. How long has Spock been friends with Pardek? **(4pts)**
8. What is the message to the Barolians which Data retrieved from the surface? **(5pts)**
9. What is a popular Klingon opera? **(4pts)**
10. Who is Spock's young Romulan friend? **(3pts)**

✪ SPECIAL ASSIGNMENT (15pts)
What song does Omag always want to hear?

MULTIPLE CHOICE QUESTIONS

1. What does Picard allow Spock to do? **(2pts)**
    A. mind-meld with Picard
    B. speak with the Proconsul
    C. help them escape
    D. stay on Romulus

2. What are the small triangular objects that Spock's young Romulan friend shows him? **(2pts)**
   A. a form of ceremonial dice
   B. Vulcan counting cubes
   C. the syllabic nucleus of the Vulcan language
   D. the basis of the early Romulan language just after the Separation

3. Where did Omag deliver the Vulcan ship? **(3pts)**
   A. Qualor II
   B. Romulus
   C. Galor IV
   D. Galorndon Core

4. Why can't Data penetrate the Romulan computer system at first? **(5pts)**
   A. it has a residual coded energy lock
   B. it has a progressive encryption lock
   C. it has a stepped-level encoded lock interface
   D. it has a multiphasic lock interface

5. What is a nasty habit that Riker never cared for? **(3pts)**
   A. eating suck salt
   B. womanizing
   C. using chewing tobacco
   D. eating gagh

ANSWERS

TRIVIA ANSWERS
1. Vulcan nerve pinch
2. the former wife of the dead smuggler
3. closed minds
4. Romulan Neutral Zone and Barolian trade route
5. a fool's errand
6. Romulan disruptor settings
7. 80 years
8. 14:00 hours
9. Aktuh and Melota
10. D'Tan

SPECIAL ASSIGNMENT SOLUTION
'Melor Famagal'
Congratulations! Starfleet Command is proud to award you the Starfleet Medal of Honour and 15 extra points.

MULTIPLE CHOICE ANSWERS
1. A. mind-meld with Picard
2. C. the syllabic nucleus of the Vulcan language
3. D. Galorndon Core
4. B. it has a progressive encryption lock
5. A. eating suck salt

MISSION PERFORMANCE RATING:
45 – 65 points **Superior:** You have successfully repelled the invaders!
40 – 44 points **Above Average:** Live long and prosper!
30 – 39 points **Average:** Your logic eludes even the Romulan child.
20 – 29 points **Fair:** Sela wants to interview you for your new position.
0 – 19 points **Poor:** Report to the bar on Qualor II for piano lessons!

A MATTER OF TIME

STARDATE: 45349.1

While en route to assist the people on Penthara IV, the *Enterprise* encounters a small craft. The pilot, Rasmussen, claims to be a historian from the future and is supposedly here to study Picard and the *Enterprise*. Although suspicious, Picard allows Rasmussen to stay on board. The *Enterprise* arrives at the rapidly cooling planet, the result of an asteroid strike.

The *Enterprise* uses phasers to release pockets of carbon dioxide to help retain the sun's heat and warm Penthara IV. Everything appears to be going smoothly. Suddenly, there is a drastic increase in volcanic activity. The planet's mantle has become unstable. Geordi devises a plan to correct the problem. The solution is a success, Penthara IV begins to stabilize and temperatures start to rise.

Rasmussen tells Picard his studies are now complete and he prepares to leave the *Enterprise*. Picard confronts Rasmussen before he can do so. Rasmussen is suspected of stealing several missing pieces of equipment. Rasmussen allows Data to inspect the inside of the time-travel pod. Once inside, Rasmussen tells Data that he is really from the past. He stole the pod from a future historian. Rasmussen tries to deactivate Data but is disarmed. As Data removes Rasmussen from the pod, an automatic timer activates and the time-travel device disappears back to the past.

TRIVIA QUESTIONS

1. What does Riker say is the most important technological development in the last 200 years? **(3pts)**
2. What phenomenon did 21st century Earth experience? **(3pts)**
3. What does Geordi want a glimpse of? **(3pts)**
4. Where on Earth is Rasmussen from? **(3pts)**
5. What type of knife did Rasmussen try stealing? **(4pts)**
6. How strong does Geordi estimate the landquakes are by Earth standards? **(3pts)**
7. How many simultaneous musical selections can Data listen to? **(4pts)**
8. Who are the five famous blind men mentioned by Rasmussen? **(1pt each)**
9. Rasmussen says that Data is the what of androids? **(3pts)**
10. What is the hull of the time-travel pod composed of? **(4pts)**

✪✪ MATHEMATICALLY SPEAKING (20pts)

Answer A to E and then insert the numbers into the formula to solve this problem.

A. What is the cloud depth reported by New Seattle in kilometres? **(2pts)**
B. How many pockets of carbon dioxide has the *Enterprise* located underground? **(2pts)**
C. How long is the time-travel pod in metres? **(2pts)**
D. What percentage of the sunlight is getting through Penthara's atmosphere says Geordi? **(2pts)**
E. Rasmussen says he should have limited Data to how many words for his answers? **(2pts)**

$$(A \div B) \times C \times D \times E = F$$

What is the significance of your answer (F) in relation to the episode? **(10pts)**

MISSION PERFORMANCE RATING:

30 – 55 points **Superior:** An ingenious solution to the problem.
25 – 39 points **Above Average:** Just a glimpse of the poker game, huh?
20 – 24 points **Average:** Thought you were from New Jersey.
10 – 19 points **Fair:** You were *told* to check the tectonic stress at the sites!
 0 – 9 points **Poor:** You are to be deported to the far distant past.

NEW GROUND

Worf's adoptive mother, Helena, visits the *Enterprise*. She brings along Worf's son, Alexander. Helena explains to Worf that Alexander needs his father and that they are getting too old to act as parents. Worf enrolls Alexander in school on the *Enterprise* until he can decide what to do. Alexander misbehaves at school and Worf gives him a stern lecture on honour and family. When Alexander continues to act up, Worf decides to send him to boarding school.

Meanwhile, the *Enterprise* is assisting in the testing of a new means of warp propulsion. Known as 'soliton waves', they propel a ship along at warp speed without need for warp engines. The *Enterprise* follows behind a test ship recording information. The experiment proceeds well until the soliton wave becomes unstable and destroys the test ship. The *Enterprise* warps to catch up with the soliton wave that has grown stronger and larger. The wave is headed for the destination planet but will overwhelm the wave dispersal equipment there and destroy the world. The *Enterprise* must fly through the soliton wave to position itself in front of the wave. Picard hopes to fire photon torpedoes into the wave to dissipate it. The aft shields are damaged in the chase and a fire breaks out, trapping Alexander. Worf and Riker are able to save him just as Picard fires the torpedoes and the wave is dispersed. Worf decides that Alexander will stay with him and together they will work things out.

CROSSWORD PUZZLE CLUES

ACROSS

1. Alexander steals a model _____ at school. **(1pt)**
3. The fire _____ equipment was not working. **(1pt)**
4. Worf would rather face ten _____ warriors than one small child. **(3pts)**
6. Geordi says the test ship will ride the soliton wave just like a _____. **(3pts)**
11. Type of school Worf considers placing Alexander in. **(1pt)**
14. Off-line after *Enterprise* goes through the soliton wave. **(1pt)**
16. Name of transport vessel that conveyed Alexander to *Enterprise*. **(3pts)**
17. Geordi had to replace three power _____. **(2pts)**
18. First human to fly faster than the speed of sound. **(3pts)**
19. Last name of warp drive inventor. **(2pts)**
21. Riker made a favourable impression on these two. **(3pts)**
22. A sister facility is located on _____ II. **(3pts)**
23. First to interrupt Worf's meeting with Picard. **(2pts)**

DOWN

2. Helena says Alexander is often _____. **(1pt)**
3. Type of field that will disperse the soliton wave. **(3pts)**
5. Earth's _____ lizards died out some three hundred years ago. **(3pts)**
7. The _____ controls for the lab were shorted out. **(1pt)**
8. The _____ men have always had beards of iron-grey. **(2pts)**
9. Protected destination of the gilvos. **(3pts)**
10. Member of Geordi's Engineering staff. **(3pts)**
12. Alexander received a hairline fracture of the _____. **(2pts)**
13. First name of warp drive inventor. **(2pts)**
15. Alexander dumps _____ onto the floor in Worf's quarters. **(2pts)**
16. Brother of Kahless. **(3pts)**
20. Level Alexander is running Worf's calisthenics program. **(2pts)**
22. A Klingon's honour is more important than his _____. **(1pt)**

✪ SPECIAL ASSIGNMENT (15pts)

What areas of the ship need to be evacuated?

ANSWERS

SPECIAL ASSIGNMENT SOLUTION

Sections 24–47 on Decks 35 and 38 Congratulations! Starfleet Command is proud to award you the Starfleet Medal of Honour and 15 extra points.

MISSION PERFORMANCE RATING:

50 – 71 points **Superior:** You'll perfect the soliton wave soon.

45 – 49 points **Above Average:** You saved the gilvos. Aren't they cute?

40 – 44 points **Average:** Your intelligence has decreased by a factor of four.

30 – 39 points **Fair:** Starfleet is going to ride you out on a soliton wave!

0 – 29 points **Poor:** Hopefully, you're an endangered species too!

HERO WORSHIP ⬈

The *Enterprise* is investigating the disappearance of the *SS Vico*. They find the badly damaged vessel near the Black Cluster. The only survivor on the ship is a young boy named Timothy. The crew of the ship, including his parents, were killed by what Timothy describes as an alien attack on the vessel.

Picard takes the *Enterprise* into the Black Cluster to try to determine what happened. The crew discovers that the *Vico* could not have been attacked inside the Cluster due to the unpredictable gravitational distortions. Timothy admits lying about the attack. He feels he is responsible for the ship's destruction by accidentally brushing against a control panel. Troi is able to persuade Timothy that the accident was a coincidence and he wasn't at fault.

The *Enterprise* prepares to leave the Black Cluster but is hit by a gravitational wave. The waves soon become stronger. Picard orders more power to the shields. Timothy tells Data that is what the *Vico* did. Data runs a quick analysis and realizes that increasing the power to the shields is what is responsible for the strengthening gravitational waves. Picard lowers the shields just before the huge wave crashes into the *Enterprise*. The wave vanishes and the *Enterprise* is able to fly out of the Cluster.

TRIVIA QUESTIONS

1. Where was Timothy found on the Vico? **(3pts)**
2. Where was Timothy's mother's body found? **(3pts)**
3. What song were the children singing in the classroom? **(3pts)**
4. What was Timothy's mother's job on the Vico? **(3pts)**
5. Timothy runs out of what colour while painting? **(3pts)**
6. What pushed the Vico out of the Black Cluster to the location where it was found? **(3pts)**
7. How much larger is this black cluster than any previously explored? **(4pts)**
8. When did the Black Cluster form? **(4pts)**
9. What does Worf say the gravitational wave front intensity is at? **(4pts)**
10. What percentage of the Vico's logs are damaged? **(5pts)**

✪ SPECIAL ASSIGNMENT (15pts)

What is Timothy attempting to recreate in his quarters?

MULTIPLE CHOICE QUESTIONS

1. What do all on board control systems on starships require? **(3pts)**
   - **A.** a user code clearance
   - **B.** an operator
   - **C.** a user recognition interface
   - **D.** a security access code

2. Why can't the *Enterprise* maintain a warp field in the Black Cluster? **(5pts)**
   - **A.** the dilithium crystals are decaying
   - **B.** the neutrino dispersal patterns are too erratic
   - **C.** the gravitational distortion is too high
   - **D.** the gravimetric fluctuations are too intense

3. What will the *Enterprise* have to push through to get to the centre of the Black Cluster? **(3pts)**
   - **A.** black matter
   - **B.** neutrino streams
   - **C.** protoplasmic residue
   - **D.** graviton wave fronts

4. What does Geordi say proves the *Vico* was attacked within the Black Cluster? **(2pts)**
   - **A.** the phaser burn marks on the hull
   - **B.** the gaping hole in the hull
   - **C.** the results of a magnetic residual analysis
   - **D.** the log records detailing the attack

5. Why are the *Vico*'s logs damaged? **(2pts)**
   - **A.** the *Enterprise*'s computer downlink damaged the fragile records
   - **B.** Geordi thinks an EM pulse hit the computer banks
   - **C.** part of the computer core was sucked out into space through the breached hull
   - **D.** an electrostatic charge knocked out the central processor core in the computer core

ANSWERS

TRIVIA ANSWERS

1. in the hallway outside the computer core
2. in the computer core
3. *Row, Row, Row Your Boat*
4. systems engineer
5. red ochre
6. graviton wave fronts
7. seven times more massive
8. nine billion years ago
9. 1,100 standard G units and rising
10. nearly 83% of the records and all of the sensor logs

SPECIAL ASSIGNMENT SOLUTION

the Dokkaran temple of Kural Hanesh

Congratulations! Starfleet Command is proud to award you the Starfleet Medal of Honour and 15 extra points.

MULTIPLE CHOICE ANSWERS

1. A. a user code clearance
2. C. the gravitational distortion is too high
3. D. graviton wave fronts
4. C. the results of a magnetic residual analysis
5. B. Geordi thinks an EM pulse hit the computer banks

MISSION PERFORMANCE RATING:

45 – 65 points **Superior:** Your empathic abilities told you Timothy was lying.

40 – 44 points **Above Average:** So, you told Data about dropping the shields!

30 – 39 points **Average:** Don't touch the controls!

20 – 29 points **Fair:** The least of your problems is being attacked by aliens.

0 – 19 points **Poor:** Weren't you on the bridge of the *Vico*?

VIOLATIONS

The *Enterprise* transports several Ullians, a race known for their telepathic abilities. After a dinner with the Ullians and the senior staff, Troi goes to her quarters. A memory keeps playing in her mind until she suddenly goes into a coma. Riker questions Jev, the son of Tarmin, since he was the last person to see Troi before she became comatose. Soon after, Riker also collapses into an unexplained coma. Dr Crusher suggests testing the Ullians during a mind probe to see if there is a connection. Sure enough, Dr Crusher becomes comatose.

Data and Geordi try to tie the Ullians to other unexplained comas on other planets they have visited. Troi awakens after several days but doesn't remember anything. Jev suggests a memory probe would exonerate the Ullians of any wrong doing. During the probe, Troi sees Tarmin, Jev's father, mentally raping her.

Data and Geordi uncover several cases of unexplained comas from past visits of Ullians to other planets. Tarmin, however, was not present in all of the cases. As Jev leaves the *Enterprise* he is drawn to Troi and tries to mentally rape her again. Data and Worf burst in, taking Jev into custody. Data and Geordi determined that only Jev was present at each location where a coma occurred.

TRIVIA QUESTIONS

1. What art form did Keiko's grandmother practise? **(3pts)**
2. What does Troi remember spilling onto the floor? **(3pts)**
3. While talking to Troi, Riker alludes to certain events from which episode? **(4pts)**
4. When was Iresine Syndrome first diagnosed? **(3pts)**
5. Which medical database does Geordi use to study electropathic patterns? **(4pts)**
6. How many nonmedical forces or agents might cause electropathic patterns? **(4pts)**
7. What was Geordi's first pet? **(5pts)**
8. What fragment did Tarmin once recover from an elderly Genton? **(3pts)**
9. What floor is actually marked on the turbolift door when Troi gets off the turbolift on Deck 8? **(4pts)**
10. How many planets have the Ullians surveyed over the years? **(3pts)**

✪ SPECIAL ASSIGNMENT (15pts)

Name the five chemical agents that could produce electropathic patterns.

MULTIPLE CHOICE QUESTIONS

1. What was the nature of the Engineering accident Riker remembered? **(4pts)**
   A. dilithium chamber explosion
   B. damage to the starboard warp nacelle
   C. antimatter containment failure
   D. emergency impulse engine shutdown

2. What is unusual about Troi and Riker's brain scans? **(3pts)**
   A. they are not the same as earlier scans
   B. they both show electropathic activity
   C. they both show abnormal activity in the occipital lobe
   D. they are identical

3. What was the chipped cup used for? **(2pts)**
   A. Miles' grandmother used it to drink tea
   B. Keiko's aunt used it as a vase
   C. Miles liked to drink coffee from it at work
   D. Keiko's grandmother used it to clean her brushes

4. What does memory retrieval require? **(3pts)**
   A. a willing mind
   B. innate talent
   C. a steady mind and innate talent
   D. special training and years of study

5. What are the Ullians building? **(2pts)**
   A. a new research centre for Ullian historical studies
   B. a library of the collected memories of many races
   C. a college for training telepathic historical researchers
   D. a treatment centre for victims of memory invasion

ANSWERS

TRIVIA ANSWERS

1. ink brush writing
2. poker chips
3. 'Shades of Gray'
4. 23rd century
5. 4 Delta-1
6. 22 nonmedical agents
7. a Circassian cat
8. a fragment of the Gentonian Trade Wars
9. Deck 3
10. 11 planets in eight star systems

SPECIAL ASSIGNMENT SOLUTION

ferizene, dardillium, manzene, hylatitine, chrysamite

Congratulations! Starfleet Command is proud to award you the Starfleet Medal of Honour and 15 extra points.

MULTIPLE CHOICE ANSWERS

1. C. antimatter containment failure
2. B. they both show electropathic activity
3. D. Keiko's grandmother used it to clean her brushes
4. D. special training and years of study
5. B. a library of the collected memories of many races

MISSION PERFORMANCE RATING:

45 – 65 points **Superior:** A most proficient telepath, but you knew I'd say that!

40 – 44 points **Above Average:** You're a natural historical researcher.

30 – 39 points **Average:** Your telepathic abilities are truly average.

20 – 29 points **Fair:** You need to quit living in the past and get a life!

0 – 19 points **Poor:** You're under arrest for memory invasion!

THE MASTERPIECE ⬡ SOCIETY

STARDATE: 45470.1

The *Enterprise* is tracking a stellar core fragment whose path will take it dangerously close to Moab IV, a supposedly uninhabited planet. The *Enterprise*'s sensors show human life on the planet. The *Enterprise* goes to Moab IV to investigate and warn the inhabitants. The colony's leader, Conor, explains that the colony has grown in total isolation from any outside contact and that everyone is genetically engineered to perform a specific role in the society. Although any interaction with outsiders will cause disruptions in the delicate balance, Conor must co-operate or the colony will perish.

Geordi works with Hannah, the top scientist in the colony, to devise a stronger tractor beam. The *Enterprise* successfully deflects the core fragment enough to minimize its effects on the planet. Another problem develops when Hannah and others in the colony want Picard to grant them asylum. They want to explore the galaxy outside their own world. Conor and Picard try to persuade them to stay but to no avail. The *Enterprise* leaves with a small contingent of colonists while the future of the colony remains uncertain.

TRIVIA QUESTIONS

1. What new equipment must be installed to strengthen the colony's biosphere? **(4pts)**
2. How powerful is the *Enterprise*'s matter/antimatter warp reaction system? **(5pts)**
3. What is Martin's job? **(3pts)**
4. What type of readings is the *Enterprise* picking up from the colony on Moab IV? **(4pts)**
5. What concerns Martin about Hannah transporting to the *Enterprise*? **(3pts)**
6. Which nursery rhyme is mentioned by Conor? **(3pts)**
7. Geordi hasn't had any sleep for so long that his eyelids feel like what? **(3pts)**
8. What would Troi book if the colony had one? **(3pts)**
9. When the *Enterprise* initially hailed the colony, what was the first thing the colonists did? **(3pts)**
10. What are deep EM readings indicative of? **(4pts)**

⊗⊗ SIGNIFICANT NUMBERS (1pt each)

Match the clues with the correct number. Some numbers may be used
more than once.

Clues

1. How many days before the core fragment passes by Moab IV?
2. How many generations have been selectively bred?
3. How many times more efficient will the emitters need to be to handle
   the high-powered pulsed energy?
4. How many personnel are on the first team that beams down from the
   Enterprise?
5. How many months does Conor suggest for a cooling off period before
   people decide to leave the colony?
6. How many colonists finally decide to leave the colony?
7. When the first emitter circuit is lost on which decks is there life
   support failure?
8. What is the minimum amount of deflection (in degrees) needed to
   adjust the core fragment's trajectory?
9. Hannah initially says that the emitters are radiating at what percentage
   over standard?
10. On which decks is there life support failure after the second lateral
    emitter circuit is lost?
11. How many degrees does the *Enterprise* deflect the core fragment just
    after the first emitter is lost?
12. Geordi and Hannah have increased the efficiency of the emitters by
    what percentage?
13. Approximately how many years has the colony been on Moab IV?
14. With the *Enterprise* using minimum life support, the emitters are
    radiating at what percentage over standard?
15. The colony's biosphere is rated to deal with quakes up to _____ on
    the Richter scale.

Numbers

A. 4
B. 9, 12, 13
C. 1.01
D. 200
E. 1.2
F. 8.7
G. 390
I. 5–9
J. 5
K. 300
L. 23
M. 8
N. 320
O. 6

ANSWERS

TRIVIA ANSWERS

1. five new shield generators and power supplies for each one
2. the most powerful in Starfleet, it takes plasma in the terawatt range
3. he acts as a judge and interpreter of the colony founder's intentions
4. deep EM
5. how molecular transport will affect her DNA
6. Humpty Dumpty
7. like they have lead weights attached to them
8. a hotel room for her next vacation
9. increased the power to their defensive shields
10. an obsolete subspace relay

SIGNIFICANT NUMBERS ANSWERS

1. O 6	2. M 8
3. A 4	4. J 5
5. O 6	6. L 23
7. B 9, 12, 13	8. E 1.2
9. N 320	10. I 5–9
11. C 1.0	12. K 300
13. D 200	14. G 390
15. F 8.7	

MISSION PERFORMANCE RATING:

30 – 50 points	**Superior:**	It is your destiny to lead!
25 – 29 points	**Above Average:**	You're a terrific theoretical physicist.
20 – 24 points	**Average:**	You were genetically engineered for mediocrity.
10 – 19 points	**Fair:**	What is your genetically engineered purpose, a door mat?
0 – 9 points	**Poor:**	You were genetically engineered to perform at this level.

CONUNDRUM

STARDATE: 45494.2

The *Enterprise* encounters a small alien craft while investigating some subspace signals. The craft overpowers the *Enterprise*'s shields and scans the ship. Afterwards, no-one on the ship remembers who they are. The *Enterprise*'s computer has also been damaged with most control systems off-line. Geordi is eventually able to access a crew manifest and they learn their identities. Information on their current mission is also discovered. The Federation is at war with an alien race known as the Lysians and the *Enterprise* is to attack the enemy's central command.

They soon arrive at the Lysian central command, easily sweeping through the defensive perimeter. Picard is troubled by the ease of the mission so far. It's clearly evident that the Lysians are no match for the Federation. When Picard refuses to destroy the central command, MacDuff, the first officer, tries to relieve the captain of duty and take control of the ship. Worf and Riker prevent MacDuff from firing on the Lysian central command. The Lysians later identify MacDuff as belonging to an alien race that the Lysians have been fighting with for decades. MacDuff hoped to end the war using the vastly superior weapons on the *Enterprise*.

TRIVIA QUESTIONS

1. What weapon does the Lysian central command have four of? **(3pts)**
2. How many sentry pods surround the Lysian central command? **(3pts)**
3. What type of warheads and how many does the Lysian central command possess? **(5pts)**
4. How many Federation ships have supposedly been captured by the Lysians? **(3pts)**
5. What book did Troi once give to Riker? **(3pts)**
6. What is holodeck programme 47-C? **(4pts)**
7. What location comes highly recommended by Dr Crusher? **(3pts)**
8. By how much does the alien vessel's scanning activity increase? **(4pts)**
9. Near what system is the *Enterprise* investigating some strange subspace signals? **(3pts)**
10. What countermove did Data expect Troi to make during their chess game? **(4pts)**

CHARACTER QUOTE
(2pts per word + 3pts for identifying the speaker.)

Unscramble the words below and then identify the character.

'I _____ as _____ I've _____ _____ a _____, _____ _____
  EFLE   GUTOHH   ENBE DNHDAE EPWANO NSTE TNIO

a _____ and _____ to _____ a _____.'
  OMOR   LTDO   OSTHO GNTARSRE

✪ SPECIAL ASSIGNMENT (15pts)

How many Lysians are in the central command?

ANSWERS

TRIVIA ANSWERS

1. laser cannon
2. 47
3. 39 cobalt fusion warheads with magnetic propulsion
4. 14
5. *Ode to Psyche* by John Keats
6. the Cliffs of Heaven on Sumiko IV
7. Emerald Wading Pool on Cirrus IV
8. 1,500%
9. Epsilon Silar system
10. the el-Mitra Exchange

CHARACTER QUOTE SOLUTION

'I feel as though I've been handed a weapon, sent into a room and told to shoot a stranger.' – Picard

SPECIAL ASSIGNMENT SOLUTION

15,311

Congratulations! Starfleet Command is proud to award you the Starfleet Medal of Honour and 15 extra points.

MISSION PERFORMANCE RATING:

55 – 75 points **Superior:** You suspected MacDuff from the beginning!

50 – 54 points **Above Average:** Chairman of Lysian Reparations Committee.

40 – 49 points **Average:** Don't remember who you are? You're still an ensign!

30 – 39 points **Fair:** Osmotic amnesia through the TV screen, huh?

0 – 29 points **Poor:** Just think, you'll be the first to fly in a sentry pod.

POWER PLAY

STARDATE: 45571.2

The *Enterprise* investigates a distress signal from the *USS Essex*, a Federation ship missing for over 200 years. Due to intense electromagnetic interference, Picard sends a shuttlecraft away team to the surface. The shuttlecraft is damaged and crashes on the moon. O'Brien is able to beam down and set up some pattern enhancers to allow the safe transport of the away team, but not before they are all knocked unconscious and small surges of energy enter Data, Troi, and O'Brien.

After the away team returns to the *Enterprise*, Data, Troi and O'Brien attempt to take over the ship. The mutineers make their way to Ten-Forward and take everyone hostage. Troi claims to be the captain of the *Essex* and that she and two of her crew became spirits when their vessel crashed. The mutineers go to a transporter to supposedly beam up the remains of the *Essex* crew for burial. Instead, they beam up other energy beings like themselves. Troi explains that they are all prisoners sent here as punishment and separated from their physical bodies. The *Enterprise* crew quickly releases a containment field that traps the entities. Picard persuades the entities to release their hold on Data, Troi, and O'Brien, and he returns them to the surface of the moon.

TRIVIA QUESTIONS

1. What is Ro prepared to do on Riker's orders? **(3pts)**
2. How long ago did the prisoners arrive at the colony? **(2pts)**
3. How does Geordi gain access to Ten-Forward to deliver the plasma shock? **(3pts)**
4. Why can't Geordi shut down computer access to Ten-Forward? **(3pts)**
5. Where does the *Enterprise* pick up a weak distress call? **(4pts)**
6. What star system are the prisoners from? **(3pts)**
7. What is the Starfleet Registry Number of the *Essex*? **(5pts)**
8. The *Essex* reported to whom in this sector? **(4pts)**
9. What inclination does Troi tell Picard to move the *Enterprise*? **(4pts)**
10. There hasn't been a Daedalus-class starship in service for how many years? **(4pts)**

SPECIAL ASSIGNMENT (10pts)

In trying to access Ten-Forward, Geordi thought they might have a problem with which conduit in the access tube?

MULTIPLE CHOICE QUESTIONS

1. Dr Crusher proposes to flood Ten-Forward with what kind of particles to contain the entities? **(5pts)**
   A. iconic
   B. neutrino
   C. tachyon
   D. ionongenic

2. What does Picard order Worf to initiate in Turbolift 4? **(3pts)**
   A. the emergency bulkheads
   B. a level-3 diagnostic
   C. a security stop override
   D. the security fields

3. What makes it virtually impossible to locate the distress call? **(2pts)**
   A. electroplasmic storms
   B. subspace distortion
   C. electromagnetic whirlwinds
   D. dust devils

4. How does Ro determine the shuttlecraft's position on the moon? **(3pts)**
   A. uses the navigational sensors
   B. calculates it from the angle of descent
   C. uses lateral sensor array
   D. calculates it from the shuttlecraft's electromagnetic signature

5. What does O'Brien want to be transferred to Ten-Forward? **(2pts)**
   A. a medical team to treat the wounded
   B. all command functions
   C. all command officers
   D. all transporter controls

ANSWERS

TRIVIA ANSWERS

1. blow the hatch in Cargo Bay 4
2. 500 years ago
3. by using a micro-optic drill
4. the mutineers have established a remote security lockout
5. on an M-class moon in orbit around Mab-Bu VI
6. Ux-Mal
7. NCC-173
8. Admiral Uttan Narsu at Starbase 12
9. 80° south
10. 172 years

SPECIAL ASSIGNMENT SOLUTION

Conduit 227

Congratulations! Starfleet Command is proud to award you the Starfleet Medal of Honour and 10 extra points.

MULTIPLE CHOICE ANSWERS

1. D. ionongenic
2. A. the emergency bulkheads
3. C. electromagnetic whirlwinds
4. B. calculates it from the angle of descent
5. D. all transporter controls

MISSION PERFORMANCE RATING:

45 – 60 points **Superior:** So you connected the scanner to the plasma inverter.

40 – 44 points **Above Average:** Well, we know you're not possessed.

30 – 39 points **Average:** Do you still hear voices inside your head?

20 – 29 points **Fair:** Mutiny will not be tolerated on this ship!

0 – 19 points **Poor:** It's time for your plasma shock therapy!

ETHICS

STARDATE: 45587.3 ▰▰▰▰▰▰▰▰▰▰▰

Worf is paralyzed in an accident and Dr Russell, a neural specialist, is brought aboard the *Enterprise* to assist Dr Crusher. Russell is working on an experimental device that can replicate organs. She wants to use the technology to replace Worf's spinal cord. Dr Crusher decides to stick with conventional therapy after she discovers that the procedure has never been tried on humanoids.

Meanwhile, Worf asks Riker to help him commit ritual suicide. Riker is disturbed by the request but says he'll think it over. Dr Crusher tries to persuade Worf to pursue a course of treatment that would give him limited mobility but he will have none of it. Russell offers the new technique to Worf. Picard also applies pressure to Dr Crusher to allow Russell to perform the procedure.

Riker tells Worf that according to Klingon tradition the eldest son should assist in the suicide ritual. Worf calls Alexander to his room and tells him he has decided to break with tradition and will allow Russell to perform the operation. The operation seems to go well but complications arise and Worf dies. Later, his physiological redundancies kick in and he comes back to life.

TRIVIA QUESTIONS

1. What is Dr Russell's opinion of Klingon anatomy? **(3pts)**
2. What is unusual about Klingon livers? **(3pts)**
3. Where did Worf's accident happen? **(3pts)**
4. At what time was Worf's death initially noted in the medical logs? **(4pts)**
5. Who was the archaeologist who died under Worf's command and what episode was it? **(5pts)**
6. When is the son of a Klingon considered a man? **(3pts)**
7. What do Klingons call the built-in redundancies in their bodies? **(4pts)**
8. How many ribs do Klingons have? **(4pts)**
9. What is unusual about Klingon hearts? **(3pts)**
10. About what has Dr Crusher written a paper? **(3pts)**

WHO AM I? (20pts)

I saw the two opposing forces do battle. The twelve rose up and stood their ground. The mighty thought they were weak and the weak became mighty. In the end the thirty-six folded under the onslaught. What was the battle and who am I?

✪ SPECIAL ASSIGNMENT (15pts)

What drug was Worf given three times and what was the *total* dosage given?

ANSWERS

TRIVIA ANSWERS

1. Klingons are over-designed; 2. they have two of them; 3. Cargo Bay 3; 4. 12:40 hours; 5. Marla Aster in 'The Bonding'; 6. the day he can first hold a blade; 7. brak' lul; 8. 23; 9. they have an eight chambered heart; 10. cybernetic regeneration

WHO AM I? SOLUTION

Geordi (via his VISOR).

EXPLANATION:

I saw the two opposing forces do battle. – Geordi saw Troi and Worf as they played this hand of poker.

The twelve rose up and stood their ground. – Troi tried to bluff Worf with a pair of sixes.

The mighty thought they were weak and the weak became mighty. – Troi's bluff succeeded.

In the end the thirty-six folded under the onslaught – Worf folded with a two pair of jacks and eights.

SPECIAL ASSIGNMENT SOLUTION

135cc inaprovaline

Worf was first given 20cc inaprovaline when there was a fluctuation in his isocortex. He was given another 40cc when he was disconnected from the life support. Worf was then given a final dose of 75cc.

Congratulations! Starfleet Command is proud to award you the Starfleet Medal of Honour and 15 extra points.

MISSION PERFORMANCE RATING:

36 – 70 points **Superior:** Your theories are brilliant even if you are unethical!

30 – 35 points **Above Average:** How many spinal cords have you replicated?

20 – 29 points **Average:** I think you crash-landed on this one.

10 – 19 points **Fair:** No you're not Klingon. Everyone has two kidneys!

 0 – 9 points **Poor:** You'd better lay off the chloromydride for a while.

THE OUTCAST

The *Enterprise* assists an androgynous race of aliens called the J'naii to find a missing shuttlecraft. The *Enterprise* discovers a large pocket of null space that absorbs energy and determines that the missing shuttle is hidden within the pocket. Riker works with a J'naii named Soren and together they map out the edges of the null space pocket. Soren tells Riker that he/she is attracted to him. Soren explains that sometimes a J'naii will favour one gender or the other. Soren has tendencies toward femaleness. The J'naii consider this aberrant behaviour and routinely treat these individuals to 'cure' them of their illness.

Riker and Soren pilot a shuttlecraft into the null space and are able to rescue the two J'naii from the trapped shuttle. Afterwards, Soren is arrested by the J'naii for exhibiting signs of gender. Riker goes to Soren's hearing and tries to take responsibility for what happened, but Soren is tired of the lies. He/she discloses the truth and accepts the verdict. That evening, Riker and Worf attempt to rescue Soren but they discover he/she has already been treated and refuses to go with them. Riker and Worf leave without Soren.

TRIVIA QUESTIONS

1. Where has Riker never been comfortable? **(3pts)**
2. What is the most important thing Riker says he looks for in a woman? **(3pts)**
3. What is split pea soup good for? **(3pts)**
4. How does Soren prefer to keep warm on a cold night? **(3pts)**
5. How much power was used in the first attempt to transport the J'naii to the rescue shuttle? **(4pts)**
6. What is the name of the J'naii shuttlecraft? **(4pts)**
7. What type of game does Worf call Federation Day? **(3pts)**
8. The failure of what system caused the lurching inside the shuttle that injured Soren? **(4pts)**
9. What are J'naii foetuses incubated in? **(3pts)**
10. What type of engines does the rescue shuttle have? **(5pts)**

MULTIPLE CHOICE QUESTIONS

1. What does Worf bring to Riker's quarters? **(3pts)**
   A. a plan for deploying warming buoys around the perimeter of the *Enterprise*'s olympic pool
   B. a plan for rescuing Soren from the J'naii therapy sessions
   C. a plan for rescuing the J'naii from their shuttlecraft in the null space
   D. a plan for deploying warning buoys around the perimeter of the null space

2. What will Geordi have installed on the rescue shuttlecraft by 08:00 hours? **(3pts)**
   - A. phase buffer inverter
   - B. buffer field generator
   - C. two microfusion phaser emitters
   - D. microfusion generator

3. Which cards are wild when playing Federation Day? **(5pts)**
   - A. sixes, threes, and nines
   - B. sevens, twos, and jacks
   - C. aces, jacks, and twos
   - D. twos, sixes, and aces

4. What did Lwaxana send to Troi? **(2pts)**
   - A. a box of her old clothes that she thought might fit Troi
   - B. a crate of Troi's childhood belongings
   - C. a box of items that belonged to one of her father's ancestors
   - D. several of Troi's old teddy bears

5. What is the purpose of the phasers mounted on the rescue shuttlecraft? **(2pts)**
   - A. to pinpoint the location of the J'naii shuttlecraft by hitting it with phaser fire
   - B. to chart the size of the null space pocket
   - C. to defend the shuttle against unknown alien forces that may be trapped in the null space
   - D. to illuminate a path through the null space since sensors won't work once the shuttle is inside

ANSWERS

TRIVIA ANSWERS

1. in crowded rooms
2. someone who laughs at his jokes
3. helps keep you warm on cold Alaskan nights
4. by sleeping with a friend
5. 10 megajoules
6. *Taris Murn*
7. a women's game
8. the failure of the inertial dampeners
9. fibrous husks
10. two 1250 millicochrane warp engines

MULTIPLE CHOICE ANSWERS

1. D. a plan for deploying warning buoys around the perimeter of the null space
2. B. buffer field generator
3. D. twos, sixes, and aces
4. C. a box of items that belonged to one of her father's ancestors
5. B. to chart the size of the null space pocket

MISSION PERFORMANCE RATING:

45 – 50 points **Superior:** You're not going to risk *your* career are you.

40 – 44 points **Above Average:** First to theorize about existence of null space.

30 – 39 points **Average:** Hey, pick a gender and then stay with it!

20 – 29 points **Fair:** You're scheduled for psychotectic therapy at 08:30 hours.

0 – 19 points **Poor:** There's a lot of null space between your ears!

CAUSE AND EFFECT

STARDATE: 45652.1

The *Enterprise* is in the midst of a major disaster. As the situation deteriorates the order is given to abandon ship. Moments later the *Enterprise* explodes into a ball of flame.

The *Enterprise* is mapping the unexplored region known as the Typhon Expanse. Dr Crusher is troubled by a feeling of déjà vu and she hears voices in her quarters as she tries to sleep. The next morning, the *Enterprise* encounters a distortion of the space-time continuum. As the *Enterprise* tries to reverse course all major systems fail. A starship appears out of the disturbance, on a collision course with the *Enterprise*. Riker suggests decompressing the shuttlebay to avoid the collision. Picard instead uses the tractor beam as Data suggests. It moves the ship but the *Enterprise* is still badly damaged by the collision. Moments later the *Enterprise* explodes into a ball of flame.

The *Enterprise* is caught in a temporal causality loop, destined to repeat the same series of events endlessly. Dr Crusher is able to record the voices she hears in her room during one of the time loops. Data extracts several significant bits of information from the recording. The officers determine that in order to break out of the cycle, they must prevent the collision with the other ship. Geordi and Data devise a means of sending a short message into the next loop to warn themselves. Just before the *Enterprise* is destroyed again, Data is able to send the message. Moments later the *Enterprise* explodes into a ball of flame.

The *Enterprise* crew begins mapping the unexplored region known as the Typhon Expanse. The events play out again. As the situation deteriorates, Data remembers the message and is able to save both ships from catastrophe. The space-time distortion disappears and the loop is ended.

TRIVIA QUESTIONS

1. Geordi has all the symptoms of what type of medical problem? **(3pts)**
2. What spice did Picard add to his insomnia remedy? **(3pts)**
3. What remedy does Picard recommend to Dr Crusher for insomnia? **(3pts)**
4. What does Data see that reminds him of the meaning of the number three? **(3pts)**
5. What is the name of the ship commanded by Captain Bateson? **(4pts)**
6. What part of the *Enterprise* sustains a direct impact from the other ship? **(3pts)**
7. After impact what is the *Enterprise* venting? **(3pts)**
8. What is Bateson's first name? **(5pts)**
9. What class of starship is Bateson's ship? **(5pts)**
10. When did Bateson say they had left the starbase? **(3pts)**

✪✪ POKER TRIVIA

1. Riker is one card short of a what? **(2pts)**
2. When Dr Crusher starts the betting at 10, what does she have? **(3pts)**
3. Dr Crusher jokingly says she knows Riker is bluffing whenever he does what? **(2pts)**
4. During time loop two, Riker realizes what during the poker game? **(3pts)**
5. The first queen Data deals to Dr Crusher is the queen of _____. **(3pts)**
6. When did the officers last play poker? **(3pts)**
7. During the fourth time loop what is the first card Data deals to everyone? **(3pts)**
8. During the fourth time loop what hand does Data deal each person? **(8pts: 2pts per person)**
9. During the third time loop what two cards does Riker have showing? **(4pts: 2pts per card)**
10. During the third time loop what three cards does Data have showing? **(9pts: 3pts per card)**

ANSWERS

TRIVIA ANSWERS
1. an inner ear infection
2. nutmeg
3. steamed milk
4. the three pips on Riker's collar
5. USS Bozeman
6. the starboard nacelle
7. drive plasma
8. Morgan
9. Soyuz-class
10. only three weeks ago

POKER TRIVIA ANSWERS
1. straight
2. pair of queens
3. by the way his left eyebrow rises when he's bluffing
4. that Dr Crusher is going to call his bluff
5. spades
6. last Tuesday night
7. three
8. Worf: three kings, Dr Crusher: three tens, Riker: three eights, Data: three sixes
9. eight of diamonds and ten of spades
10. four of hearts, nine of diamonds, and six of clubs

MISSION PERFORMANCE RATING:

30 – 75 points **Superior:** Wow, decompressing the shuttlebay was your idea!

25 – 29 points **Above Average:** You were one card from a straight flush.

20 – 24 points **Average:** What year do *you* think it is?

10 – 19 points **Fair:** You're caught in a FAIR temporal causality loop.

0 – 9 points **Poor:** No loop for you, you've slept through the last 90 years!

THE FIRST DUTY

The *Enterprise* is en route to Earth so Picard can give the commencement address at the graduation ceremonies at Starfleet Academy. Picard learns that Wesley was injured while training for a precision flight demonstration as part of the graduation ceremonies. One pilot named Albert was killed in the accident.

Picard and Dr Crusher attend the official inquiry into the accident. Locarno, the squadron leader, blames the dead cadet for the accident. Wesley supports Locarno's account of the accident. Several discrepancies between the evidence and the cadets' testimony occur. New evidence is introduced that contradicts Wesley's version of the events.

Picard assigns Geordi and Data to assist in the investigation of the evidence. Picard realizes after listening to their report that the cadets were attempting a dangerous manoeuvre that Starfleet banned long ago. Picard gives Wesley a choice to come forward with the truth or he will. Wesley comes forward and confesses. The cadets are punished.

TRIVIA QUESTIONS

1. Where was Wesley's ship at the beginning of the squadron's run to Titan? **(4pts)**
2. Whose flight recorder was recovered? **(3pts)**
3. How far apart are the ships when they collide? **(3pts)**
4. What rank is Joshua's father? **(3pts)**
5. What is Wesley's punishment besides a formal reprimand on his permanent record? **(3pts)**
6. What is the name of the banned manoeuvre that Nova Squadron was attempting? **(5pts)**
7. Which tournament does Boothby mention that the Academy won against Minsk in the final? **(4pts)**
8. What was the only course Wesley says Joshua needed help in? **(3pts)**
9. What was wrong with the squadron's low-apogee turn around Titan? **(3pts)**
10. Where will the memorial service be held for Joshua? **(4pts)**

SPECIAL ASSIGNMENT (10pts)

What move did Picard once use to pin an opponent in the first 14 seconds of a wrestling match at the Academy?

MULTIPLE CHOICE QUESTIONS

1. What does Brand revoke from the cadets? **(2pts)**
   - A. any previous job offers
   - B. conjugal visits
   - C. flight privileges
   - D. driving privileges

2. Why is purging a plasma exhaust while in-flight extremely hazardous? **(3pts)**
   - A. it can lead to a fusion plasma failure
   - B. the plasma stream could interfere with sensor readings
   - C. the plasma could be sucked into the Bussard intakes causing the ship to explode
   - D. the engine could ignite the plasma

3. What does Wesley tell his mother not to do? **(2pts)**
   - A. treat him like a child
   - B. try to protect him
   - C. worry about him
   - D. stare at him

4. What does Wesley say Locarno led the squadron in after clearing Titan? **(3pts)**
   - A. Parrises Starburst
   - B. Yeager Loop
   - C. Picard Manoeuvre
   - D. Kobayashi Maru Sequence

5. What injuries did Wesley sustain from the accident? **(5pts)**
   - A. second degree burns to his chest and multiple fractures in his right arm
   - B. brain trauma and compound fractures in his right leg
   - C. third degree burns to his legs and multiple fractures to his left arm
   - D. a tension pneumothorax and second degree burns to his chest

ANSWERS

TRIVIA ANSWERS

1. right wing
2. Wesley's
3. 10 metres apart
4. lieutenant commander
5. his academic credits for the last year are voided and he will not advance with his class
6. Kolvoord Starburst
7. Parrises Squares tournament of '24
8. Statistical Mechanics
9. it was at least 2,000 kilometres closer to the moon than the flight plan stated
10. in the West Garden

SPECIAL ASSIGNMENT SOLUTION

a reverse body lift

Congratulations! Starfleet Command is proud to award you the Starfleet Medal of Honour and 10 extra points.

MULTIPLE CHOICE ANSWERS

1. C. flight privileges
2. D. the engine could ignite the plasma
3. B. try to protect him
4. B. Yeager Loop
5. A. second degree burns to his chest and multiple fractures in his right arm

---

MISSION PERFORMANCE RATING:

45 – 60 points **Superior:** You knew the first duty of a Starfleet officer.

40 – 44 points **Above Average:** Ex-Blue Angel, huh?

30 – 39 points **Average:** You stretched the truth a little, didn't you, Cadet?

20 – 29 points **Fair:** Expelled from the Academy in disgrace!

0 – 19 points **Poor:** Blown up during a Kolvoord Starburst attempt!

COST OF LIVING ⌖

The *Enterprise* destroys an asteroid on a collision course with a nearby planet and flies through the debris. Later, Troi discovers that her mother, Lwaxana, has beamed aboard the *Enterprise*. Lwaxana informs Troi that she is getting married to a man she's never met.

Meanwhile, sporadic problems begin occurring all over the *Enterprise*. The problems are traced to metal parasites that eat an alloy found throughout the ship. The crew works to rid the ship of the parasites before they damage critical systems.

Lwaxana's fiancé, Campio, joins the *Enterprise* with his escort. The crew finally remove the parasites from the *Enterprise* and the wedding goes ahead as planned. Lwaxana decides at the last minute to turn up in traditional Betazoid fashion – naked. Campio is quickly escorted off by his attendant and the wedding is cancelled.

TRIVIA QUESTIONS

1. What is Lwaxana's favourite part of the Parallax Colony? **(3pts)**
2. What did Campio send Lwaxana? **(3pts)**
3. Who stands guard at the entrance to the Parallax Colony? **(4pts)**
4. What's the hottest thing at the Parallax Colony? **(3pts)**
5. Lwaxana says contracts are usually what? **(3pts)**
6. Where does Lwaxana want to have the wedding? **(3pts)**
7. How many reports of malfunctioning food replicators does Geordi receive? **(3pts)**
8. With which planet is the asteroid on a collision course? **(5pts)**
9. Why can't the *Enterprise* get a positive tractor beam lock on the asteroid core? **(3pts)**
10. What is Campio's full title? **(5pts)**

✪ SPECIAL ASSIGNMENT (15pts)

What statue is visible on the table in Worf's quarters and which other episode was it first seen in?

MULTIPLE CHOICE QUESTIONS

1. What is failing at random spots around the ship, according to Riker? **(3pts)**
    A. structural integrity of the ship
    B. replicators
    C. ventilation and life support
    D. computers and life support

2. Atmospheric systems are down by how much, says Riker? **(5pts)**
    A. 35% and going below minimum oxygen levels
    B. 25% and rising above CO_2 safety limits
    C. 27% and going below tolerable oxygen levels
    D. 12% and going below comfortable oxygen levels

3. Children and servants can't be present during what, according to Campio's escort? **(2pts)**
    A. the divorce proceedings
    B. the wedding
    C. the honeymoon
    D. the prenuptial consultation

4. What does the particle beam from the deflectors create in the asteroid core? **(3pts)**
    A. a disruptive nuclear effect
    B. a disruptor-like phase inversion
    C. a sonic boom
    D. a resonance wave

5. What honour is bestowed on Picard? **(2pts)**
    A. he gets to meet Minister Campio
    B. he is to give the bride away
    C. he will officiate at the wedding
    D. he gets to take Lwaxana's luggage to her quarters

ANSWERS

TRIVIA ANSWERS

1. the mud baths
2. his mother's wedding gown
3. Wind Dancer
4. the fire sculptor
5. between people who don't really trust one another
6. Ten-Forward
7. over 200
8. Tessen III
9. magnetic interference from asteroid metals
10. the Third Minister of the Conference of Judges

SPECIAL ASSIGNMENT SOLUTION

The statue of Morath and Kahless the Unforgettable fighting that was first seen in the episode 'New Ground'.

Congratulations! Starfleet Command is proud to award you the Starfleet Medal of Honour and 15 extra points.

MULTIPLE CHOICE ANSWERS

1. C. ventilation and life support
2. C. 27% and going below tolerable oxygen levels
3. D. the prenuptial consultation
4. A. a disruptive nuclear effect
5. B. he is to give the bride away

MISSION PERFORMANCE RATING:

45 – 65 points **Superior:** You got rid of the parasites without any problems!

40 – 44 points **Above Average:** You'd make a good protocol minister!

30 – 39 points **Average:** You are sentenced to the mud baths at Shiralea VI.

20 – 29 points **Fair:** Ever thought about juggling for a career?

0 – 19 points **Poor:** You are sentenced to a gelatinous pool of metal parasites.

THE PERFECT MATE

STARDATE: 45761.3

The *Enterprise* hosts peace negotiations between the planets Valt Minor and Krios. The Kriosian Ambassador stores a gift for the Valtese leader in the cargo bay in stasis. The *Enterprise* rescues two Ferengi en route to the conference. The Ferengi end up destabilizing the stasis field around the gift in the cargo bay. The field dissolves and a beautiful woman steps out. She is Kamala, the future wife of the Valtese leader. Kamala is an empathic metamorph. She is able to sense what a mate wants or needs and then becomes that type of person. She will imprint herself with her husband's ideal of a perfect mate.

The Ferengi hope to bribe the Ambassador into selling Kamala to them. When he refuses to and tries to leave, the Ambassador is injured in the ensuing scuffle. Picard must assume the duties of the Ambassador until he can recover from his injuries. Kamala instructs Picard in the performance of various rituals and discusses the trade issues that need to be negotiated. Kamala decides to imprint Picard's ideal of a perfect mate. However, she goes on with the ceremony anyway and marries the Valtese leader who cares more about the trade agreements than Kamala.

TRIVIA QUESTIONS

1. How long has it been since a female metamorph was born? **(4pts)**
2. What did the Ferengi tell Worf they hoped Picard would do? **(3pts)**
3. What term did Geordi use that the Ambassador didn't understand? **(3pts)**
4. What type of instrument did Kamala learn to play when young? **(3pts)**
5. How old is the Ambassador? **(4pts)**
6. What do Valtese horns sound like? **(5pts)**
7. What was the total amount of the bribe that the Ferengi offered to the Ambassador? **(3pts)**
8. How often are female metamorphs born? **(4pts)**
9. Where was Kamala held in stasis? **(3pts)**
10. What is holodeck programme Krios 1? **(3pts)**

SPECIAL ASSIGNMENT (10pts)

What is the final stage of an empathic metamorph's sexual maturation called?

CHARACTER QUOTE
(2pts per word + 5pts for identifying the speaker.)

Unscramble the words below and then identify the character.

'_____ has _____ very _____, but I _____ it a _____ _____
ITSH   EBNE   ITDNEULAAOC   KAME   CPLYIO ENRVE

to _____ _____ _____ ____.'
   EONP TNAHROE NMSA FGTI

ANSWERS

TRIVIA ANSWERS
1. over 100 years
2. invite them to dinner
3. ball park
4. the entire orchestra
5. 200 years old
6. braying Targhee moon beasts
7. 20,000 pieces of Ludugial gold
8. only once every seven generations
9. Cargo Bay I
10. a recreation of the ancient Temple of Akadar

SPECIAL ASSIGNMENT SOLUTION
Finiis'ral
Congratulations! Starfleet Command is proud to award you the Starfleet Medal of Honour and 10 extra points.

CHARACTER QUOTE SOLUTION
'This has been very educational, but I make it a policy never to open another man's gift.' – Riker

---

MISSION PERFORMANCE RATING:

55 – 70 points **Superior:** You're as old and wise as the Ambassador.

50 – 54 points **Above Average:** The Captain often invites you to dine with him.

40 – 49 points **Average:** You must schedule the Ambassador's appointments.

30 – 39 points **Fair:** You're just a meddlesome Ferengi at heart!

0 – 29 points **Poor:** You've got the brain of a redneck Harodian miner!

The *Enterprise* enters an interesting nebula and begins exploring it. An energy being enters the ship and takes the form of a little girl's imaginary friend named Isabella. Clara shows Isabella around the *Enterprise*. Troi counsels Clara, thinking that she is only going through a lonely phase.

Meanwhile, the *Enterprise* is becoming entangled in a web of energy strands that threaten the ship. Other energy beings show up and begin feeding on the *Enterprise*'s shields. Picard confronts the alien and learns that she thinks that adults are cruel to their children and should die. The alien has been viewing humans through the eyes of a child. Picard explains that adults make rules only to protect their young. The aliens are convinced and leave the ship. The *Enterprise* makes its way safely out of the nebula.

TRIVIA QUESTIONS

1. What is Alexander making? **(3pts)**
2. What image did Data say he could visualize within the nebula? **(3pts)**
3. How does Clara make purple omelettes? **(3pts)**
4. What is a majestic name for the nebula? **(3pts)**
5. How old is Isabella according to Troi's estimate? **(3pts)**
6. Approximately how many energy strands compose the nebula? **(4pts)**
7. How does Geordi make the energy strands visible? **(4pts)**
8. What does Ensign Sutter jokingly propose to call the nebula? **(3pts)**
9. What does Isabella take in her tea? **(4pts)**
10. What is the name of the nebula? **(5pts)**

SPECIAL ASSIGNMENT (10pts)

Nurse Ogawa and her date walked along what on the holodeck?

MULTIPLE CHOICE QUESTIONS

1. What hits Alexander in the back of his head? **(2pts)**
    A. ceramic cup
    B. lump of clay
    C. ball of crumpled paper
    D. lump of ceramic

2. Why can't the *Enterprise* go to warp speed in the nebula? **(3pts)**
    A. the energy strands interfere with creating a warp field
    B. the warp engines are off-line

C. the stress on the hull would be too great
D. warp power is being diverted to the shields

3. What does Troi order in her quarters from the replicator? **(2pts)**
   A. chocolate cake
   B. hot chocolate
   C. Valerian root tea
   D. chocolate fudge sundae

4. How many samples are taken from the nebula? **(5pts)**
   A. eight samples from random sections of the nebula
   B. five samples from various sections of the nebula
   C. ten samples from specific regions within the nebula
   D. six samples from random sections of the nebula

5. Clara and her father have been moving from starship to starship since when? **(3pts)**
   A. since Clara was four years old
   B. since her mother died
   C. since Clara was two years old
   D. since her father graduated from the Academy

ANSWERS

TRIVIA ANSWERS
1. a ceramic cup for his father
2. a bunny rabbit
3. puts grape juice in the eggs
4. the La Forge Nebula
5. 11 or 12 years old
6. 47 million energy strands
7. he runs the warp field generators through the deflector grid
8. Sutter's Cloud
9. two cubes of sugar
10. FGC-47

SPECIAL ASSIGNMENT
Champs Elysées
Congratulations! Starfleet Command is proud to award you the Starfleet Medal of Honour and 10 extra points.

MULTIPLE CHOICE ANSWERS
1. B. lump of clay
2. C. the stress on the hull would be too great
3. B. hot chocolate
4. A. eight samples from random sections of the nebula
5. C. since Clara was two years old

MISSION PERFORMANCE RATING:

45 – 60 points   **Superior:** You knew better than to even go into the nebula!

40 – 44 points   **Above Average:** You got us out of the nebula!

30 – 39 points   **Average:** Not too good with ceramics, huh?

20 – 29 points   **Fair:** You have lots of imaginary friends, don't you?

0 – 19 points   **Poor:** I bet you can talk to starships with a spoon!

I, BORG

The *Enterprise* comes across the wreckage of a small Borg ship on a nearby moon. An away team beams down to investigate and discovers a survivor. Picard allows Dr Crusher to beam the injured Borg aboard the *Enterprise*. Picard orders Geordi to create new Borg implants modified with an invasive programme that will destroy the Borg collective after the surviving Borg is returned.

Geordi begins testing the Borg to learn more about how it functions so that he can replicate the needed implants. Geordi eventually becomes friends with the Borg he has named Hugh. Hugh attains a degree of individuality, something he never had while within the Borg collective. Picard decides to stop the mission after he talks with Hugh and realizes that using him to destroy his whole race would be wrong. Hugh is returned to the crash site and is picked up by a Borg rescue ship.

TRIVIA QUESTIONS

1. How many Borg beam down to the crash site from the rescue ship? **(3pts)**
2. What is the wounded Borg's designation? **(3pts)**
3. How many other Borg were on the ship that crashed? **(3pts)**
4. What does Geordi use to neutralize any transmissions coming from the Borg's cell? **(3pts)**
5. What is an advantage in fencing and bartending? **(4pts)**
6. Until when will the star's radiation shield the *Enterprise* from the Borg ship's sensors? **(3pts)**
7. In which test did Hugh get all eight questions correct? **(5pts)**
8. What two signals is the Borg emitting in his cell? **(4pts)**
9. What do Borg eat? **(3pts)**
10. What is the source of the self-repeating transmission? **(4pts)**

MULTIPLE CHOICE QUESTIONS

1. When will the Borg suffer total systems failure after the invasive programme is introduced? **(2pts)**
   A. not until the geometric shape has gone through several hundred computational cycles
   B. not until the geometric saturation level is reached by over half of the Borg collective
   C. a matter of months
   D. A and C

2. What does Hugh remove to let Geordi look at it? **(3pts)**
   A. power coupling adapter
   B. prosthetic eye
   C. left arm
   D. brain implant

3. Why does Geordi have to go into the Borg's cell? **(3pts)**
   A. to rescue Dr Crusher after the Borg seizes her
   B. to study his spatial abilities
   C. to connect the power conduit
   D. to modify the power coupling adapter

4. Where would an invasive programme be introduced into the Borg's programming? **(5pts)**
   A. vital command pathways
   B. basic command structure
   C. command pathway structure
   D. root command structure

5. What might Dr Crusher have to remove from the injured Borg? **(2pts)**
   A. damaged brain implants
   B. prosthetic eye
   C. left arm
   D. neurolinguistic chip

ANSWERS

TRIVIA ANSWERS

1. two
2. Third of Five
3. four
4. subspace damping field
5. a strong forearm
6. until the Borg ship enters the star system
7. Spatial Acuity
8. a homing signal and a second subspace beacon
9. they don't, their implants synthesize any organic molecules their tissues may require
10. a small moon orbiting the fourth planet of a nearby system in the Argolis Cluster

MULTIPLE CHOICE ANSWERS

1. D. A and C
2. B. prosthetic eye
3. C. to connect the power conduit
4. D. root command structure
5. A. damaged brain implants

MISSION PERFORMANCE RATING:

45 – 50 points **Superior:** You developed the invasive programme for the Borg.

40 – 44 points **Above Average:** Cyborg specialist, huh?

30 – 39 points **Average:** Go transport onto the Borg rescue ship.

20 – 29 points **Fair:** The Borg have started to assimilate you.

 0 – 19 points **Poor:** You are Borg, go assimilate yourself!

THE NEXT PHASE

STARDATE: 45892.4

The *Enterprise* assists a badly damaged Romulan vessel. Ro and Geordi disappear while beaming back to the *Enterprise*. No trace of them can be found and Picard must assume that they are dead. In actuality, the Romulans were testing a new cloaking device that changes the phase state of matter. Geordi and Ro were accidentally cloaked during transport. They awake on the *Enterprise* but find that no-one can see or hear them and that they are also able to walk through walls.

The Romulans decide to sabotage the *Enterprise* before they can learn about the new cloaking device. They set up a dangerous feedback wave in the power transfer beam between the two ships. The *Enterprise* will explode when it goes to warp drive. Geordi and Ro overhear the Romulans' plan but are unable to warn anyone.

Geordi and Ro discover that they are leaving a trail of chroniton particles wherever they go on the *Enterprise*. While Data decontaminates the areas involved, Geordi's hand is struck by the decontaminating beam. Geordi realizes that the beam returned his hand momentarily to a more normal state. Geordi and Ro create larger chroniton fields, forcing Data to inadvertently increase the strength of the beams. Geordi and Ro become momentarily visible at their memorial service. Data understands what is happening and increases the strength of the decontamination beam. Geordi and Ro, now uncloaked, are able to warn the crew about the Romulan sabotage.

TRIVIA QUESTIONS

1. What do the Romulans have to do manually? **(3pts)**
2. What is over two hours long? **(3pts)**
3. Data has researched the funerary rites of how many other cultures? **(4pts)**
4. What did Geordi once stay up all night doing to impress Picard? **(3pts)**
5. Where are the Romulans hiding the feedback wave? **(3pts)**
6. What is the only way the *Enterprise* could detect the feedback wave from the Romulan ship? **(3pts)**
7. What is the official time of death listed on the death certificates? **(5pts)**
8. What is the Engineering team modifying to act as a new engine core? **(3pts)**
9. How many Romulans are still alive according to Worf's scans? **(4pts)**
10. What type of problem did the Romulans have with their engine core? **(4pts)**

CHARACTER QUOTE
(2pts per word + 4pts for identifying the speaker.)

Unscramble the words below and then identify the character.

'I _____ _____ ____. I'm _____, you can't _____ _____ me

   T'OND EIBEELV IHTS   AEDD   NEEV AHRE

and I'm _____ _____ by you.'

      LTISL   EIDTMAITDIN

✪ SPECIAL ASSIGNMENT (15pts)

Where does Ro report her position on the *Enterprise* after changing phases?

ANSWERS

TRIVIA ANSWERS

1. eject the engine core
2. the Bajoran death chant
3. 5,000
4. refitting the fusion initiators on a shuttlecraft
5. in the sensor return signal
6. by running a level-3 diagnostic
7. 14:30 hours
8. subspace resonator
9. at least 73
10. a forced chamber explosion in the resonator coil

CHARACTER QUOTE SOLUTION

'I don't believe this. I'm dead, you can't even hear me, and I'm still intimidated by you.' – Ensign Ro

SPECIAL ASSIGNMENT SOLUTION

Section 23-Baker near sickbay
Congratulations! Starfleet Command is proud to award you the Starfleet Medal of Honour and 15 extra points.

MISSION PERFORMANCE RATING:

50 – 70 points **Superior:** You created the first working interphase generator!

45 – 49 points **Above Average:** Always staying one step ahead of the Romies.

40 – 44 points **Average:** You're on chroniton decontamination detail.

30 – 39 points **Fair:** You are sentenced to listen to fifty Bajoran death chants.

  0 – 29 points **Poor:** Your brain is still out of phase with reality.

The *Enterprise* investigates an unknown probe. The probe suddenly emits a powerful particle stream towards the ship and Picard drops unconscious to the floor. When he regains consciousness a woman is by his side and he is no longer on the *Enterprise*. The woman, Eline, claims to be Picard's wife and she calls him Kamin. Meanwhile, the bridge crew try to disconnect Picard from the probe's beam. Picard starts to die and Data must re-establish the connection.

Picard's mind accepts this alternate reality and his life as Kamin. Time takes on a different meaning as well. A minute on the bridge translates into several years of Kamin's life. Kamin and Eline go on to have two children. Kamin is a scientist and is studying the causes of a drought. He finally determines that the planet is doomed. Kamin tries to warn the Administrator but is told that the government's scientists came to the same conclusions.

As an older Kamin plays with his grandchild, his daughter reminds him of the missile launching later that day. The missile will release a probe that will seek out other humanoids. It will then interact with one of them to instill a knowledge of Kamin and his people. The people of Kataan hope that, in this way, a small part of their civilization will be remembered. Picard is the person found by the probe. With this knowledge, Picard wakes up on the bridge of the *Enterprise* and must begin separating the events of his real life from Kamin's.

TRIVIA QUESTIONS

1. How long was Picard under the influence of the probe? **(4pts)**
2. What might the Administrator recommend in all of his communities? **(3pts)**
3. Batai says Eline was always what? **(3pts)**
4. What position does Batai hold in the village? **(3pts)**
5. What does Kamin insist on collecting? **(3pts)**
6. Kamin says that rationing won't be enough if what doesn't change? **(3pts)**
7. What is the name of the propellant used in the Kataan probe? **(5pts)**
8. What does Kamin suggest to the Administrator to increase the water supplies? **(3pts)**
9. How many years have elapsed when Kamin is charting the sun? **(4pts)**
10. What is the first gift Kamin ever gave to Eline? **(4pts)**

✪ SPECIAL ASSIGNMENT (15pts)

What drug and dosage does Dr Crusher order after Picard starts to die when the beam is disconnected?

MULTIPLE CHOICE QUESTIONS

1. Name three fleeting areas of interest for the young Batai? **(5pts)**
   A. sculpture, ceramics, physics
   B. mathematics, zoology, painting
   C. botany, sculpture, mathematics
   D. music, botany, painting

2. What helps Kamin to think? **(2pts)**
   A. playing the flute
   B. walking
   C. taking soil samples
   D. staring at the stars through his telescope

3. What is a Kataan farewell salutation? **(3pts)**
   A. Be safe.
   B. Hurry back.
   C. Until the next.
   D. Go carefully.

4. Why is Kamin charting the progress of the sun's course? **(2pts)**
   A. to develop a new calendar
   B. to determine his position
   C. to discover a clue to the cause of the drought
   D. to determine the date when the sun will go supernova

5. How do the Kataans exchange messages with other villages? **(3pts)**
   A. couriers
   B. voice-transit conductors
   C. message transfer conduits
   D. orbiting communications satellites

ANSWERS

TRIVIA ANSWERS

1. 20–25 minutes
2. a symbolic tree
3. strong-minded
4. council leader
5. soil samples
6. weather patterns
7. crystalline emiristol
8. building atmospheric condensers to extract water from the air
9. five years
10. a medallion with a replica of the Kataan probe

SPECIAL ASSIGNMENT SOLUTION

2cc delactovine

Congratulations! Starfleet Command is proud to award you the Starfleet Medal of Honour and 15 extra points.

MULTIPLE CHOICE ANSWERS

1. C. botany, sculpture, mathematics
2. A. playing the flute
3. D. Go carefully.
4. C. to discover a clue to the cause of the drought
5. B. voice-transit conductors

MISSION PERFORMANCE RATING:

45 – 65 points **Superior:** You figured out how to leave the planet!

40 – 44 points **Above Average:** Nice job on the probe. It really does work!

30 – 39 points **Average:** You live in a doomed world.

20 – 29 points **Fair:** Do you have alternate realities often?

0 – 19 points **Poor:** You've fallen and you can't get up!

TIME'S ARROW

The *Enterprise* is recalled to Earth to investigate a mystery. Construction crews have unearthed what appears to be Data's severed head. The excavation site has also been exposed to triolic waves, a by-product of certain energy sources. Data confirms that the head is his and therefore infers that he will travel back in time at some point and die. Geordi determines that Devidia II is the source of a fossil found near Data's head. On Devidia II, an away team is unable to detect an alien presence because of a time differential; the aliens exist slightly in the future. Data is able to create a subspace field and synchronize with the aliens' time frame. Data is caught in a temporal distortion and transported back to 19th century Earth.

On Earth, Data sees Guinan's picture in the local newspaper and he goes to meet her. While trying to sort out Data's temporal difficulties, they discover an eavesdropping Samuel Clemens.

Meanwhile back on Devidia II, Geordi constructs a larger version of the device Data used to synchronize with the aliens' time frame. Picard joins the away team, after Guinan tells him that he should be there. The device works and the away team are able to view the aliens. The away team determines that a pair of the aliens are stealing the life force of humans from 19th century Earth and returning to Devidia II to feed it to others of their race. At the end of the episode, the away team follows the alien pair through the time vortex and back to 19th century Earth.

TRIVIA QUESTIONS

1. How old is the Earth according to the best geologic estimates of the 19th century? **(3pts)**
2. What is the name of the newspaper Data picks up from the ground? **(4pts)**
3. How tall are the aliens Data describes on Devidia II? **(3pts)**
4. How much does Data sell his communicator pin for at the start of the poker game? **(3pts)**
5. Whose hat does Data win during the poker game? **(4pts)**
6. Whose vest does Data win during the poker game? **(4pts)**
7. What bet does the bellboy place with a man in the street? **(3pts)**
8. What building is in front of Data when he first stands up in the street? **(3pts)**
9. What is the date on the newspaper Data picks up from the ground? **(3pts)**
10. What types of phase discriminating amplifiers do Data and Lore's positronic brains use? **(5pts)**

✪ SPECIAL ASSIGNMENT (15pts)

What is the inscription inside the pocket watch found near Data's head?

_____

MULTIPLE CHOICE QUESTIONS

1. What does the headline on the newspaper read that Data picks up
   from the ground? **(2pts)**
   - **A.** Smallpox Outbreak
   - **B.** Dysentery Outbreak
   - **C.** Cholera Outbreak
   - **D.** Typhoid Outbreak

2. What is the level of synchronic distortion in the caverns of Devidia II?
   (3pts)
   - **A.** positive displacement of .4%
   - **B.** positive displacement of .004%
   - **C.** positive displacement of 4%
   - **D.** positive displacement of .04%

3. Where was Data's head found? **(2pts)**
   - **A.** a mile beneath San Francisco
   - **B.** in an old storage room under Starfleet Academy
   - **C.** in a cavern on Devidia II
   - **D.** attached to the top of his shoulders

4. What type of cellular fossil did Geordi discover in the cavern near
   Data's severed head? **(5pts)**
   - **A.** 54401HX
   - **B.** LB10445
   - **C.** LBJ 55410
   - **D.** amoeba

5. Data estimates that his head was severed how long ago? **(3pts)**
   - **A.** 475 years ago
   - **B.** 525 years ago
   - **C.** 375 years ago
   - **D.** 500 years ago

_____

ANSWERS

TRIVIA ANSWERS

1. 100 million years old
2. The San Francisco Register
3. 2–3 metres in height
4. $3
5. Joe Falling Hawk
6. Frederick La Rouque
7. Gentleman Jim – knockout in the 5th (boxing match)
8. No. 5 Fire House
9. Sunday, 13 August, 1893
10. Data uses a Type R phase discriminating amplifier and Lore uses a Type L

SPECIAL ASSIGNMENT SOLUTION

To ACC / With Love / 30 November / 1889

Congratulations! Starfleet Command is proud to award you the Starfleet Medal of Honour and 15 extra points.

MULTIPLE CHOICE ANSWERS

1. C. Cholera Outbreak
2. B. positive displacement of .004%
3. A. a mile beneath San Francisco
4. B. LB10445
5. D. 500 years ago

MISSION PERFORMANCE RATING:

45 – 65 points **Superior:** You figured it all out and we don't need a Part II.

40 – 44 points **Above Average:** Seen any Ophidians lately?

30 – 39 points **Average:** Hey, don't lose your head over this!

20 – 29 points **Fair:** I think you lost your shirt on this one!

0 – 19 points **Poor:** Are you also a Forty-Niner that fell down a mine?

DARMOKISMS

Refer to the episode 'Darmok' to get a feel for how the Tamarians communicated through metaphor. Then try your hand at the Darmokisms below and guess which episodes they are describing. **(2pts each)**

1. Data and Tasha with arms opened wide.
2. Riker at Bourbon Street, his glass raised.
3. Worf, when armadillos ruled.
4. Korris, his heart ablaze.
5. Data and Marley on the holodeck.
6. Data and the Grand Master wired for battle.
7. Picard, his beard white and full.
8. Riker, his chest bared, with the mistress
9. Cleponji at Orelious IX.
10. Noonian, when his eyes closed.
11. Picard with Horga'hn held high.
12. Morgan and Picard at Typhon.
13. Dexter, his head in pieces.
14. Riker and gagh at Pagh.
15. Yamato scattered across the heavens.
16. Riker and Ro, their arms wide.
17. Beverly on the ocean.
18. Jalad at Tanagra.
19. Ishikawa one last day.
20. Q with fork in hand.
21. Guinan, when the children reigned.
22. Picard, when the turbolift fell.
23. Troi, when the bricks fell.
24. Worf, when he lost his nerve.
25. Berlinghoff with his pockets full.
26. Picard, his face muddied at Labarre.
27. Riker with his costal struts missing.
28. Leah, her fury unleashed.
29. Timicin, when the sun set.
30. Salia, her crown ready.
31. Geordi and Susanna at Tarchannen III.
32. Juliana and Data at Atria IV.
33. Neela, when the marshmallows burned.
34. Riva, when the music stopped.
35. Picard and Data, with faces covered.
36. Deanna flying, her arms outstretched.
37. Lwaxana, when the lights went out.
38. Regina, her eyes open.
39. Ro, her loyalties swayed.

---

40. Felisa and Ronin at the caber toss.
41. Worf with honour restored.
42. Minos on the ocean.
43. Troi, a cake in her image.
44. Worf and Duras at the crossroads.
45. Enterprise with crimson force field raised.
46. Kamin, his music lives on.
47. Riker with his spit and image.
48. Roga with fists raised in anger.
49. Kila, when the crystal shattered.
50. Hutch, when the room grew silent.
51. Geordi inverted at Delphi Ardu
52. T'Jon with his hand out.
53. Pickerd with pointed edge protruding.
54. Goss with his hand extended.
55. Montgomery on the ocean at Dyson.
56. Sleeping Klingons now awakened.
57. Riker, when the clicking began.
58. Aries and Riker with his thumb down.
59. Picard and Picard near Endicor.
60. Thadiun with the Jewel of Thesia grasped tightly.
61. Troi when the voices grew silent.
62. Geordi and Ro on the ocean.
63. Doe at Zeta Gelis.
64. Pressman, his ship a rock.
65. Kamala at Valt Minor.
66. Worf and Pulaski with teacups raised.
67. Data with bearded face.
68. Garrett with fist closed at Narendra III.
69. The Phoenix rises above Cuellar.
70. The Iceman at Barkon IV.
71. Picard, his fingernails long.
72. Tam at Ghorusda.
73. Data, his finger squeezing the trigger.
74. Pulaski before her time.
75. Uxbridge under three moons.

SPECIAL SECTION

ANSWERS

1. 'The Naked Now'
2. '11001001'
3. 'A Fistful of Datas'
4. 'Heart of Glory'
5. 'Devil's Due'
6. 'Peak Performance'
7. 'All Good Things . . .'
8. 'Angel One'
9. 'Booby Trap'
10. 'Brothers'
11. 'Captain's Holiday'
12. 'Cause and Effect'
13. 'Conspiracy'
14. 'A Matter of Honor'
15. 'Contagion'
16. 'Conundrum'
17. 'Remember Me'
18. 'Darmok'
19. 'Data's Day'
20. 'Déjà Q'
21. 'Rascals'
22. 'Disaster'
23. 'Emergence'
24. 'Ethics'
25. 'A Matter of Time'

26. 'Family'
27. 'First Contact'
28. 'Galaxy's Child'
29. 'Half a Life'
30. 'The Dauphin'
31. 'Identity Crisis'
32. 'Inheritance'
33. 'Lessons'
34. 'Loud as a Whisper'
35. 'Masks'
36. 'Night Terrors'
37. 'Dark Page'
38. 'Ship in a Bottle'
39. 'Preemptive Strike'
40. 'Sub Rosa'
41. 'Redemption'
42. 'The Arsenal of Freedom'
43. 'Phantasms'
44. 'Reunion'
45. 'Samaritan Snare'
46. 'The Inner Light'
47. 'Second Chances'
48. 'The Hunted'
49. 'Silicon Avatar'
50. 'Starship Mine'

51. 'The Last Outpost'
52. 'Symbiosis'
53. 'Tapestry'
54. 'The Price'
55. 'Relics'
56. 'The Emissary'
57. 'Schisms'
58. 'The Icarus Factor'
59. 'Times Squared'
60. 'The Outrageous Okona'
61. 'The Loss'
62. 'The Next Phase'
63. 'Transfigurations'
64. 'The Pegasus'
65. 'The Perfect Mate'
66. 'Up the Long Ladder'
67. 'The Schizoid Man'
68. 'Yesterday's Enterprise'
69. 'The Wounded'
70. 'Thine Own Self'
71. 'Timescape'
72. 'Tin Man'
73. 'The Most Toys'
74. 'Unnatural Selection'
75. 'The Survivors'

MISSION PERFORMANCE RATING:

126 – 150 points	**Superior:** You and Dathon can talk over subspace! (SEE BELOW)
101 – 125 points	**Above Average:** Do you always speak in metaphors?
76 – 100 points	**Average:** Not bad, all things considered.
51 – 75 points	**Fair:** You haven't a clue, have you?
0 – 25 points	**Poor:** You did so badly, it isn't worth talking about!

If you have received a SUPERIOR Mission Performance Rating –

Congratulations!
Starfleet Command is proud to award you
the Legion of Honour and 50 extra points.

SPECIAL SECTION

SEASON SIX

TIME'S ARROW – PART II

STARDATE: 46001.3

The away team walks through the time portal and ends up in 19th century San Francisco. There they encounter the alien pair and are able to steal their time travel device. Guinan helps the away team to gain entry to the cavern where Data's severed head was found at the start of 'Time's Arrow'.

While the away team inspects the cavern, Samuel Clemens, with gun in hand, confronts the group. He is determined to capture them and hand them over to the police. The aliens suddenly reappear and grab the time travel device. One of the aliens begins to activate the time portal but Data over-powers him and takes the device from him. Data is unable to control the energy forces and there is a terrific explosion. Everybody is thrown to the ground and Data's head is blown off as the time portal is established. One of the aliens escapes through the energy field, while Picard orders the away team to go back through the portal, while he remains behind to take care of an injured Guinan. Just as the portal is about to close Clemens jumps through as well.

The remaining alien who is injured tells Picard that any attempt to destroy the cavern on Devidia II will end in failure. Picard picks up Data's head and programmes a message into his static memory. Meanwhile, Geordi reattaches Data's 500-year-old head originally found in the cavern on Earth to Data's body. Data immediately receives Picard's message and is able to warn Riker not to use their weapons on the site. They begin to modify some photon torpedoes to destroy the cavern. Clemens is sent back to his time to allow Picard to return. Riker can't wait any longer and orders torpedoes away. Just then Picard appears as the torpedoes are about to destroy the cavern. O'Brien's quick actions beam Picard up to safety.

TRIVIA QUESTIONS

1. The policeman tells Riker he's been doing what for three years? **(3pts)**
2. What play does Picard tell the landlady his troupe is rehearsing? **(3pts)**
3. What excuse does Clemens use to get into Data's room? **(4pts)**
4. What three words does Data say after his head is reattached? **(5pts)**
5. What was causing Data's input polarizers to function intermittently? **(3pts)**
6. Clemens wonders if the *Enterprise* ever saw what while travelling through space? **(3pts)**
7. What was Data looking for information about from the county assayer's office? **(4pts)**
8. What book did Clemens write concerning time travel? **(3pts)**
9. What is strange about the bodies that Dr Crusher examines? **(3pts)**
10. What is the name of the charity hospital? **(4pts)**

CHARACTER QUOTE
(2pts per word + 7pts for identifying the speaker.)

Unscramble the words below and then identify the character.

'All _____ _____ _____ _____ to _____ _____ _____ 'EIFLS
  ITSH   OOEHYTLCGN   LOYN SVSREE   EAKT YWAA 'EIFLS

_____ _____.'
EMLSPI ERSELAUSP

DOUBLE SPECIAL ASSIGNMENT (10pts each)

Assignment I: Who is Titania?

Assignment II: What is Data's room number at the hotel?

ANSWERS

TRIVIA ANSWERS
1. working at the downtown station
2. A Midsummer Night's Dream
3. he needs to get a letter of intent that Data left for him or a major investor will pull out
4. torpedoes, phasing, alien
5. iron filing
6. Halley's comet
7. mining operations during the 1850s
8. A Connecticut Yankee in King Arthur's Court
9. their nervous systems have been depleted of electrochemical energy
10. Sisters of Hope Infirmary

CHARACTER QUOTE SOLUTION
'All this technology only serves to take away life's simple pleasures.' – Clemens

SPECIAL ASSIGNMENT SOLUTION
Assignment I: Queen of the Fairies in Shakespeare's play, A Midsummer Night's Dream
Assignment II: Room 314
Congratulations! Starfleet Command is proud to award you the Starfleet Medal of Honour and 10 or 20 extra points.

MISSION PERFORMANCE RATING:

55 – 80 points **Superior:** Gee, you're so smart you could be an android!

50 – 54 points **Above Average:** Samuel Clemens is *your* pen name?

40 – 49 points **Average:** Starfleet got you a job at the Sisters of Hope Infirmary.

30 – 39 points **Fair:** You stole the wrong cane! Go back and get the other one.

0 – 29 points **Poor:** Report to Sisters of Hopelessness Infirmary for an exam!

REALM OF FEAR

STARDATE: 48041.1

The *Enterprise* checks on a Federation science vessel studying a remote plasma streamer. The away team finds everybody either dead or missing. Lieutenant Barclay sees a wormlike creature in the matter stream as he beams back to the *Enterprise*. The creature floats up to Barclay and bites his arm just as he rematerializes on the ship. Barclay's arm later has a bluish glow to it.

Data and Geordi determine that the science vessel crew beamed aboard a plasma sample to study it. During a scan of the sample, life forms in the plasma reacted violently and caused an explosion. The blast knocked out the computer and exposed the crew to high-energy plasma and the organisms living in it. Geordi and O'Brien modify the transporter to screen out the plasma organisms in Barclay's arm. While suspended in the matter stream, Barclay sees more of the wormlike creatures. He quickly grabs one as it comes closer to him. Barclay then rematerializes with a member of the science vessel in his arms. A security team rescues several more crew members from the matter stream. The science vessel crew were also trying to remove the plasma organisms from their bodies but became trapped in the matter stream.

TRIVIA QUESTIONS

1. What damage did the explosion do to the science vessel? **(3pts)**
2. Where did the explosion on the science vessel originate? **(3pts)**
3. Why is it unlikely the science vessel crew abandoned their ship? **(3pts)**
4. How long does Geordi have to suspend Barclay in the matter stream? **(4pts)**
5. What type of life forms are living in the distortion field of the plasma streamer? **(4pts)**
6. Why didn't the biofilters initially screen out the new life forms? **(3pts)**
7. What hasn't there been a case of in over 50 years? **(3pts)**
8. How many years has O'Brien been working with transporters? **(5pts)**
9. How long were the legs on the hook spiders O'Brien saw? **(3pts)**
10. What other situation occurring in the sector does Starfleet apprise Picard of? **(4pts)**

TRANSPORTER PSYCHOSIS (1pt each)

Match the symptoms with the correct type.

Symptoms	Type of Symptom
1. tactile hallucinations	A. primary symptom
2. acute myopia	B. peripheral symptom
3. muscular spasms in the extremities	C. not a symptom

---

4. paranoid delusions
5. psychogenic hysteria
6. sleeplessness
7. visual hallucinations
8. fever
9. dehydration
10. multi-infarct dementia
11. difficulty breathing
12. accelerated heart rate

✪ SPECIAL ASSIGNMENT (15pts)

In what year was transporter psychosis first diagnosed?

ANSWERS

TRIVIA ANSWERS

1. destroyed the ship's computer core memory
2. in the centre of the transport chamber
3. the escape pods haven't been used
4. 30–40 seconds
5. quasi-energy microbes
6. because the microbes exist simultaneously as both matter and energy
7. transporter psychosis
8. 22 years
9. half a metre long
10. the Ferengi claim that two of their freighters were destroyed by a Cardassian warship

TRANSPORTER PSYCHOSIS ANSWERS

1. A primary symptom; 2. B peripheral symptom;
3. B peripheral symptom; 4. A primary symptom;
5. A primary symptom; 6. B peripheral symptom;
7. A primary symptom; 8. C not a symptom;
9. B peripheral symptom; 10. A primary symptom;
11. C not a symptom; 12. B peripheral symptom

SPECIAL ASSIGNMENT SOLUTION

2209 *Congratulations! Starfleet Command is proud to award you the Starfleet Medal of Honour and 15 extra points.*

MISSION PERFORMANCE RATING:

44 – 62 points **Superior:** Keep up the good work. You'll soon be an admiral!

40 – 43 points **Above Average:** You're not scared of worms.

30 – 39 points **Average:** Just close your eyes in the transporter matter stream.

20 – 29 points **Fair:** Seeing worms are you? That doesn't surprise me.

0 – 19 points **Poor:** Your brain's still trapped in the transporter matter stream!

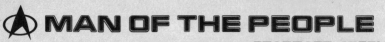
The *Enterprise* renders aid to a transport ship under attack. The Captain requests that the *Enterprise* transports an important mediator who is on his way to nearby peace talks. Picard agrees to the request and beams aboard the Ambassador and his mother. The Ambassador's mother dies several days later and Dr Crusher is at a loss to explain the death. Troi participates in a meditation with the grieving Ambassador.

Almost immediately Troi begins to act strangely. She soon becomes a jealous wretch. Her physical condition also deteriorates as she quickly ages. Dr Crusher soon discovers similarities between Troi and the Ambassador's mother. The Ambassador explains to Picard that he uses people to dump his negative emotions into so that he can stay focused and calm during his negotiations. Picard tells him to break his link with Troi but the Ambassador refuses, saying one life is worth sacrificing for the sake of peace.

After Picard returns to the *Enterprise,* Dr Crusher suggests killing Troi to break the link between her and the Ambassador. Picard gives Dr Crusher the go-ahead and Troi is killed. The Ambassador is forced to seek another link with someone else. Troi is revived by Dr Crusher and the next intended victim beamed to safety. The Ambassador is instantly overwhelmed by the negative emotions coming back from Troi. With nowhere to dump the negative emotions, the Ambassador quickly ages and dies. Troi returns to normal.

TRIVIA QUESTIONS

1. The autopsy revealed Maylor's body systems to be those of what? **(3pts)**
2. For how long after she dies can Dr Crusher resuscitate Troi? **(3pts)**
3. On what deck are the Ambassador's quarters located? **(3pts)**
4. When did Troi die and from what, according to Dr Crusher? **(3pts)**
5. What is Troi's blood pressure reported to be after she is resuscitated? **(4pts)**
6. What are Troi's neurotransmitter levels first reported at? **(4pts)**
7. What's wrong with the turbolift that Riker escorts Troi to directly from Ten-Forward? **(5pts)**
8. What drug does Dr Crusher order given to Maylor? **(4pts)**
9. How old did the Ambassador say his 'mother' was? **(3pts)**
10. Who is the first crew member on the evaluation list? **(3pts)**

✪ SPECIAL ASSIGNMENT (15pts)

What variance is considered within specifications concerning routine diagnostics on the sensor pallets?

MULTIPLE CHOICE QUESTIONS

1. What will be Troi's reward for finishing the crew evaluations? **(2pts)**
    A. a soothing bath
    B. a chocolate fudge sundae
    C. two ice cream sundaes
    D. a one-night stand with an ensign

2. What does Troi dread doing with Riker? **(2pts)**
    A. explaining the claw marks on his face
    B. doing the crew evaluation reports
    C. becoming old and grey
    D. confronting the Ambassador

3. How did Dr Crusher know that Maylor was not the Ambassador's mother? **(3pts)**
    A. they had different last names
    B. Maylor told her she wasn't his mother
    C. no family resemblance between the two
    D. their DNA didn't match

4. How long after Maylor joined the *Enterprise* did she die? **(3pts)**
    A. three days
    B. two days
    C. the next morning
    D. 56 hours

5. Where did Dr Crusher find high levels of neurotransmitter residue in Maylor's brain? **(5pts)**
    A. medulla oblongata
    B. cerebral cortex
    C. frontal lobe
    D. isocortex

ANSWERS

TRIVIA ANSWERS

1. a 30-year-old woman
2. up to 30 minutes
3. Deck 9
4. she died at 14:30 hours from respiratory and renal failure
5. 90/40
6. 300% above normal
7. The door identifies the location as Deck 8 but Ten-Forward is on Deck 10
8. 40cc inaprovaline
9. 93 years old
10. Lieutenant Jeffrey Fraytis

SPECIAL ASSIGNMENT SOLUTION

a variance of .023

Congratulations! Starfleet Command is proud to award you the Starfleet Medal of Honour and 15 extra points.

MULTIPLE CHOICE ANSWERS

1. C. two ice cream sundaes
2. B. doing the crew evaluation reports
3. D. their DNA didn't match
4. A. three days (Dr Crusher says when comparing biofilter logs and tricorder readings on body)
5. B. cerebral cortex

MISSION PERFORMANCE RATING:

45 – 65 points **Superior:** How come you're such a good negotiator?

40 – 44 points **Above Average:** Nice cease-fire, Ambassador!

30 – 39 points **Average:** You have an emotional maelstrom inside you.

20 – 29 points **Fair:** Say, you don't look a day over 95!

0 – 19 points **Poor:** Here, take this piece of moon rock and repeat after me.

The *Enterprise* discovers a Dyson sphere while searching for the long lost Federation ship, the *USS Jenolen*. Upon closer scrutiny, the *Jenolen* is found crashed on the outer surface of the sphere. On board the *Jenolen*, Geordi finds a viable pattern still in the transporter and activates the device. Montgomery Scott appears as a modern day Rip Van Winkle. The away team returns to the *Enterprise* with Scotty so Dr Crusher can tend to his injuries. Scotty is in awe of the technological improvements that have been made. He tries to help Geordi in Engineering but feels inadequate. Picard gives Scotty something to do by sending him back to the *Jenolen* with Geordi to retrieve the ship's logs.

Data locates an entryway into the sphere. As the *Enterprise* opens a hailing frequency, the doors open and tractor beams pull the ship inside. Meanwhile, Geordi tries to communicate with the *Enterprise* and discovers the ship is missing. Scotty and Geordi are able to patch the *Jenolen* up and get it running. The *Jenolen* traces the *Enterprise*'s path up to the entryway. Keeping a safe distance, Scotty and Geordi trigger the door mechanism to open the entryway. They use the *Jenolen*'s shields to hold the door open until the *Enterprise* can fly out. Picard transports Geordi and Scotty out at the last moment and destroys the *Jenolen* to allow the *Enterprise* enough space to fly through.

TRIVIA QUESTIONS

1. What hasn't changed much in 200 years? **(3pts)**
2. What does Riker compare the size of the Dyson sphere to? **(3pts)**
3. What does Scotty bet Geordi that the *Enterprise* is inside the Dyson sphere? **(5pts)**
4. What does Guinan keep in Ten-Forward? **(3pts)**
5. How could Scotty tell how fast the original *Enterprise* was travelling? **(3pts)**
6. What is at the centre of the Dyson sphere? **(3pts)**
7. What planet was Scotty's original destination? **(4pts)**
8. What caused the *Jenolen*'s warp engines to fail? **(4pts)**
9. What exploded on the *Jenolen* as they completed their initial orbital scan? **(4pts)**
10. What component did isolinear chips replace? **(3pts)**

✪✪ SIGNIFICANT NUMBERS (1pt each)

Match the clues with the correct number.

Clues
1. How many years ago was the *Jenolen* reported missing?
2. How many kilometres from the Dyson sphere does the *Jenolen* stay, when the doors open?
3. What percentage signal degradation is there in Scotty's pattern?
4. By what percentage has the second pattern degraded in the pattern buffer?
5. What is the interior surface area of the Dyson sphere in square kilometres?
6. What is the diameter of the Dyson sphere in million kilometres?
7. Which starbase does the *Enterprise* head to after leaving the Dyson sphere?
8. How many million kilometres is the *Enterprise* from the star's photosphere when the ship is first pulled into the Dyson sphere?
9. After the *Enterprise* establishes an orbit around the star, how many kilometres are they from it?
10. How many ships has Scotty served aboard?
11. The location of the antenna array on the sphere is _____ kilometres south of the *Enterprise*'s present position.
12. The interior surface area of the Dyson sphere is equivalent to how many million class-M planets?
13. How many years has Scotty been an engineer?
14. When does Picard want the spectrographic analysis done by?
15. How old is Scotty, according to Dr Crusher?

Numbers
A. 53
B. 150,000
C. 55
D. 400,000
E. 500,000
F. 52
G. 1300
H. 10^{16}
I. 90
J. 250
K. 75
L. 147
M. 200
N. 11
O. .003

ANSWERS

TRIVIA ANSWERS

1. impulse engines
2. he says it's almost as large as the Earth's orbit around the sun
3. two bottles of scotch
4. a limited supply of non-syntheholic products
5. by the feel of the deck plates
6. a G-type star
7. Norpin V
8. an overload in one of the plasma transfer conduits
9. aft power coils
10. duotronic enhancers

SIGNIFICANT NUMBERS ANSWERS

1. K 75; 2. E 500,000; 3. O .003; 4. A 53; 5. H 10^{16}; 6. M 200;
7. C 55; 8. I 90; 9. B 150,000; 10. N 11; 11. D 400,000; 12. J 250;
13. F 52; 14. G 300; 15. L 147

MISSION PERFORMANCE RATING:

30 – 50 points	**Superior:** *You* beamed Geordi and Scotty through the shields!
25 – 29 points	**Above Average:** Compute the surface area of the sphere in cm^2.
20 – 24 points	**Average:** Your mission is to survey the sphere . . . on foot!
10 – 19 points	**Fair:** Sorry, there was a fly in the transporter with you and . . .
0 – 9 points	**Poor:** You're suffering from a wee bit of signal degradation.

Riker, having difficulty sleeping, becomes haggard as the *Enterprise* begins charting a dense globular cluster. Riker later experiences a flashback and tells Troi about it. Several other crew members have also reported vague recollections and having strange reactions to everyday objects. Troi gathers some of them on the holodeck. There they reconstruct a strange looking examination table from their shared memories.

A spatial rupture develops in one of the cargo bays. The instability doesn't appear to be a naturally occurring phenomenon; it is controlled from deep within subspace. Geordi thinks his modifications to the sensor array may have attracted someone's attention. The rupture continues to grow in size, threatening to breach the *Enterprise*'s hull. Geordi determines that a graviton pulse will close the spatial rupture, but he must first know the source of the signal. Riker dons a homing device in the hopes that the aliens will again take him to their laboratory in subspace.

That night, Riker is abducted by the aliens. Geordi is able to get a fix on Riker's position and begins firing the graviton pulse. Riker grabs a crew member from another examination table and jumps through the rift moments before it closes.

TRIVIA QUESTIONS

1. What does Riker ask Geordi to do at 07:00 hours? **(3pts)**
2. What is the title of Data's ninth poem? **(3pts)**
3. How long will the neural stimulant work? **(3pts)**
4. What did Geordi do to Riker's tricorder? **(3pts)**
5. What is the name of the unusually dense globular cluster that the *Enterprise* is charting? **(4pts)**
6. Riker's skeletal structure in his radius and ulna is offset by how much? **(4pts)**
7. How many classifications of tables can the holodeck computer recreate? **(5pts)**
8. What does Geordi have around his neural inputs? **(3pts)**
9. How much of the cluster will the *Enterprise* be able to map in three days? **(3pts)**
10. What style of poetic metre did Data write his eighth poem in? **(4pts)**

HOLODECK WORKSHOP 101 (3pts each)

Match the modifications with the correct holodeck participant.

Modifications
1. Who says it was a long table?
2. Who decreases the table's height by 25%?
3. Who remembers a chest restraint?
4. Who inclines the table's top by 15°?
5. Who tells the computer to create a restraining arm attached to the right side of the table at midpoint?
6. Who decreases the table's surface area by 20%?
7. Who attaches a pair of scissors to the armature?
8. Who says it was a rectangular table?
9. Who says the sounds were more like clicks?
10. Who says the table was smoother and not made of wood?
11. Who says one blade curved inward?
12. Who asks the computer to show a rectangular conference table?
13. Who makes the scissors' handle a single piece grip 10cm long and made of solid metal?
14. Who says the room sounds were louder, faster, and had more clicking noises?
15. Who changes the table to metal?

Holodeck Participant
A. Troi
B. Worf
C. Riker
D. Geordi
E. woman

SPECIAL ASSIGNMENT (10pts)

Where is the subspace homing signal coming from?

ANSWERS

TRIVIA ANSWERS

1. stop by his quarters
2. 'Ode to Spot'
3. 12 hours
4. locked it into a continuous cycle so it will record whether he opens it or not
5. Amargosa Diaspora
6. .02 microns
7. 5,047
8. a slight bacterial infection
9. 1/10
10. anapaestic tetrametre

HOLODECK WORKSHOP 101 ANSWERS

1. E woman; 2. D Geordi; 3. C Riker; 4. B Worf; 5. A Troi;
6. B Worf; 7. B Worf; 8. D Geordi; 9 E woman; 10. C Riker;
11. B Worf; 12. A Troi; 13. B Worf; 14. C Riker; 15. A Troi

SPECIAL ASSIGNMENT SOLUTION

a subspace energy level of 16.2 KEB
Congratulations! Starfleet Command is proud to award you the Starfleet Medal of Honour and 10 extra points.

MISSION PERFORMANCE RATING:

70 – 90 points **Superior:** Your sensor modifications would never attract aliens.

60 – 69 points **Above Average:** Good job on sealing the spatial rupture.

40 – 59 points **Average:** Oh no! The aliens have turned your stomach into jelly!

20 – 39 points **Fair:** Your brain has been surgically reattached backwards.

0 – 19 points **Poor:** MIA: You were trapped on the other side of the spatial rift!

The *Enterprise* is preparing for a major relief effort to assist the planet Tagra IV. A young medical intern named Amanda Rogers joins the crew. Although she appears human, she soon demonstrates Q-like powers. Amanda saves Riker's life in the cargo bay and contains an explosion in Engineering. Q appears during a staff meeting and explains who Amanda really is. Q says her parents were from the Continuum but decided to take human form. Q's mission is to determine if Amanda is a Q or a hybrid of human and Q qualities.

Meanwhile, the *Enterprise* arrives at Tagra IV where the situation is deteriorating. Geordi beams down to assist in stabilizing the Tagrans' reactor. Q continues to study Amanda and shows her how to focus her powers. Data discovers that the Continuum destroyed Amanda's parents when they would not return.

Q is convinced that Amanda is truly Q and gives her the choice of joining the Continuum or refraining from using her powers. Amanda chooses to stay but is unable to prevent herself using her powers to resolve Tagra IV's problem. Amanda realizes that she should return to the Continuum and leaves with Q.

TRIVIA QUESTIONS

1. How old is Amanda? **(3pts)**
2. What type of accident occurs in Engineering? **(3pts)**
3. When did Jack Crusher die? **(4pts)**
4. What do Amanda's adoptive parents do? **(4pts)**
5. What are the contaminant levels after Amanda cleans the Tagran atmosphere? **(5pts)**
6. Who is taking Amanda out to dinner? **(3pts)**
7. What does Q turn Dr Crusher into? **(3pts)**
8. When did Amanda first begin to notice she had special powers? **(3pts)**
9. What happens when Q tries to take Amanda back to the Continuum after first meeting her? **(3pts)**
10. How many light and dark puppies appear in Amanda's quarters? **(4pts)**

CHARACTER QUOTE
(2pts per word + 4pts for identifying the speaker.)

Unscramble the words below and then identify the character.

'___ ___ ___ ___ ___ ___ ___ ___.'

SREUCRH TGSE RMEO LHLRSI TWHI CEHA SNPGSIA AYRE

⭐ SPECIAL ASSIGNMENT (15pts)

What type of fish does Q admire in Picard's aquarium?

ANSWERS

TRIVIA ANSWERS

1. 18 years old
2. warp core breach
3. when Wesley was five years old
4. marine biologists
5. less than one part per trillion
6. Dr Crusher and Troi
7. an Irish setter
8. about six months ago
9. she flings him into a corner of the room
10. five light and five dark puppies

CHARACTER QUOTE SOLUTION

'Crusher gets more shrill with each passing year.' – Q

SPECIAL ASSIGNMENT SOLUTION

Australian lionfish

Congratulations! Starfleet Command is proud to award you the Starfleet Medal of Honour and 15 extra points.

MISSION PERFORMANCE RATING:

50 – 70 points **Superior:** You're so smart you could join the Q Continuum.

45 – 59 points **Above Average:** You must be Q's understudy.

40 – 44 points **Average:** Q turned you into a Markoffian sea lizard.

30 – 39 points **Fair:** You definitely don't have any Q powers.

0 – 29 points **Poor:** No one will ever accuse you of being a Q!

Picard, Keiko, Ro, and Guinan, returning to the *Enterprise* on a shuttlecraft, encounter a strange energy field. The four occupants must be evacuated before the craft explodes. Upon rematerialization on the transporter pads, all four have regressed to childhood.

The *Enterprise* responds to a distress call. Just after arriving, two Klingon ships decloak and attack the *Enterprise*. The shields fail and the *Enterprise* is boarded by Ferengi. Riker is able to lock out all computer functions before the Ferengi takeover the bridge. All adults are beamed to the planet's surface; only Riker and the children remain onboard.

Picard, Keiko, Ro, and Guinan plot to retake the ship. Picard is able to see Riker and give him a message. Riker returns control of the computer to a terminal Picard can access. The 'children' then use the ship's transporter to round up the Ferengi and contain them. The *Enterprise* is retaken and the Ferengi arrested. Later, Dr Crusher uses the transporter to return Picard, Keiko, Ro, and Guinan to their respective ages.

TRIVIA QUESTIONS

1. Approximately how old are Picard and the others? **(3pts)**
2. What does the young Picard order while talking to Dr Crusher in his ready room? **(3pts)**
3. What does Picard tell Dr Crusher to convert Shuttlebay 3 into? **(3pts)**
4. What colour crayon does Guinan ask Ro for? **(4pts)**
5. What is the crew complement of the *Enterprise*? **(3pts)**
6. Which ship's system is initially damaged when the *Enterprise* is attacked? **(3pts)**
7. How many years has Picard been on starships? **(3pts)**
8. How old are the artefacts Picard recovered during his shore leave? **(4pts)**
9. What makes O'Brien think he lost someone while beaming the occupants out of the shuttle? **(4pts)**
10. The artefacts Picard found on the tertiary level of the dig are examples of what? **(5pts)**

WHO AM I? (25pts)

I am the Pied Piper but I have no flute, for remoteness is my ally. I steal the means to administer justice to the foemen, but I willingly give a bit of gold to see them go.

SPECIAL ASSIGNMENT (10pts)

What four numerals are written on the side of the plant container Keiko is carrying on the shuttlecraft?

ANSWERS

TRIVIA ANSWERS

1. 12 years old; 2. tea, Earl Grey, hot; 3. a triage centre for any wounded science team members; 4. royal blue; 5. 1,014; 6. Primary Life Support; 7. 30 years; 8. 700 years old; 9. there was a 40% drop in mass; 10. 2nd century Marlonian cookware

WHO AM I? SOLUTION

Alexander

EXPLANATION:

I am the Pied Piper but I have no flute, – Alexander used his toy to lead the Ferengi down the corridor.

for remoteness is my ally, – Alexander's toy was remote controlled and he was safely out of sight.

I steal the means to administer justice to the foemen, – Alexander stole some hyposprays from sickbay. Keiko used one to sedate a Ferengi.

but I willingly give a bit of gold to see them go. – Alexander gave a com badge to the Ferengi who was then transported away. Gold is a component of the insignia communicator.

SPECIAL ASSIGNMENT SOLUTION

0520

Congratulations! Starfleet Command is proud to award you the Starfleet Medal of Honour and 10 extra points.

MISSION PERFORMANCE RATING:

36 – 70 points **Superior:** You single-handedly saved the *Enterprise*.

30 – 35 points **Above Average:** You must have been a child prodigy.

20 – 29 points **Average:** You can only use the kids' computers from now on!

10 – 19 points **Fair:** Even the Ferengi did better than this!

0 – 9 points **Poor:** Go play with Alexander's toy spaceship.

A FISTFUL OF DATAS ⟨⧉⟩

STARDATE: 46271.5 ━━━━━━━━━

The *Enterprise* crew enjoy a brief layover between missions. Worf joins his son, Alexander, and Troi for a holodeck adventure set in the Ancient West. At the same time, Geordi is testing a new interface between Data and the ship's computer. A power surge in Data's neural net affects several secondary systems including the holodecks. Worf and the others are unable to access the main computer to control the holodeck programme.

The villains in the holoprogramme take on Data's appearance. Worf is injured and realizes that the holodeck is not functioning properly. Alexander is captured by the bad guys and will be swapped for the lead villain's son who is in Worf's jail. Worf knows he's no match for a holodeck character with Data's speed and accuracy. Luckily, he is able to fashion a small force field generator using his communicator. During the prisoner exchange, the villain pulls out his gun and fires at Worf. The bullets bounce harmlessly off the force field. Worf is then able to disarm the villain and banish him from the town. Geordi, meanwhile, has initiated corrective measures to restore Data and the main computer to normal. The holodeck programme ends and Worf, Alexander, and Troi are able to leave.

TRIVIA QUESTIONS

1. Where will Frank be for the prisoner exchange? **(3pts)**
2. What does Geordi use to restore Data's programming and fix the ship's computer? **(3pts)**
3. How much is Eli worth dead or alive? **(3pts)**
4. What is the name of Dr Crusher's current production? **(3pts)**
5. What music selection does the computer play for Picard instead of Mozart? **(5pts)**
6. Whose work was Data recently studying? **(4pts)**
7. What does Data order from the replicator for Spot? **(4pts)**
8. Where does Annie think Worf is seeing another woman from? **(3pts)**
9. What type of dessert did Annie make for Worf? **(4pts)**
10. How many men has Eli killed? **(3pts)**

SPECIAL ASSIGNMENT (10pts)

What poem does Riker start reciting from and in which episode did Data read it?

MULTIPLE CHOICE QUESTIONS

1. The affected computer programme controls what three functions? **(5pts)**
   A. gravitational control, recreational programming, and auxiliary life support
   B. library computer access, replicator selection, and recreational programming
   C. solid waste recycling, gravitational control, and turbolift control
   D. turbolift control, recreational programming, library computer access

2. How long does Worf think his force field generator will last? **(3pts)**
   A. 45 seconds
   B. long enough
   C. 30 seconds
   D. 15 seconds

3. What state is the holographic town in? **(3pts)**
   A. South Dakota
   B. Wyoming
   C. Nebraska
   D. North Dakota

4. Eli is known as what? **(2pts)**
   A. The Killer of Billings
   B. The Butcher of Bozeman
   C. The Chef of Barcelona
   D. The Butcher of Bohemia

5. How does Picard describe Dr Crusher's latest play? **(2pts)**
   A. a breathtaking thriller
   B. an intriguing drama
   C. a real snoozer
   D. a brilliantly plotted mystery

ANSWERS

TRIVIA ANSWERS

1. in front of the livery stable
2. a progressive memory purge
3. $5,000
4. *Something For Breakfast*
5. *The Slavonic Dances*
6. Antonín Dvořák
7. Feline Supplement 127
8. Miss Langford's House of Pleasure
9. gooseberry cobbler
10. 23

SPECIAL ASSIGNMENT SOLUTION

'Ode to Spot' from the episode 'Schisms'

Congratulations! Starfleet Command is proud to award you the Starfleet Medal of Honour and 10 extra points.

MULTIPLE CHOICE ANSWERS

1. B. library computer access, replicator selection, and recreational programming
2. D. 15 seconds
3. A. South Dakota
4. B. The Butcher of Bozeman
5. B. an intriguing drama

MISSION PERFORMANCE RATING:

45 – 60 points **Superior:** You figured out the progressive memory purge!

40 – 44 points **Above Average:** You could outshoot Frank at any level.

30 – 39 points **Average:** You thought the replicator food tasted great!

20 – 29 points **Fair:** You thought Frank was an honourable man who kept his word.

0 – 19 points **Poor:** Your force field generator gave out after five seconds.

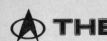

THE QUALITY OF LIFE
STARDATE: 46307.2

The *Enterprise* evaluates a new mining technology at an orbiting station. Geordi beams over and finds the project rife with technical problems. Dr Farallon, the project director, has developed several robotic tools known as exocomps to assist in performing difficult tasks. After an explosion, Data determines that an exocomp refused to perform a task as an act of self-preservation. Data concludes that the exocomps are a new life form.

Picard tours the station when another accident occurs and he and Geordi are trapped. Dr Farallon wants to send the exocomps to stabilize the situation long enough to beam Picard and Geordi out. Data maintains it is wrong to sacrifice one life form for another. Riker agrees to allow the exocomps to choose whether or not to go on the mission. The exocomps accept and beam down. Through their efforts, Picard and Geordi are able to beam safely off the station.

TRIVIA QUESTIONS

1. What is wild during the poker hand Dr Crusher deals? **(3pts)**
2. Dr Crusher has always been suspicious of whom? **(3pts)**
3. What tools do the exocomps create before beaming down to the station? **(4pts)**
4. Once Dr Farallon watched an exocomp do what? **(3pts)**
5. What did Data simulate in a small conduit breach? **(5pts)**
6. To master the bat'leth, what must Dr Crusher do? **(3pts)**
7. What is ready to be sealed in one of the access tunnels? **(3pts)**
8. What did the exocomp activate at 13:40 hours? **(4pts)**
9. What is the basis of the exocomp? **(4pts)**
10. What do the men have to do if Dr Crusher wins the poker hand? **(3pts)**

✪✪ MATHEMATICALLY SPEAKING (15pts)

Answer A to C and then insert the numbers into the formula to solve this problem.

A. The original plans called for the particle fountain to lift how many kilograms per minute of material from the planet's surface? **(3pts)**
B. How many minutes before Geordi's force field collapses on the station? **(3pts)**
C. How many years has Dr Farallon been working on the particle fountain project? **(3pts)**

$A + (B \times C) = D$
What is the significance of your answer (D) in relation to the episode? **(6pts)**

ANSWERS

TRIVIA ANSWERS

1. one-eyed jacks
2. men wearing beards
3. power taps
4. enter a reaction chamber and vaporize itself
5. a plasma cascade failure in progress
6. she must learn to strike and avoid in the same motion
7. plasma conduit
8. a self repair programme
9. a common industrial servomechanism
10. shave their beards

MATHEMATICALLY SPEAKING SOLUTION

A. 500
B. 22
C. 6
$500 + (22 \times 6) = 632$
In the exocomp Data examines, the number of new circuit pathways in Section Gamma-4 has increased by 632%.

MISSION PERFORMANCE RATING:

30 – 50 points **Superior:** You're not going to let the exocomps get in your way.

25 – 29 points **Above Average:** Starfleet mining engineer, huh?

20 – 24 points **Average:** Crawl inside the access tunnel and fix the plasma leak.

10 – 19 points **Fair:** The exocomps are mad at you and they've got phasers.

0 – 9 points **Poor:** The exocomps voted not to help you on the station.

CHAIN OF COMMAND
– PART I

STARDATE: 46357.4

Picard goes on a special mission for Starfleet and Captain Jellico assumes command of the *Enterprise*. The Cardassians are suspected of preparing for an incursion into Federation space over some disputed systems. Jellico heads a diplomatic mission aimed at defusing the situation. Jellico proves to be very demanding on the *Enterprise* crew as they strive to adjust to their new captain.

Meanwhile, Picard leads a special away team that includes Worf and Dr Crusher. They travel to a remote planet and infiltrate a secret Cardassian base. The base is supposed to be the site of a devastating new biological weapon that the Cardassians are developing. Picard soon realizes it's a trap and signals a hasty retreat. Cardassians suddenly appear and Picard is captured in the ensuing fight. Picard is transferred to a detention centre where a Cardassian prepares to interrogate him.

TRIVIA QUESTIONS

1. What runs for 75 metres beyond the rock wall? **(3pts)**
2. What are used to create anchor points for rappelling? **(4pts)**
3. How current is the Starfleet intelligence concerning the Cardassian installation? **(3pts)**
4. What phaser level does Worf use to cut through solid rock? **(3pts)**
5. How deep is the crevasse Picard's team must rappel down? **(3pts)**
6. What has Jellico done to ⅓ of Geordi's Engineering crew? **(3pts)**
7. What will be required to improve warp coil efficiency by 15%? **(5pts)**
8. When does Jellico want to have his first senior staff meeting as captain of the *Enterprise*? **(4pts)**
9. What did Jellico do two years ago? **(3pts)**
10. When will the change of command ceremony take place on the *Enterprise*? **(4pts)**

✪ SPECIAL ASSIGNMENT (15pts)

Where are Jellico's quarters on the *Enterprise*?

MULTIPLE CHOICE QUESTIONS

1. What does Starfleet think the Cardassians are planning to do? **(2pts)**
    A. start a full scale war
    B. use disinformation to lure Picard to a desolate planet, detain him and proceed to torture him
    C. seize one of the disputed star systems along the border
    D. prepare to have routine training operations

2. Where does Jellico meet with Gul Lemec? **(2pts)**
    A. observation lounge
    B. diplomatic conference room
    C. Ten-Forward
    D. ready room

3. What are metagenic weapons? **(3pts)**
    A. selectively bred viruses that can wipe out an entire species within weeks
    B. genetically engineered viruses that can destroy whole ecosystems within a few days
    C. triolic wave based weapons that destroy all life after prolonged exposure
    D. microscopic nanites that seek out and kill only life forms they are programmed to harm

4. Name three areas that would be affected by the secondary distribution grid going off-line. **(5pts)**
    A. arboretum, geophysical labs, and exobotany
    B. cartography, biomedical labs, and exobiology
    C. exobiology, astrophysics lab, and geological research
    D. Cargo Bay 4, junior officers' quarters, and cartography

5. What tasks does Jellico want Science Stations I and II dedicated to? **(3pts)**
    A. sensor logistics and secondary engineering control
    B. damage control and weapons status
    C. auxiliary power status and environmental control
    D. ship repairs and logistics

ANSWERS

TRIVIA ANSWERS

1. lava tube
2. fusing pitons
3. two years old
4. level 16
5. over 500 metres
6. transferred them to security
7. realigning the warp coil and taking the secondary distribution grid offline
8. 15:00 hours
9. he helped to negotiate the original armistice between the Federation and Cardassians
10. 13:00 hours

SPECIAL ASSIGNMENT SOLUTION

Cabin 735 on Deck 7
Congratulations! Starfleet Command is proud to award you the Starfleet Medal of Honour and 15 extra points.

MULTIPLE CHOICE ANSWERS

1. C. seize one of the disputed star systems along the border
2. A. observation lounge
3. B. genetically engineered viruses that can destroy whole ecosystems within a few days
4. C. exobiology, astrophysics lab, and geological research
5. B. damage control and weapons status

MISSION PERFORMANCE RATING:

45 – 65 points **Superior:** Metagenic weapons, yeah right.

40 – 44 points **Above Average:** You knew it was a trap to start with.

30 – 39 points **Average:** Rescue mission is on the way. Hang in there!

20 – 29 points **Fair:** What is your serial number?

0 – 19 points **Poor:** You know nothing! You're not even worth interrogating!

CHAIN OF COMMAND ⌖
– PART II

STARDATE: 46360.8

Picard is interrogated by a Cardassian known as Gul Madred. Madred is trying to learn Starfleet's plans for defending the contested area of Federation space that the Cardassians are preparing to invade. Picard tells him nothing about Starfleet's plans because he doesn't know what they are. Gul Madred tries to elicit the needed information through torture. Picard is fitted with a pain producing device in the Gul's effort to break Picard's spirit.

Meanwhile, the talks continue between Jellico and the Cardassians. The Cardassians provide evidence that they have Picard in their possession and want Jellico to admit that Picard was acting under Starfleet orders. Jellico denies any Starfleet involvement and refuses to negotiate for his release.

The *Enterprise* crew determines the Cardassian invasion force is hiding in a nearby nebula and they mine it. Jellico is then able to negotiate the safe return of Picard and the surrender of the Cardassians. Picard returns to active duty as captain of the *Enterprise*.

TRIVIA QUESTIONS

1. What must each Cardassian ship eject as it emerges from the nebula? **(3pts)**
2. Where did Jellico first start as a shuttle pilot? **(3pts)**
3. How many mines does Jellico want sown in the nebula? **(3pts)**
4. Which mine does Jellico make Worf detonate as a warning? **(5pts)**
5. How close to the Cardassian ships do the mines need to be laid? **(3pts)**
6. How many Cardassians did Picard's team supposedly kill? **(4pts)**
7. Where is the closest molecular dispersion field that could have affected Gul Lemec's vessel? **(4pts)**
8. What is Gul Madred's daughter's name? **(3pts)**
9. The burial vaults of which ancient civilization can still be viewed on Cardassia? **(4pts)**
10. When were the ancient ruins on Cardassia first uncovered? **(3pts)**

CHARACTER QUOTE
(3pts per word + 4pts for identifying the speaker.)

Unscramble the words below and then identify the character.

'_____ has _____ _____ a _____ _____
EUOTRRT   ENVRE EBNE   EBIRLLEA ASNME
of _____ _____.'
   CGTTENXRIA NIRMTFOIANO

ANSWERS

TRIVIA ANSWERS

1. primary phaser coil
2. Jovian run
3. 500
4. Alpha 42
5. within two kilometres
6. over 55
7. McAllister C-5 Nebula
8. Jil Orra
9. the First Hebitian
10. 200 years ago

CHARACTER QUOTE SOLUTION

'Torture has never been a reliable means of extracting information.' – Picard

SPECIAL ASSIGNMENT SOLUTION

31

Congratulations! Starfleet Command is proud to award you the Starfleet Medal of Honour and 15 extra points.

MISSION PERFORMANCE RATING:

55 – 75 points	**Superior:**	CAUTION: Soon to be Admiral.
50 – 54 points	**Above Average:**	Laid mines before, huh? Good job!
40 – 49 points	**Average:**	Would you like a Taspar egg? They're very good.
30 – 39 points	**Fair:**	Jellico wants to see you; something about incompetence.
0 – 29 points	**Poor:**	You need to be strung up by your thumbs and twirled.

SHIP IN A BOTTLE Ⓐ

While Lieutenant Barclay is troubleshooting a minor glitch with the holodeck, Professor Moriarty appears (see 'Elementary, My Dear Data'). Moriarty is upset that Picard has not kept his promise to find a way for him to leave the holodeck. Picard meets with Moriarty and explains that Starfleet hasn't figured out how to make holodeck matter real. Moriarty decides to try walking off the holodeck and succeeds. What Picard doesn't realize is that Moriarty has programmed the holodeck to simulate the *Enterprise*.

Picard eventually gives his command codes to the 'computer' only to discover Moriarty's ruse. Moriarty then seizes control of the *Enterprise* and demands that Riker find a way to allow him to leave the holodeck. Picard and the others programme their own version of the *Enterprise* on the holodeck. A simulated Riker gives in to Moriarty, beams him off the holodeck and lets him leave in a shuttlecraft. Once he is safely in simulated space, Moriarty returns control of the *Enterprise* to Picard. Picard stores this holodeck simulation in active memory so that Moriarty will think he is experiencing life 'outside' the confines of the holodeck.

TRIVIA QUESTIONS

1. What does Moriarty do to convince Riker to help find a way for him to leave the holodeck? **(3pts)**
2. Is Moriarty right- or left-handed? **(3pts)**
3. What are Moriarty's command codes? **(5pts)**
4. What is the name of the simulated programme that Moriarty and the Countess are kept alive in? **(4pts)**
5. Which transport log does Data ask the computer to display? **(3pts)**
6. What are Picard's command codes? **(5pts)**
7. Which holodeck is used in this episode? **(3pts)**
8. What is Sherlock Holmes' address? **(3pts)**
9. Is the simulated Geordi right- or left-handed? **(3pts)**
10. Where does Moriarty want to meet Picard the first time? **(3pts)**

✪ SPECIAL ASSIGNMENT (15pts)

Strychnine is derived from the seeds of what plant?

MULTIPLE CHOICE QUESTIONS

1. What is blocking Worf's attempts to reach the holodeck? **(2pts)**
   A. emergency bulkheads
   B. containment fields
   C. force fields
   D. holodeck matter

2. What does Barclay place in the sitting room on Baker Street? **(2pts)**
   A. three pattern enhancers
   B. a leather chair
   C. transporter testing module
   D. two molecular pattern reinforcers

3. When did the Countess go on safari with her uncle? **(3pts)**
   A. after her first wedding
   B. when she was 27 years old
   C. when she was but a child
   D. when she was 17 years old

4. What will the collision of the two planets initiate? **(3pts)**
   A. an explosive chain-reaction
   B. a massive loss of life on the planets
   C. a self-sustaining fusion reaction
   D. a planetary core meltdown

5. Which holodeck program did Data and Geordi use initially? **(5pts)**
   A. La Forge Adventure 7C
   B. Data Holmes programme 12D
   C. Sherlock Holmes programme 3A
   D. Sherlock Holmes programme 21B

ANSWERS

TRIVIA ANSWERS

1. makes the warp core temperature rise to critical levels
2. left-handed
3. Moriarty, Alpha 24159
4. Picard-Delta 1
5. Transport Log 759
6. Picard, Epsilon 793
7. Holodeck 3
8. 221B Baker Street
9. left-handed
10. in the sitting room in Baker Street

SPECIAL ASSIGNMENT SOLUTION

Strychnos nux-vomica

Congratulations! Starfleet Command is proud to award you the Starfleet Medal of Honour and 15 extra points.

MULTIPLE CHOICE ANSWERS

1. C. force fields
2. A. three pattern enhancers
3. D. when she was 17 years old
4. C. a self-sustaining fusion reaction
5. C. Sherlock Holmes programme 3A

MISSION PERFORMANCE RATING:

45 – 65 points **Superior:** At least you know none of this is real!

40 – 44 points **Above Average:** Professor Moriarty I presume.

30 – 39 points **Average:** Are you left- or right-handed?

20 – 29 points **Fair:** You are trapped inside a false reality.

0 – 19 points **Poor:** Don't try to leave the holodeck. You're no Moriarty!

The *Enterprise* makes a routine stop at a communication relay station, but the ship's hails go unanswered. An away team investigates and finds the station deserted with a shuttlecraft missing. They also discover some charred remains and the pet dog of a lieutenant named Aquiel.

Geordi begins investigating Aquiel's station logs, looking for clues to what might have happened. He finds several references to Klingon harassment. Picard contacts the local Klingon governor and asks him to look into the matter. A short time later, the Klingons produce Aquiel, having found her in the shuttlecraft. She says she was attacked by Rocha, the other station officer, but was able to fend him off. Aquiel doesn't seem to remember much after that.

Dr Crusher determines that the charred remains found on the station belong to a coalescent organism. It absorbs its victims and assumes their shape. Rocha had apparently been absorbed by the creature. The coalescent organism then attacked Aquiel in order to assume her body. Dr Crusher places Aquiel and a Klingon who boarded the station under observation to determine which one is the coalescent organism. Soon after, Aquiel's dog turns into a blob of coalescent protoplasm and attacks Geordi. He kills the creature with his phaser.

TRIVIA QUESTIONS

1. How often does the Klingon commander's patrol take him close to the relay station? **(3pts)**
2. How long has Aquiel been stationed at the relay station? **(3pts)**
3. What hasn't there been in more than seven years? **(3pts)**
4. What schedule does Geordi tell the computer to display? **(3pts)**
5. What is the official designation of the relay station? **(4pts)**
6. What is missing from the encrypted message bank? **(4pts)**
7. What is the name of the Klingon governor's ship? **(5pts)**
8. What novel did Aquiel get the name of her dog from? **(4pts)**
9. Aquiel agreed to handle comtraffic from where? **(3pts)**
10. What is very nutritious but is an aquired taste? **(3pts)**

✪ SPECIAL ASSIGNMENT (15pts)

What phaser setting does Geordi use to vaporize the coalescent organism?

MULTIPLE CHOICE QUESTIONS

1. What did Aquiel place a request for at three different times? **(2pts)**
    A. a transfer
    B. extra rations
    C. a message delay buffer
    D. a subspace field inverter

2. What did Aquiel do that was risky? **(4pts)**
    A. countermanded Lieutenant Rocha's order
    B. flew a shuttle into Klingon territory
    C. all of the above and below
    D. fell in love with Geordi
    E. tampered with evidence during a murder investigation

3. Why did the *Enterprise* stop at the relay station? **(2pts)**
    A. to answer their distress signal
    B. to investigate a missing shuttle
    C. to investigate reports of Klingon harassment
    D. to deliver supplies

4. Aquiel's family has lived where? **(4pts)**
    A. all over the sector
    B. in the same city all their lives
    C. on the same planet for four generations
    D. in the same house for five generations

5. What noise does the away team first hear on the relay station? **(3pts)**
    A. a loose panel flapping
    B. several thousand subspace messages playing all at once
    C. a dog barking
    D. a coalescent organism talking to itself

ANSWERS

TRIVIA ANSWERS

1. every six days
2. nine months
3. a Klingon raid against the Federation
4. Engineering Duty Roster for the next three days
5. Relay Station 47
6. 27 priority Starfleet messages
7. Qu'Vat
8. Cold Moon Over Blackwater
9. Relay Station 194
10. Muskan seed punch

SPECIAL ASSIGNMENT SOLUTION

level-10 (Assuming it was properly stored at level-1. He first fired at level-4 and then raised it six levels.)

Congratulations! Starfleet Command is proud to award you the Starfleet Medal of Honour and 15 extra points.

MULTIPLE CHOICE ANSWERS

1. C. a message delay buffer
2. C. all of the above and below
3. D. to deliver supplies
4. D. in the same house for five generations
5. B. several thousand subspace messages playing all at once

MISSION PERFORMANCE RATING:

45 – 65 points   **Superior:** You can spot a coalescent organism a mile away!

40 – 44 points   **Above Average:** Nothing's going to absorb you.

30 – 39 points   **Average:** You could be mistaken for a coalescent organism.

20 – 29 points   **Fair:** A coalescent organism must have drained your memory!

0 – 19 points   **Poor:** Aren't you about due to change bodies? You look horrible!

FACE OF THE ENEMY ⌖

Troi awakens on a Romulan warbird and discovers she has been surgically altered to look Romulan. Troi has been pressed into service by the Romulan underground movement. N'Vek, a member of the underground, explains the situation to Troi. She is to pose as an officer of the Tal Shiar, the Romulan intelligence agency. The warbird is carrying several defectors who are hidden in some cargo containers. The ship is to meet with a freighter and transfer the illicit cargo. Troi will then accompany the freighter to Federation space. Unknown to either, Picard has received a request from the Romulan underground to meet with the freighter.

During the meeting with the freighter, Troi senses deception from its captain and N'Vek immediately destroys the ship. Meanwhile, Picard begins searching for the freighter after it fails to meet with the *Enterprise* on schedule. The Romulan ship, now cloaked, watches the approaching *Enterprise*. The Romulan commander decides to attack the *Enterprise*, so Troi relieves her of command. Troi orders the warbird decloaked and speaks with Picard. She *persuades* him to lower his shields and N'Vek beams the defectors over to the *Enterprise*. The Romulans discover his treason and kill N'Vek while Troi is taken into custody. The crew of the *Enterprise* beams Troi off the warbird at the last second and race off to safety.

TRIVIA QUESTIONS

1. What does Troi say is the reason she ordered the freighter destroyed? **(3pts)**
2. Why did DeSeve return to the Federation? **(3pts)**
3. How long does Troi say she has been in Intelligence? **(3pts)**
4. What do the Romulans use as a power source? **(3pts)**
5. Where is there a Starfleet base, according to N'Vek? **(5pts)**
6. What would not be consistent with the debris pattern? **(3pts)**
7. Where did Troi tell Toreth she supposedly trained at? **(4pts)**
8. What is the name of the facility Troi did not train at? **(4pts)**
9. What was Toreth once awarded? **(4pts)**
10. What is the precise nature of the cargo? **(3pts)**

CHARACTER QUOTE
(2pts per word + 3pts for identifying the speaker.)

Unscramble the words below and then identify the character.

'_____ _____ the _____ for the _____ that we are '_____
  LOEPEP MLEAB   TIRMLYAI   RWSA   SDKAE
to _____, but I _____ it is _____ _____ _____, that will be
  HFTGI   NHKTI   UYRO NKDI JRMOA
the _____ of us all.'
  AHDTE

ANSWERS

TRIVIA ANSWERS

1. she recognized the captain as a known Federation spy
2. Romulus had lost its appeal
3. several months
4. forced quantum singularity
5. on Draken IV
6. a reactor core breach
7. Intelligence Academy
8. Imperial War College
9. the Sotarek Citation
10. Vice-Proconsul M'ret and his top two aides in stasis

CHARACTER QUOTE SOLUTION

'People blame the military for the wars that we are asked to fight, but I think it is your kind Major, that will be the death of us all.' – Toreth

---

MISSION PERFORMANCE RATING:

55 – 60 points **Superior:** Aren't you with Federation Intelligence?

50 – 54 points **Above Average:** Spock would be proud of you!

40 – 49 points **Average:** Well Vice-Proconsul, how do you like the Federation!

30 – 39 points **Fair:** You flunked out of the Imperial War College.

0 – 29 points **Poor:** The Tal Shiar is looking for you and they're not smiling.

TAPESTRY ◬

Picard is severely injured during an away team mission and dies from complications arising from his artificial heart. Picard awakens in a white room and discovers Q there. He informs Picard that if he had had his real heart, he would still be alive. Q decides to let Picard relive the events of his youth leading up to his heart replacement. Q tells Picard that if he can avoid the fight that leads to a dagger piercing his heart, he will survive the fatal injury he receives in the future.

After Picard prevents the brawl from happening, Q returns him to the present. Since Picard acted more responsibly in his youth, his future has changed. Picard is now a low ranking officer with a very safe future. The Captain, viewing this dreary life with disdain, urges Q to allow him a chance to return events to the way they were. Q agrees and Picard relives the brutal fight that led to his artificial heart. Picard finds himself in sickbay on the operating table, alive once again.

TRIVIA QUESTIONS

1. Where was Captain Picard attacked? **(3pts)**
2. What is Picard's position on the *Enterprise* after he avoids being stabbed by the Nausicaan? **(4pts)**
3. What is Q wearing in the 'afterlife' scene? **(3pts)**
4. Who does Picard wake up next to? **(3pts)**
5. What is Picard's new rank on the *Enterprise* after he avoids being stabbed by the Nausicaan? **(3pts)**
6. What were Captain Picard's fatal wounds made by? **(3pts)**
7. Where was Picard once assigned that was near a Nausicaan outpost? **(5pts)**
8. Who is the captain of the *Enterprise* after Picard avoids being stabbed by the Nausicaan? **(4pts)**
9. What game is Corey usually quite good at? **(3pts)**
10. How does Q pronounce Picard's name when he appears as a deliveryman? **(4pts)**

✪ SPECIAL ASSIGNMENT (15pts)

What time is it according to the computer when Picard is talking to Q in his quarters?

MULTIPLE CHOICE QUESTIONS

1. Where was there once a Nausicaan outpost? **(2pts)**
   - **A.** on a planetoid .2 light years distant
   - **B.** on an outlying asteroid
   - **C.** on a nearby planet
   - **D.** near Starbase 212

2. Who did Picard threaten to go to if Corey didn't stop trying to rig the game table? **(2pts)**
   - **A.** the gaming commissioner
   - **B.** the gambling foreman
   - **C.** the Nausicaans
   - **D.** the rec facility commander

3. Why is Picard's face wet? **(3pts)**
   - **A.** perspiration
   - **B.** he's been crying
   - **C.** Penny threw her drink in his face
   - **D.** Marta stuck Picard's head in the shower

4. How soon before Picard fought with the Nausicaans, when Q first sends him back to the past? **(5pts)**
   - **A.** two days
   - **B.** less than 18 hours
   - **C.** one day
   - **D.** six hours

5. How old was Picard when he was just out of the Academy? **(3pts)**
   - **A.** 20 years old
   - **B.** 21 years old
   - **C.** 22 years old
   - **D.** 23 years old

ANSWERS

TRIVIA ANSWERS

1. outside the conference room
2. assistant astrophysics officer
3. white robes
4. Q
5. lieutenant, junior grade
6. a compressed teryon beam
7. Morikin VII
8. Thomas Halloway
9. dom-jot
10. John-Luck Pickerd

SPECIAL ASSIGNMENT SOLUTION

16:11 hours

Congratulations! Starfleet Command is proud to award you the Starfleet Medal of Honour and 15 extra points.

MULTIPLE CHOICE ANSWERS

1. B. on an outlying asteroid
2. B. the gambling foreman
3. C. Penny threw her drink in his face
4. A. two days
5. B. 21 years old

MISSION PERFORMANCE RATING:

45 – 65 points **Superior:** You aren't scared of a few Nausicaans.

40 – 44 points **Above Average:** You're no Q, but you're still pretty smart!

30 – 39 points **Average:** You don't play dom-jot very well.

20 – 29 points **Fair:** You're an insignificant nonentity – an ensign.

0 – 19 points **Poor:** Quit acting like a big, hairy, bone-headed Nausicaan.

BIRTHRIGHT – PART I

STARDATE: 46578.4

The *Enterprise* docks at Deep Space 9 to work on a project with the Bajorans. Data assists Dr Bashir in examining an alien device. During an experiment, Data is stunned. While unconscious, Data experiences images of his father, Dr Soong. Further testing reveals that Dr Soong had implanted components in Data to allow him to dream. Dr Soong had planned to activate them when Data had reached a certain level of development. Data begins to explore this added dimension in his life.

Meanwhile, Worf receives information that his father is still alive in a Romulan prison camp. Worf finds the Yridian who told him the story and *persuades* him to take him to the site of the prison camp. Worf sneaks into the camp under the cover of darkness and indeed finds Klingons there. They tell him that his father died in battle with honour. Unfortunately, Worf is also not allowed to leave the camp.

TRIVIA QUESTIONS

1. What was Soong making on the anvil? **(3pts)**
2. Which journal does Bashir want to write a paper on Data for? **(3pts)**
3. What is the name of the Klingon woman Worf first meets in the jungle near the stream? **(3pts)**
4. How many paintings has Data done in the last six and a half hours? **(4pts)**
5. How many religious and philosophical systems has Data analyzed during his investigation? **(3pts)**
6. What culture views the hammer as an icon of hearth and home? **(4pts)**
7. What likes to attack from above in the jungle? **(4pts)**
8. How long was Data inactive during his first dream experience? **(5pts)**
9. Worf participated in what rite as a child? **(3pts)**
10. What antique is Geordi excited about? **(3pts)**

✪✪ REMBRANDT (2pts each)

First choose the ten paintings from the left column that Data mentions creating. Then list these paintings in the right column in the order that Data painted them.

Paintings	Order Data Painted
A. an individual feather	1.
B. anvil	2.
C. a bird	3.
D. bridge	4.

Paintings	Order Data Painted
E. Soong's face	5.
F. Spot	6.
G. blacksmith	7.
H. a flock of birds flying in formation	8.
I. bluebird	9.
J. hammer	10.
K. bird's foot	
L. smoke coming from a bucket	
M. corridor	
N. Soong's hands	
O. bird's wing	
P. two birds in a tree	

ANSWERS

TRIVIA ANSWERS

1. a bird's wing
2. Starfleet Cybernetics Journal
3. Ba'el
4. 23
5. over 4,000
6. the Taqua tribe of Nagor
7. Arboreal Needle Snake
8. 47 seconds
9. the Klingon Rite of MajQa
10. a 21st century plasma coil in near perfect condition

REMBRANDT ANSWERS

1. G. blacksmith; 2. M. corridor; 3. B. anvil; 4. J. hammer; 5. E. Soong's face; 6. L. smoke coming from a bucket; 7. O. bird's wing; 8. C. a bird; 9. H. a flock of birds flying in formation; 10. A. an individual feather

---

MISSION PERFORMANCE RATING:

30 – 55 points **Superior:** You have discovered the meaning of your vision!

25 – 29 points **Above Average:** A painter of rare birds?

20 – 24 points **Average:** You got lost in the jungle looking for the camp.

10 – 19 points **Fair:** Here, go test this unknown device from the gamma quad.

0 – 9 points **Poor:** You have brought dishonour on your family for generations!

BIRTHRIGHT - PART II

STARDATE: 46759.2

Worf learns that the Klingons in the prison camp, captured decades ago at Khitomer, don't want to be rescued. The Romulans tried to release them but they did not want to dishonour their families by returning. Over the years, the Romulans and Klingons in the camp have lived in peace and intermarried. In order to protect the secret of the prison camp, Worf is not allowed to leave.

After a failed escape attempt, Worf resigns himself to staying at the camp for the time being. He soon discovers that the young Klingons have no knowledge of their heritage. He begins instructing them in the ways of the warrior. The Romulan commander decides that Worf must be executed to preserve the peaceful coexistence of the camp inhabitants. As the commander prepares to have Worf executed, the young Klingons gather around Worf to protect him. The commander, realizing that he cannot carry out the execution, allows Worf and the young Klingons who choose to go, to leave the camp. They all promise never to reveal the existence of the camp.

TRIVIA QUESTIONS

1. What does Ba'el try to remove from Worf? **(3pts)**
2. What did Worf not think was possible? **(3pts)**
3. What does Picard say is their only chance of finding Worf? **(3pts)**
4. What sacrifice did Tokath make? **(3pts)**
5. How does Worf explain the Klingon children with him? **(3pts)**
6. What is the Klingon game called that hones one's hunting skills? **(4pts)**
7. What is the name of the Klingon exercises that Worf teaches to the children? **(5pts)**
8. What kind of knife is in the chest Ba'el and Worf examine? **(4pts)**
9. What is Toq tilling the soil with? **(4pts)**
10. What lie have the Klingon parents been telling their children about why they live in the camp? **(3pts)**

CHARACTER QUOTE
(3pts per word + 4pts for identifying the speaker.)

Unscramble the words below and then identify the character.

'I _____ _____ _____ _____ _____ _____ my _____.'
 VDSDCIEEOR AHTT RSWORIRA' OLOBD NRSU GTUHRHO ISVNE

ANSWERS

TRIVIA ANSWERS

1. tracking device
2. that he could love a Romulan
3. If the Yridian filed a flight plan with DS9
4. he stayed as commander of the camp to prevent the Klingons from being executed
5. survivors of a vessel that crashed four years ago
6. qa'vak
7. Mok'bara
8. d'k tahg
9. gin'tak spear
10. that they came to this planet to escape the war and make a safe place to raise their children

CHARACTER QUOTE SOLUTION

'I discovered that warrior's blood runs through my veins.' – Toq

---

MISSION PERFORMANCE RATING:

55 – 60 points **Superior:** Your heart is Klingon forever!

50 – 54 points **Above Average:** You never did trust the Yridians.

40 – 49 points **Average:** It isn't your fault; you were not raised Klingon.

30 – 39 points **Fair:** *You* were supposed to file the flight plan!

0 – 29 points **Poor:** Romulan dog, stay clear!

⚓ STARSHIP MINE

The *Enterprise* is scheduled for a baryon sweep at a Federation facility. Since the sweep is lethal to living tissue, the crew must be evacuated for a short time. While Picard is at a welcoming reception, he learns of an opportunity to ride horses. He excuses himself and leaves to get his saddle from the *Enterprise*.

Just as Picard prepares to leave the *Enterprise* with his saddle, he is attacked by one of the baryon sweep workers. Picard knocks him out but is unable to beam off the ship. Picard learns that the baryon sweep workers aboard the *Enterprise* are actually terrorists trying to steal a toxic resin material.

Picard uses his ingenuity and knowledge of the ship to attack the terrorists in a series of raids. Eventually Picard fights the leader of the group who successfully beams off the *Enterprise* to a waiting vessel. The vessel explodes as it flies off due to Picard removing the control rod from the highly volatile resin container. Picard frantically calls the base on a communicator as the baryon sweep closes in on him. Data shuts down the sweep just in time.

TRIVIA QUESTIONS

1. What did Picard do to the Jefferies tube that the terrorists tried to use to get to Ten-Forward? **(3pts)**
2. When will the baryon sweep begin? **(3pts)**
3. The *Enterprise* has logged more warp time in five years than what? **(3pts)**
4. What does Picard do to Pomet? **(3pts)**
5. At what rate is the resin material drained from the engine core? **(4pts)**
6. Where does the terrorist leader want Kiros to bring Picard to meet her? **(5pts)**
7. How much of the resin material is loaded into the transport assembly? **(4pts)**
8. What does Neil use as a control rod in the transport assembly? **(3pts)**
9. What is considered an awful place? **(3pts)**
10. Hutch says they could take horses to go where? **(4pts)**

✪ SPECIAL ASSIGNMENT (15pts)

Troi asks Geordi to get her more of what at the reception?

MULTIPLE CHOICE QUESTIONS

1. What is the purpose of a baryon sweep? **(3pts)**
   A. to remove the toxic waste that accumulates around warp nacelles
   B. to remove accumulated tachyon particles from the ship's hull
   C. to evenly distribute the baryon fields throughout the ship
   D. to remove accumulated baryon particles from starships

2. Tyrellia is one of only three inhabited planets without what? **(3pts)**
   A. fresh water
   B. a molten core
   C. a magnetic pole
   D. North Pole

3. Data says at what body temperature do humans operate most efficiently? **(4pts)**
   A. 37 °C
   B. 45 °C
   C. 15 °C
   D. 21 °C

4. Geordi has requested two additional field diverters for where? **(2pts)**
   A. Ten-Forward and the bridge
   B. Engineering
   C. the computer core and the bridge
   D. Engineering and the computer core

5. What does Picard find open in the corridor when he goes back for his saddle? **(3pts)**
   A. EPS tap
   B. Jefferies tube access hatch
   C. ODN junction box
   D. corridor access panel

ANSWERS

TRIVIA ANSWERS

1. cut the rungs off the ladder
2. at 15:00 hours
3. most starships log in ten years
4. shoots him in the left thigh with a drugged arrow that renders him unconscious
5. 100 mg per minute
6. Intersection 41
7. 300 mg
8. dynamic stabilizer
9. Starbase 97
10. the nesting grounds of the Arkarian horn fowl on the southern promontory

SPECIAL ASSIGNMENT SOLUTION

fruit salad (only her voice is heard in the background as the camera pans across the room)

Congratulations! Starfleet Command is proud to award you the Starfleet Medal of Honour and 15 extra points.

MULTIPLE CHOICE ANSWERS

1. D. to remove accumulated baryon particles from starships
2. C. a magnetic pole
3. D. 21 °C
4. C. computer core and the bridge
5. C. ODN junction box

MISSION PERFORMANCE RATING:

45 – 65 points **Superior:** You sent Data to fetch your saddle!

40 – 44 points **Above Average:** You can spot terrorists from a mile away.

30 – 39 points **Average:** Duh, you forgot to install the dynamic stabilizer.

20 – 29 points **Fair:** Hold this vial of trilithium and wait for the baryon sweep.

0 – 19 points **Poor:** You just had to look at Picard's jacket, didn't you?

Picard meets Daren, a new department head, and is fascinated by her. After Daren plays in a concert in Ten-Forward, Picard discovers that they have a mutual interest in music. She stops by Picard's quarters one evening and unfolds a portable piano. She persuades Picard to join her with his flute. As time goes on the feelings between them deepen and they fall in love.

A Federation colony needs to be evacuated due to dangerous firestorms that are approaching. Daren leads a crucial part of the mission to set up a screen of thermal deflector units to allow the colonists extra time to evacuate. After the firestorm passes, the crew is able to recover Daren and many of the team members who were missing. Picard tells Daren that he could never place her in danger again. They realize that they can't work together on the same ship and Daren puts in for a transfer.

TRIVIA QUESTIONS

1. What position does Daren hold on the *Enterprise*? **(3pts)**
2. What French folksong did Picard and Daren play together? **(3pts)**
3. What rank is Daren? **(3pts)**
4. Which two teams are missing? **(3pts)**
5. The archaeologist Picard wants to contact is working on a site where? **(4pts)**
6. Where did Daren once lead a team of geologists? **(5pts)**
7. Where is the most acoustically perfect spot on the *Enterprise* located? **(4pts)**
8. What musical selection is performed during the concert in Ten-Forward? **(4pts)**
9. What tea does Daren order for Picard from the replicator? **(3pts)**
10. What time is it when Picard walks in on an experiment in Stellar Cartography? **(4pts)**

✪✪ SIGNIFICANT NUMBERS (2pts each)

Match the clues with the correct number. Some numbers may be used more than once.

Clues
1. Riker says it will take ten minutes longer to evacuate how many colonists?
2. What was the population of the Bersallis outpost?
3. How many people will be required to deploy the thermal deflector units?

---

4. During a firestorm on Bersallis how high can the winds get? (km per hour)
5. What is the total number of thermal deflector units needed?
6. How wide a field, in metres, can be generated by a thermal deflector unit?
7. How many months before the next firestorm was expected?
8. Which starbase did some new crew members recently come aboard at?
9. How high can temperatures get in a firestorm on Bersallis? (°C)
10. Bersallis firestorms normally occur every _____ years.
11. How many different tea blends has Daren programmed into the replicators?
12. How many hours of work did Picard ruin when he visited Stellar Cartography?

Numbers
A. 200
B. 7
C. 400
D. 643
E. 8
F. 300
G. 12
H. 4
I. 73
J. 218
K. 6

ANSWERS

TRIVIA ANSWERS

1. Head of Stellar Sciences
2. Frère Jacques
3. lieutenant commander
4. Team 3 and Team 6
5. Landris II
6. to study the plasma geyser on Melnos IV
7. at the fourth intersect on Jefferies tube 25
8. Chopin's Trio in G Minor
9. Daren Herbal Tea – Blend #3
10. 03:00 hours

SIGNIFICANT NUMBERS ANSWERS

1. I 73; 2. D 643; 3. G 12; 4. A 200; 5. K 6; 6. C 400; 7. E 8; 8. J 218; 9. F 300; 10. B 7; 11. E 8; 12. H 4

MISSION PERFORMANCE RATING:

30 – 60 points **Superior:** Impressive! Carry on the good work!

25 – 29 points **Above Average:** Musician, huh?

20 – 24 points **Average:** Go fix the defective thermal deflector unit.

10 – 19 points **Fair:** Go stand over by Richardson.

0 – 9 points **Poor:** Stand in front of this approaching firestorm.

THE CHASE

Picard's former archaeology professor visits him on the *Enterprise*. Professor Galen is on the verge of a dramatic discovery and wants Picard to join him on his expedition. Picard says no and the Professor abruptly leaves in his shuttlecraft.

The *Enterprise* later receives a call from Galen's shuttlecraft which is under attack. The *Enterprise* destroys the attacker's ship but Professor Galen dies from injuries sustained in the attack.

Picard and the crew piece together Galen's work and discover a computer programme dispersed in the genetic material of life forms from many planets. When the samples are joined, the programme is complete.

The Cardassians, Klingons, and Romulans are also interested in gaining the secret of the ancient computer programme. The four groups finally confront each other at the site of the last DNA fragment needed to complete the programme. The programme turns out to be a holographic message from an ancient humanoid race that seeded scattered worlds with the DNA that eventually evolved into humanoid life. This message was encoded in the DNA to provide a testimonial to their shared ancestry.

TRIVIA QUESTIONS

1. What is the figurine called that Picard receives as a gift in the observation lounge? **(4pts)**
2. Who is responsible for destroying all life on Indri VIII? **(3pts)**
3. Who is the female commander of the Cardassian warships? **(4pts)**
4. What is the name of the Klingon cruiser that uncloaks? **(5pts)**
5. What is the true name of the system where the last DNA fragment may be found? **(3pts)**
6. How old is the figurine given to Picard as a gift? **(4pts)**
7. How old is the DNA computer programme? **(3pts)**
8. Data's reputation for what is known throughout the Klingon Empire? **(3pts)**
9. What does Nu'Daq offer Data? **(3pts)**
10. What does Riker release to simulate a complete shield failure on the *Enterprise*? **(3pts)**

✪✪ P SOUP (20pts)

Decipher the following formula:

$$V = F_3K(CR_2)_2$$

CHARACTER QUOTE
(3pts per word + 4pts for identifying the speaker.)

Unscramble the words below and then identify the character.

'You're like some _____ _____ out _____ the
      NOAMR ITNEUCNRO   LGAORLNPTI

_____, _____ a dull and _____ _____.'
VCOISPNRE NIAITGNMIAN   ALDTEOB RPEIME

ANSWERS

TRIVIA ANSWERS

1. Naiskos
2. Klingons
3. Gul Ocett
4. *Maht-H'a*
5. Vilmoran
6. 12,000 yrs +
7. four billion years
8. strength
9. bribe
10. inertial dampers

P(RIMORDIAL) SOUP SOLUTION

V = the planet in the Vilmoran system where the 'chase' ends.

The rest of the formula is based on the number of each group present during the holographic encounter.

F_3 = 3 Federation officers
K = 1 Klingon
z = 2 Cardassians + 4 Romulans

CHARACTER QUOTE SOLUTION

'You're like some Roman centurion out patrolling the provinces, maintaining a dull and bloated Empire.' – Professor Galen

---

MISSION PERFORMANCE RATING:

55 – 80 points **Superior:** You are descended from an ancient humanoid race.

50 – 54 points **Above Average:** The Yridians have a job opening.

40 – 49 points **Average:** You did well in biochemistry, didn't you?

30 – 39 points **Fair:** You couldn't even bake Klingon biscuits.

0 – 29 points **Poor:** You must be descended from partially fossilized lichen!

FRAME OF MIND

STARDATE: 46678.1

Riker is rehearsing for a play called *Frame of Mind*. In five days he is to go undercover to the planet Tilonus IV to evacuate some Federation researchers. After performing the play, Riker suddenly finds himself in the Tilonus Institute for Mental Disorders where he is told that he was admitted after killing a man. As Riker struggles with an attendant, he wakes up in his bed on the *Enterprise*.

The next night Riker performs *Frame of Mind*, and again images from real life and the play interact. He's on board the *Enterprise* one moment and the next he is at the Institute in his cell. This time Worf and Data attempt to rescue him from his cell. Back on board the *Enterprise*, Riker realizes it's just one more illusion. He grabs a phaser and fires at himself to find out what is actually real. One illusion after another collapses until he finally regains consciousness in a Tilonian laboratory. Riker grabs his communicator and signals for an emergency transport to the *Enterprise*. Riker was kidnapped after his arrival on the planet and was undergoing experimental techniques in an effort to extract vital Federation information from his mind.

TRIVIA QUESTIONS

1. What ward does Riker find himself in at the Tilonus Institute for Mental Disorders? **(4pts)**
2. Which admiral did the Tilonians contact at Starbase 29 concerning Riker? **(5pts)**
3. Whose voice does Riker hear in sickbay coming from Troi? **(3pts)**
4. Dr Syrus says which part of Riker's brain could be reconstructed as a possible treatment? **(3pts)**
5. Dr Syrus tells Riker that Suna is actually whom? **(3pts)**
6. Who was recently assassinated on Tilonus IV? **(4pts)**
7. What was the burned crewman in sickbay working on when the accident occurred? **(3pts)**
8. Data tells Riker he gave a good demonstration of what at the end of the play? **(4pts)**
9. During reflection therapy, who represents Riker's feelings of anger and violence? **(3pts)**
10. What have the Tilonians been trying to access in Riker's brain? **(3pts)**

WHO AM I? (25pts)

The one saw me but knew me not. Others rose to the occasion but I did not. I was the key but the lock could not be found. In the end, I alone stood with you.

ANSWERS

TRIVIA ANSWERS

1. Ward 47
2. Admiral Budron
3. Dr Syrus
4. cerebral cortex
5. hospital administrator
6. Prime Minister
7. conduit
8. multi-infarct dementia
9. Worf
10. long-term memory

WHO AM I? SOLUTION

Suna

EXPLANATION:

The one saw me but knew me not. – Riker (Number One) almost ran into Suna on the Enterprise but did not recognize the alien.

Others rose to the occasion but I did not. – The audience gives Riker a standing ovation on the opening night performance of the play except Suna who remained sitting.

I was the key but the lock could not be found. – In another imagined performance of the play Riker sees Suna in the audience again and confronts the alien saying, "You're the key to all this, aren't you?"

In the end, I alone stood with you. – In the end when all of Riker's false realities are shattered, Suna remains in 'actual' reality as the Tilonian government scientist experimenting on Riker.

MISSION PERFORMANCE RATING:

36 – 60 points **Superior:** Your brain holds vital Federation information!

30 – 35 points **Above Average:** You're good at mind games.

20 – 29 points **Average:** You should join your local theatre group.

10 – 19 points **Fair:** What? You can't remember your name?

0 – 9 points **Poor:** A penny for your thoughts? Sorry, that's too much to pay!

Dr Crusher invites four prominent scientists to the *Enterprise* to learn about a Ferengi scientist's theory on a new shielding technology. The field allows a spacecraft to penetrate the outer layers of a star without harm. After Dr Reyga presents his evidence, the other scientists are still not convinced of the validity of his theory.

A test appears successful but then something goes wrong. Dr Reyga is soon found dead and suicide is suspected. Dr Crusher believes he was killed by one of the other scientists and that the test was sabotaged. However, Crusher can find no evidence of foul play in Reyga's death even after disobeying Picard's orders not to examine the body. Convinced that the field works, Dr Crusher pilots a refitted shuttlecraft into the star's corona and the saboteur emerges from hiding. Crusher fights with the saboteur and kills him.

TRIVIA QUESTIONS

1. What is the name of the Vulcan scientist? **(3pts)**
2. The Vulcan scientist is the director of what facility? **(4pts)**
3. After Jo'Bril steers away from the star, how is the shuttlecraft retrieved? **(3pts)**
4. What kind of signal does Jo'Bril send from Crusher's shuttlecraft that the *Enterprise* interprets as a warp engine breach? **(4pts)**
5. What is Kurak's area of expertise? **(3pts)**
6. During the initial meeting on the *Enterprise*, which scientist is sitting down? **(5pts)**
7. How fast is Jo'Bril flying the shuttlecraft during the test flight? **(3pts)**
8. How far from the star's corona does the shuttle need to be before Jo'Bril can be transported off? **(4pts)**
9. Where was Dr Christopher when he heard Reyga and Kurak arguing? **(3pts)**
10. What type of search does Picard initiate to find Dr Crusher's shuttlecraft? **(3pts)**

CHARACTER QUOTE
(2pts per word + 4pts for identifying the speaker.)

Unscramble the words below and then identify the character.

_____ can _____ their _____ at a _____ _____.
NKSAARTA   LTORCNO   YOHPOYILSG   UCLALREL ELELV
We can _____ the _____ of _____.'
　　ETACRE   RPACANEPAE   TADHE

✪ SPECIAL ASSIGNMENT (15pts)

Data states that a phased ionic pulse could be generated from three areas on the *Enterprise*:
1. bridge science stations
2. science labs 1, 4, 16

What is the third area that Data states?

ANSWERS

TRIVIA ANSWERS

1. T'Pan
2. Vulcan Science Academy
3. tractor beam
4. transient subspace signal
5. warp field specialist
6. Jo'Bril
7. 3/4 impulse
8. 500,000 kilometres
9. storage room in the science laboratory
10. Phase 1

CHARACTER QUOTE SOLUTION

'Takarans can control their physiology at a cellular level. We can create the appearance of death.' – Jo'Bril

SPECIAL ASSIGNMENT SOLUTION

lateral sensor array

Congratulations! Starfleet Command is proud to award you the Starfleet Medal of Honour and 15 extra points.

MISSION PERFORMANCE RATING:

50 – 70 points **Superior:** What? Dr Reyga stole your ideas?

45 – 49 points **Above Average:** The game is afoot, Watson!

40 – 44 points **Average:** You've been promoted to Shuttlecraft Maintenance.

30 – 39 points **Fair:** Stay away from the shuttlebays.

0 – 29 points **Poor:** Dr Crusher wants to see you in the morgue.

RIGHTFUL HEIR

Worf seeks spiritual answers on Boreth, a sacred Klingon planet. Boreth is the prophesied site for the return of Kahless, a great Klingon spiritual leader. During one of his meditations Worf has a vision of Kahless. He says he is Kahless and has physically returned. The Klingon has special knowledge only known by a sacred few and is proclaimed by the clerics to be the true Kahless.

The *Enterprise* takes Kahless and his entourage to a meeting with Gowron, the leader of the Klingon High Council. Gowron tries to disprove Kahless' claim, but all tests prove he is indeed the historical figure. Worf later discovers that Kahless is actually a clone of the original Klingon leader and persuades Gowron to establish Kahless as a spiritual leader for the Klingon Empire.

TRIVIA QUESTIONS

1. What makes Kahless more than just a clone of the original? **(3pts)**
2. What is not written in the Klingon sacred texts? **(3pts)**
3. What type of weapon do Gowron and Kahless fight with? **(4pts)**
4. What city is mentioned by Kahless? **(4pts)**
5. How long does Gowron say Kahless has been dead? **(3pts)**
6. Where did Worf once have a vision of Kahless? **(4pts)**
7. Who were the only people who knew the story of Kahless' sword? **(3pts)**
8. Where did Kahless supposedly cut off a lock of his hair? **(5pts)**
9. How long is it since Kahless once lived? **(3pts)**
10. What is the name of the Klingon afterworld? **(3pts)**

CHARACTER QUOTE
(3pts per word + 7pts for identifying the speaker.)

Unscramble the words below and then identify the character.

'_____ are the _____ of _____. The _____
  UINEOQSST   GNBIIENGN MDIWSO   RMKA
of a _____ _____.'
    URET RORARWI

SPECIAL ASSIGNMENT (10pts)

What time was the minor injury reported in sickbay according to Data?

ANSWERS

TRIVIA ANSWERS

1. he has been imprinted with specific information about Kahless as written in the sacred texts
2. the story of how Kahless' bat'leth was forged
3. d'k tahgs
4. Quin'lat
5. 1,000 years
6. in the caves of No'Mat
7. high clerics
8. Kri'stak Volcano
9. 15 centuries according to Korath
10. Sto-Vo-Kor

CHARACTER QUOTE SOLUTION

'Questions are the beginning of wisdom. The mark of a true warrior.' – Worf

SPECIAL ASSIGNMENT SOLUTION

04:20 hours

Congratulations! Starfleet Command is proud to award you the Starfleet Medal of Honour and 10 extra points.

MISSION PERFORMANCE RATING:

55 – 70 points **Superior:** Indeed, you must be Kahless himself!

50 – 54 points **Above Average:** Kahless wants to speak with you.

40 – 44 points **Average:** You almost set fire to your quarters.

30 – 39 points **Fair:** The only thing you can summon is the family dog.

0 – 29 points **Poor:** Sto-Vo-Kor is only for honourable warriors.

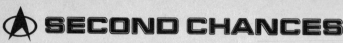

SECOND CHANCES

STARDATE: 46915.2

The *Enterprise* is to retrieve scientific data from an abandoned research station on a planet with a distortion field surrounding it. Transport down to the planet is possible only once every so many years when several 'windows' appear through the field. Riker, once a lieutenant stationed aboard another ship, had led an evacuation team the last time the planet was in phase. The transport was a difficult one and he almost didn't make it out.

An away team beams down and discovers an identical Will Riker at the station. Dr Crusher and Geordi determine that both Rikers are exact duplicates resulting from the difficult transport from the planet eight years before. Commander Riker's double, Lieutenant Will Riker, is still deeply in love with Troi.

Lieutenant Riker tries to rekindle his relationship with Troi while Commander Riker struggles with the choices he made in the past. Lieutenant Riker helps the *Enterprise* to recover the scientific data from the research station's computer. Commander Riker saves him in the caverns below the research station and reconciles with his 'twin'.

CROSSWORD PUZZLE CLUES

ACROSS

3. Troi is exercising with _____ before Lieutenant Riker enters. **(1pt)**

4. The third scroll directs Troi to go to _____. **(2pts)**

5. The servolink that needs repairs is located in the _____. **(1pt)**

7. Song Troi requests Commander Riker to play. **(3pts)**

8. Sector Lieutenant Riker's new mission is in. **(3pts)**

9. Commander Riker hosts the poker game in his _____. **(1pt)**

11. Worf has two of these at the beginning of the poker game. **(1pt)**

12. It will be eight years before the next time the planet will be in _____. **(1pt)**

14. Lieutenant Riker _____ his arm several years ago. **(1pt)**

17. Type of new assignment Lieutenant Riker will be on. **(3pts)**

18. After serving six months on his newly assigned ship, Lieutenant Riker can bring _____ aboard. **(2pts)**

20. Number of years ago that Starfleet evacuated Nervala IV. **(2pts)**

22. During the second transporter window, the computer _____ is found to be damaged. **(3pts)**

26. The *Enterprise* is trying to retrieve the _____ from the research station. **(2pts)**

28. Betazoid word meaning 'love of his life'. **(1pt)**

29. In Ten-Forward Troi finds a gift-wrapped box and a _____ on the table. **(2pts)**

DOWN

1. Number of cymbals the band drummer has. **(2pts)**

2. Lieutenant Riker used a _____ to make the etching of Janaran Falls. **(1pt)**

3. The third scroll Troi finds is attached to a heart made of _____. **(3pts)**

4. Geordi examines the _____ logs to determine how Riker's double could exist. **(2pts)**

6. Ship that evacuated the researchers. **(3pts)**

10. The *Enterprise*'s scans show the caverns to be _____. **(2pts)**

13. The away team's tricorder picks up _____ readings on their initial beam down. **(2pts)**

15. Data tells Worf that humans value their _____. **(3pts)**

16. The intense distortion field makes _____ difficult. **(1pt)**

19. Name Lieutenant Riker decides to go by. **(1pt)**

21. The _____ EPS coupling is fused. **(3pts)**

23. Picard secures a posting for Lieutenant Riker on the _____. **(3pts)**

24. Led the evacuation team to Nervala IV. **(1pt)**

25. Type of flower Troi finds in the transporter room. **(2pts)**

27. Commander Riker turned down a command on the _____. **(2pts)**

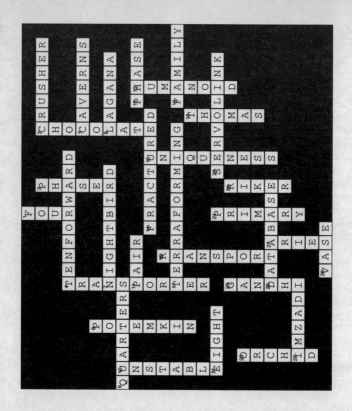

MISSION PERFORMANCE RATING:

55 – 60 points **Superior:** Keep this up and you'll be promoted again!

50 – 54 points **Above Average:** Spelunking instructor, huh?

40 – 44 points **Average:** You could be lieutenant some day.

30 – 39 points **Fair:** Your Primary EPS coupling may be fused.

0 – 29 points **Poor:** Number of years since you've seen a *TNG* episode.

While returning from a conference, Picard and three senior staff officers on the Captain's runabout encounter several areas of space/time distortion. The runabout encounters the *Enterprise* trapped in such an area along with a Romulan warbird.

Geordi beams Picard, Data, and Troi over to the *Enterprise* to investigate. Using modified emergency transporter armbands the officers are able to move freely about the ship even though the rest of the crew appears frozen in time. They discover that an explosion in the warp engines will destroy the *Enterprise* in approximately nine hours.

On the Romulan ship, the officers discover the engine inactive. Data determines that the temporal disturbances are due to life forms located in the core chamber. The officers find an alien assuming Romulan form. It appears aliens were attempting to incubate their young in the Romulan engine core. The result shut down the warbird's engine. The *Enterprise*, transferring power to the Romulan ship, unwittingly threatened this plan. The aliens had assumed Romulan form in an effort to destroy the *Enterprise* and protect their young.

Using a tricorder, Picard and the officers are able to activate the time rift. They reverse time to a point before the warp engines overloaded. The officers then act to prevent the catastrophe, saving the *Enterprise* and the alien young.

TRIVIA QUESTIONS

1. What kind of disturbances do the officers on the Captain's runabout encounter? **(3pts)**
2. The aliens mistook the Romulan engine core for what? **(3pts)**
3. What did the *Enterprise* pick up on long range sensors? **(3pts)**
4. What do the Romulans claim is wrong with their ship? **(3pts)**
5. What is Picard doing during the runabout's first encounter with the space/time distortion? **(3pts)**
6. Where does Data say the space/time disturbance intersects? **(4pts)**
7. Picard talks about a subspace force field used in the past on what planet? **(4pts)**
8. In Engineering, what does Picard draw in the explosion cloud? **(4pts)**
9. What were the Romulans trying to eject from their ship? **(3pts)**
10. How many times has Data boiled a kettle of water? **(5pts)**

A FAIRY TALE (25pts)
Explain this fairy tale and identify the dwarfs and how they got their names.

Once upon a time four dwarfs – Happy, Zappy, Pushy, and Sleepy – came upon Siamese twins. Both twins looked dead but the dwarfs weren't sure. Finally, the dwarfs determined that one of the twins had eaten a bad batch

---

of bird's nest soup and indeed was not far from giving up the spirit. The infection had spread to the other twin but the dwarfs were only able to remotely save him from certain death.

ANSWERS

TRIVIA ANSWERS

1. temporal; 2. black hole (gravity well); 3. distress call; 4. complete engine failure; 5. sipping his cup of tea; 6. table; 7. Devidia II; 8. happy face; 9. engine core; 10. 62

FAIRY TALE SOLUTION

EXPLANATION:

The four dwarfs are the Enterprise officers on the runabout:

Happy – Picard (He draws a smiling 'happy face' in the frozen explosion cloud.)

Zappy – Data (He is shocked by the alien touching his containment field.)

Pushy – Troi (She pushes Crusher out of the disruptor's discharge path in sickbay.)

Sleepy – Geordi (He is put into the slower time fragment by removing his armband.)

came upon Siamese twins. – The warbird and the Enterprise (the energy transfer uniting them).

Both twins looked dead – Both ships are frozen in the temporal distortion.

one of the twins had eaten a bad batch of bird's nest soup – The warbird has the alien embryos 'nesting' in its engine core.

The infection had spread to the other twin – The Enterprise is experiencing a warp core breach.

but the dwarfs were only able to remotely save him from certain death. – The dwarfs 'remotely' save the one twin (Enterprise) by using the runabout to sever the energy transfer.

MISSION PERFORMANCE RATING:

36 – 60 points **Superior:** Certified Starfleet temporal distortion expert!

30 – 35 points **Above Average:** Don't quit your day job just yet.

20 – 29 points **Average:** You spend too much time drawing happy faces.

10 – 19 points **Fair:** You must be trapped in a temporal fragment.

0 – 9 points **Poor:** Using your toothbrush, scrub those dark spots off the engine core.

DESCENT – PART I ⚜

The *Enterprise* comes to the aid of a Federation outpost under attack and finds a large ship in orbit around the planet. An away team beams down to investigate and battles a group of Borg that ambushes them. The *Enterprise* prepares to pursue the Borg ship as it leaves orbit when it suddenly vanishes.

Data, during the encounter with the Borg at the outpost, experienced a burst of emotions. He tries to recreate the experience without success. Later, another colony is attacked and the *Enterprise* responds. The *Enterprise* pursues the Borg vessel and is drawn into an energy vortex. On the other side of the vortex, the Borg attack the *Enterprise*. Several Borg beam onto the bridge to create a diversion while the Borg ship vanishes into yet another energy vortex. One of the Borg survives and is placed in the brig. Data is manipulated by the Borg into helping him escape and together they leave in a shuttlecraft.

The *Enterprise* tracks the shuttlecraft to a distant planet. A search team finds a building and they investigate further. Inside they are surrounded by Borg. Lore appears and declares he is their leader. Data also steps out of the shadows, apparently allied with his brother.

TRIVIA QUESTIONS

1. What device is the security extra in Picard's search team carrying? **(3pts)**
2. Which shuttlebay does Data steal a shuttlecraft from? **(3pts)**
3. What is the name of the shuttlecraft Data stole? **(3pts)**
4. What does Picard tell Worf to transmit to the colony that had the false alarm? **(3pts)**
5. The Admiral says there will be how many starships in the sector within two days? **(3pts)**
6. What is Hawking's winning poker hand? **(4pts)**
7. How far has the *Enterprise* travelled after the ship emerges from the energy vortex? **(4pts)**
8. What range are tricorders limited to on the planet's surface? **(4pts)**
9. What is the time of the recording Picard reviews on the Borg known as Hugh? **(5pts)**
10. What percentage increase in the holodeck Borg's strength would exceed safety limits? **(3pts)**

✪ SPECIAL ASSIGNMENT (15pts)

The Transwarp Topologic Analysis that Geordi looks at shows an extrapolated termination point ending where?

MULTIPLE CHOICE QUESTIONS

1. How does Geordi generate a pulse to open the transwarp conduit? **(2pts)**
    - **A.** he creates a temporary tachyon flux field in the main deflector
    - **B.** he creates a temporary tachyon matrix in the main deflector
    - **C.** he creates a temporary tachyon pulse in the lateral sensor array
    - **D.** he creates a temporary baryon matrix in the main sensor array

2. What is the name of the second colony that is attacked by the Borg ? **(5pts)**
    - **A.** MS I
    - **B.** Ohniaka III
    - **C.** NS I
    - **D.** Jouret IV

3. How fast does a ship travel in a transwarp conduit? **(3pts)**
    - **A.** Warp 20
    - **B.** no more than 20 times faster than maximum warp
    - **C.** at least 20 times faster than maximum warp
    - **D.** 20 times faster than Warp 9

4. The leader of the Borg is known by what title? **(3pts)**
    - **A.** Sir Lore of Gisbourne
    - **B.** The Only One
    - **C.** The Son Of Soong
    - **D.** The One

5. The wounds on the bodies at the Ohniaka III outpost were caused by what? **(2pts)**
    - **A.** plasma extrusion beams
    - **B.** photon grenades
    - **C.** disruptor blasts
    - **D.** forced plasma beams

ANSWERS

TRIVIA ANSWERS

1. a type-3 phaser rifle
2. Shuttlebay 2
3. El-Baz
4. a copy of Starfleet Ship Recognition Protocols
5. 15
6. four sevens
7. 65 light years
8. 100 metres
9. 07:19 hours
10. 30%

SPECIAL ASSIGNMENT SOLUTION

Delta Quadrant

Congratulations! Starfleet Command is proud to award you the Starfleet Medal of Honour and 15 extra points.

MULTIPLE CHOICE ANSWERS

1. B. he creates a temporary tachyon matrix in the main deflector
2. A. MS 1
3. C. at least 20 times faster than maximum warp
4. D. The One
5. D. forced plasma beams

MISSION PERFORMANCE RATING:

45 – 65 points **Superior:** You're one of those Borg specialists, aren't you?

40 – 44 points **Above Average:** You could play poker with Stephen Hawking!

30 – 39 points **Average:** Your brain got transwarped somewhere else.

20 – 29 points **Fair:** Congratulations, you've won what's behind Door Number 1!

0 – 19 points **Poor:** Don't worry, the Borg aren't going to assimilate you.

TECHNICAL MATTERS AND KLINGON CULTURE

LOCATIONS (5pts each)

1. Where are Riker's quarters located (deck and room number)?
2. Where are Worf's quarters?
3. What deck is Cargo Bay 4 on?
4. What is on Deck 42?
5. Where are Troi's quarters located (deck and room number)?
6. Where is the arboretum?
7. What is the room number of Dr Crusher's office?
8. What deck is the nacelle tube control room in?

WEAPONS (5pts each)

1. How many phaser banks does the *Enterprise* have?
2. How many photon torpedoes does the *Enterprise* carry?
3. What is standard procedure for phaser storage?
4. What type of phaser beam is good for melting comets?
5. What were the only three *TNG* episodes that featured the type-3 phaser rifle?

KLINGON (5pts each)

1. Death is immediate in a Klingon if the cranial exo-skeleton is shattered at the _____ lobe.
2. Which Klingon ceremony involves the use of painstiks?
3. Where is the most sacred of places for Klingons?
4. When does the path of a warrior begin?
5. What two things are tested during the First Rite of Ascension?
6. What does the *kor'tova* candle represent?

ENGINEERING (5pts each)

1. In the episode 'Skin of Evil', the chief engineer tells the *Enterprise* computer to prime the matter/antimatter injectors. What does he set the ratio at?
2. A highly toxic waste product formed by the warp engines.
3. How large is Engineering?
4. On the *Enterprise*, the secondary plasma vent has what type of bypass?
5. How long after raising the isolation door in the nacelle tube control room does the plasma venting system engage to prevent the degradation of the force field?

IMPORTANT EVENTS (5pts each)

1. What year was the Federation founded?
2. Approximately what year were isolinear chips invented?
3. In *TNG* episode 'Legacy', the *Enterprise* must bypass an archaeological survey of Camus II. What is the significance of this planet and why was this an important episode?
4. When did *TNG* first use a shuttlecraft in an episode?
5. What year did the world government form on Earth?

MINUTIAE (10pts each)

1. How wide is Picard's ready room?
2. How many duty watches does the *Enterprise* crew stand?
3. Which military unit is Gul Dolak's warship assigned to?
4. What does it take to disable the safety routine on the holodeck?
5. What is the crew complement of a Ferengi D'Kora class transport ship?
6. What is one of the *Enterprise* children's favourite school activities?
7. How often are crew evaluation reports done?
8. What time is Alpha shift relieved?
9. Which two *TNG* episodes mentioned the Federation ship *USS Lalo*?
10. Which two *TNG* episodes were the only ones that didn't have any scenes on the bridge of the *Enterprise*? **(20pts)**

TECHNICAL (5pts each)

1. What does Data say his communicator pin is made of?
2. Each transporter pad has four redundant what?
3. What is the normal length of time for a transport cycle?
4. Which sensors give readings on ambient radiation exposure and exterior hull temperature?

ANSWERS

SPECIAL SECTION

LOCATIONS TRIVIA ANSWERS

1. Cabin 0912 on Deck 8 ('Chain of Command – Part II')
2. Deck 7, Section 25-Baker ('Rightful Heir')
3. Deck 18 ('Power Play')
4. antimatter storage facility ('Liaisons')
5. Cabin 0910 on Deck 8 – ('Inheritance' & 'Eye of the Beholder')
6. Deck 17, Section 21-Alpha ('Genesis')
7. 1629 (visible on closeup of door as Picard leaves – 'Genesis')
8. Deck 25 (as seen on closeup of door – 'Eye of the Beholder')

WEAPONS TRIVIA ANSWERS

1. ten ('Conundrum')
2. 250 ('Conundrum')
3. all phasers are set to level–1 when placed in storage ('Aquiel')
4. a dispersed wide-field beam set at 10% of maximum power ('Masks')
5. 'Mind's Eye', 'Descent', 'Lower Decks'

KLINGON TRIVIA ANSWERS

1. Tricipital ('Descent')
2. the Second Rite of Ascension ('Firstborn')
3. Boreth, the site of Kahless' prophesied return ('Rightful Heir')
4. with the First Rite of Ascension ('Firstborn')
5. fighting skills and knowledge of the teachings of Kahless ('Firstborn')
6. the fire that burns in the heart of a Klingon warrior ('Firstborn')

ENGINEERING TRIVIA ANSWERS

1. 25:1
2. trilithium resin ('Starship Mine')
3. it encompasses 12 decks of the secondary hull ('Liaisons')
4. triple redundant bypass ('Thine Own Self')
5. 90 seconds ('Eye of the Beholder')

IMPORTANT EVENTS TRIVIA ANSWERS

1. 2161 ('The Outcast')
2. 2329 (current year = 2369, Geordi said isolinear chips replaced duotronic enhancers about 40 years ago, 'Relics')
3. Camus II was the site of the 79th and last episode of the original *Star Trek* series. 'Legacy' was *TNG*'s 80th episode and was thus an important mile stone in the new series.
4. when Jake Kurland steals Shuttle 13 ('Coming of Age')
5. 2150 ('Attached')

MINUTIAE TRIVIA ANSWERS

1. 7 metres as measured by Rasmussen pacing across the room ('A Matter of Time')
2. three shift rotation ('Chain of Command – Part I')
3. Cardassian Militia 41 ('Ensign Ro')
4. voice authorizations of two senior officers ('Descent')
5. 450 (Force of Nature')
6. Captain Picard Day ('The Pegasus')
7. every three months ('Lower Decks')
8. 12:00 hours ('Lower Decks')
9. 'We'll Always Have Paris' and 'The Best of Both Worlds'.
10. 'Family' and 'Liaisons'

TECHNICAL TRIVIA ANSWERS

1. a crystalline composite of silicon, beryllium, carbon 70, and gold ('Time's Arrow')
2. imaging scanners ('Realm of Fear')
3. 2–2.5 seconds. In 'Realm of Fear', O'Brien says it will take 4–5 seconds to transport to the science ship and says it's twice as long as normal.
4. Primary Hull Exterior Sensors (from display screen in 'Descent – Part II')

MISSION PERFORMANCE RATING:

126 – 275 points	**Superior:** You possess a keen mind! (SEE BELOW)
101 – 199 points	**Above Average:** Starfleet's best chief engineer!
76 – 149 points	**Average:** You don't even know what a magnaspanner is!
51 – 99 points	**Fair:** You just caused a diplomatic incident with the Klingon Empire!
0 – 49 points	**Poor:** Not very technically orientated are you?

If you have received a SUPERIOR Mission Performance Rating –

Congratulations!
Starfleet Command is proud to award you
the Grankite Order of Tactics, Class of Excellence and 100 extra points.

SEASON SEVEN

DESCENT - PART II

STARDATE: 47453.7

Dr Crusher, in command of the *Enterprise*, breaks orbit, leaving some crew members behind, as the Borg ship prepares to attack. The doctor takes the ship to the transwarp conduit and prepares to return to Federation space to get reinforcements.

Data has formed an alliance with his brother, Lore. Picard, Geordi, and Troi believe Data's programming has been altered by Lore, who is transmitting negative emotions to control his brother.

Meanwhile, Riker and Worf come across Hugh, who explains what happened when he returned to his ship (see 'I, Borg'). His new sense of individuality spread throughout the Borg collective and resulted in chaos. Lore brought stability back into their lives, but his experiments on the Borg haven't been successful.

The *Enterprise* returns and uses some new shielding technology to hide from the Borg ship in a nearby star's corona. The *Enterprise* induces a solar flare, destroying the Borg ship.

Picard is able to reboot Data's programming and restore him to a more normal state. Lore suspects something is different and tests Data's loyalty by telling him to kill Picard. Data refuses and Lore prepares to fire on Data. Hugh rushes out and saves Data, aided by Riker and Worf. Lore tries to escape but Data disables him.

TRIVIA QUESTIONS

1. What did Taitt do her senior honours thesis on? **(3pts)**
2. What does Picard use as an energy source to trigger the pulse? **(3pts)**
3. How does Picard disable the Borg that enters the detention cell? **(3pts)**
4. What could Geordi see with his VISOR radiating from Lore? **(3pts)**
5. Where is Lore's control mechanism for his emotional transmitter? **(3pts)**
6. What hull temperature does Taitt report before the *Enterprise* engages the shielding programme? **(4pts)**
7. What radiation level does Taitt report before the *Enterprise* engages the shielding programme? **(4pts)**
8. Geordi asks Picard if anything on the device removed from the Borg could be used as what? **(4pts)**
9. What chance is there that Geordi won't survive the procedure? **(5pts)**
10. How do Riker and Worf know that somebody stood on the hillside? **(3pts)**

SPECIAL ASSIGNMENT (10pts)

How far did Data once have to walk underwater to reach the shore?

_____

MULTIPLE CHOICE QUESTIONS

1. What has given Lore such a strong sense of family? **(2pts)**
    A. Data's new found loyalty
    B. Lore's family values chip
    C. helping the Borg find purpose
    D. Lore's emotion chip

2. After Data once went swimming, it took almost two weeks to get the water out of his what? **(5pts)**
    A. ears
    B. servos
    C. circulatory system
    D. subprocessors

3. During the failed escape attempt, Data tells Troi to drop her weapon or he'll do what? **(3pts)**
    A. make Geordi kill Picard
    B. fry her like a piece of bacon
    C. break Geordi's neck
    D. blast her into smithereens

4. What do some of the tunnels connect to under the compound? **(2pts)**
    A. detention cells
    B. waste disposal conduits
    C. environmental control ducts
    D. damping field generators

5. How does Dr Crusher transmit the log entries to Starfleet via the transwarp conduit? **(3pts)**
    A. a class-8 sensor probe
    B. a tightly compressed encrypted subspace signal
    C. a subspace transponder beam boosted by a quantum pulse generator
    D. an emergency buoy

ANSWERS

TRIVIA ANSWERS

1. Solar Dynamics
2. detention cell force field
3. he pulls one of the tubes loose near the Borg's neck region
4. carrier wave
5. under his left index fingernail
6. 12,000 °C
7. 10,000 Rads
8. a flux inhibitor
9. 60%
10. they found residual thermal traces with the tricorder

SPECIAL ASSIGNMENT SOLUTION

1.046 kilometres

Congratulations! Starfleet Command is proud to award you the Starfleet Medal of Honour and 10 extra points.

MULTIPLE CHOICE ANSWERS

1. D. Lore's emotion chip
2. B. servos
3. C. break Geordi's neck
4. C. environmental control ducts
5. D. an emergency buoy

MISSION PERFORMANCE RATING:

45 – 60 points **Superior:** King of the Borgs.

40 – 44 points **Above Average:** Hugh, that was a close one.

30 – 39 points **Average:** It's not your fault you've got a few negative emotions.

20 – 29 points **Fair:** Crosis scored better than this without his prosthetic eye.

0 – 19 points **Poor:** What's this tube coming out of your neck for? Oops!

The *Enterprise* participates in the first cultural exchange between the Federation and the Iyaarans. Two Iyaaran ambassadors, Byleth and Loquel, board the *Enterprise*. Picard leaves in an Iyaaran shuttlecraft to travel to their home world. En route, the shuttle crashes on a remote planet, injuring the pilot. Picard leaves in search of help but is himself injured during a storm. He awakens inside the hulk of a freighter under the watchful eye of Anna, the sole survivor of the crashed vessel.

Anna attempts to keep Picard there and frustrates his every attempt at rescue. She tells him she loves him but he refuses her advances. Anna leaves the wreckage, upset. The shuttle pilot appears and helps Picard search for Anna. Picard finds Anna and figures out that she and the pilot must be working together. Anna suddenly changes into the pilot. He explains that the Iyaarans were trying to study the human emotion of love. Picard and the pilot return to the *Enterprise*.

TRIVIA QUESTIONS
1. Why does Byleth leave Riker's quarters after fighting with Worf? **(3pts)**
2. Where did Picard leave the necklace? **(3pts)**
3. What three qualities does Data tell Worf he shares with Byleth? **(3pts)**
4. Picard is knocked unconscious by what? **(3pts)**
5. What did Worf just do for 11 hours? **(3pts)**
6. What does Byleth steal from Worf? **(3pts)**
7. How do Iyaarans procreate? **(5pts)**
8. What does Byleth want to know in Engineering that Worf is unsure of? **(4pts)**
9. What does the Iyaar home world have? **(4pts)**
10. What dessert is made with 17 varieties of chocolate? **(4pts)**

CHARACTER QUOTE
(2pts per word + 5pts for identifying the speaker.)

Unscramble the words below and then identify the character.

'It's _____ _____ to ____ a _____ _____ is _____ to _____
    RVYE CIEN   NFDI TCEURUL AHTT ILGLWNI   KTEA
an _____ to it's _____ _____.'
    EEPRCXNIEE   HFSRTEUT EMTXEER

✪ SPECIAL ASSIGNMENT (15pts)
What stardate did Anna crash on the planet?

ANSWERS

TRIVIA ANSWERS

1. to document the experience
2. by the fire
3. temperamental, demanding, and rude
4. a plasma discharge
5. engaged Byleth in holodeck battle exercises
6. a couple of poker chips (Worf says two, but camera shot showed three)
7. post-cellular compounding
8. the antimatter replenishment rate
9. the most spectacular crystal formations in the sector
10. Ktarian chocolate puff

CHARACTER QUOTE SOLUTION

"It's very nice to find a culture that is willing to take an experience to its furthest extreme." – Picard

SPECIAL ASSIGNMENT SOLUTION

Stardate: 40812

Congratulations! Starfleet Command is proud to award you the Starfleet Medal of Honour and 15 extra points.

MISSION PERFORMANCE RATING:

55 – 75 points **Superior:** The Iyaarans sent you to experience superior intellect.

50 – 54 points **Above Average:** I wonder if you are whom you appear to be?

40 – 49 points **Average:** The Iyaarans sent you to experience mediocrity.

30 – 39 points **Fair:** The Iyaarans sent you to experience failure.

0 – 29 points **Poor:** Next mission is to crash on a planet and not be rescued!

Geordi tests a new probe-interface combination that allows him to receive information directly through his neural inputs as if he were actually the probe. The *Enterprise* comes to the aid of a science vessel in orbit around a gas giant. Geordi hooks up to the probe and finds the crew of the science vessel all dead. Later, Geordi/probe returns to the science vessel in an effort to retrieve the ship. This time he sees his 'mother' whose ship had recently been reported missing. She tells Geordi that they are dying and must go down towards the planet's surface.

Picard and Dr Crusher think Geordi was hallucinating. Picard decides the probe is too risky to use again and goes with an alternative plan to retrieve the science vessel. Geordi believes his mother is alive and disobeys Picard's orders. Geordi/probe discovers that the science vessel picked up several subspace beings from the lower atmosphere. The beings began to die as the vessel rose into a higher orbit. Direct communication between the subspace beings and the ship's crew resulted in the crew's accidental deaths. Geordi/probe descends in the science vessel and returns the beings to the surface.

TRIVIA QUESTIONS

1. What is the first body found on the science vessel trapped under? **(3pts)**
2. Who does Geordi's mother want him to meet? **(3pts)**
3. The Admiral says the Ferengi have been accused of what? **(5pts)**
4. How far away from the *Enterprise* was the *Hera*'s last reported position? **(4pts)**
5. The particular poem Data is studying when Geordi visits him has a gap of how long in it? **(4pts)**
6. What type of phaser burst does Geordi/probe ask Data for? **(4pts)**
7. How long ago did the *Hera* leave DS3? **(3pts)**
8. How long did DS3 maintain contact with the *Hera*? **(3pts)**
9. What will kick in at 98% of tolerance? **(3pts)**
10. What did Geordi/probe activate to put out the fire? **(3pts)**

SPECIAL ASSIGNMENT (10pts)

The science vessel was to sample the atmosphere how many kilometres below its current position?

MULTIPLE CHOICE QUESTIONS

1. Where on the science vessel is the probe taken since the bridge is badly damaged? **(2pts)**
   - **A.** Captain's quarters
   - **B.** auxiliary control room
   - **C.** engine room
   - **D.** magnetic storage bay

2. When did Geordi receive the last messages from his mother? **(3pts)**
   - **A.** two weeks ago
   - **B.** three days ago
   - **C.** five days ago
   - **D.** three weeks ago

3. What point of entry does Picard recommend for the probe to enter the science vessel? **(3pts)**
   - **A.** aft section through the primary airlock
   - **B.** fore section through the primary airlock
   - **C.** aft section through the secondary airlock
   - **D.** fore section through the secondary airlock

4. The probe transmits information via what? **(5pts)**
   - **A.** focused particle beam
   - **B.** annular confinement beam
   - **C.** encoded carrier wave
   - **D.** subspace amplifier beam

5. Where does Geordi/probe find the rest of the crew's bodies? **(2pts)**
   - **A.** in the Captain's quarters
   - **B.** in the auxiliary control room
   - **C.** on the bridge
   - **D.** in a magnetic storage bay

ANSWERS

TRIVIA ANSWERS

1. some conduit from the bulkhead
2. her Chief Engineer
3. trying to bribe a Breen pilot participating in DS3's palio into throwing the race
4. 300 light years
5. 47 minutes
6. narrow focus, level-4 intensity
7. nine days ago on a routine courier mission
8. for five of nine days since ship left DS3
9. safety override that will disengage the interface
10. emergency suppression system

SPECIAL ASSIGNMENT SOLUTION

approx. 11,000 kilometres
Congratulations! Starfleet Command is proud to award you the Starfleet Medal of Honour and 10 extra points.

MULTIPLE CHOICE ANSWERS

1. B. auxiliary control room
2. D. three weeks ago
3. C. aft section through the secondary airlock
4. A. focused particle beam
5. D. in a magnetic storage bay

MISSION PERFORMANCE RATING:

45 – 60 points **Superior:** You are able to remotely probe distant starships!

40 – 44 points **Above Average:** You *also* converse with subspace beings.

30 – 39 points **Average:** If you can find the *Hera*, you can be her new captain!

20 – 29 points **Fair:** You've been transfered to the *Raman*, so get cracking!

0 – 19 points **Poor:** Hey, weren't you on the *Hera*?

GAMBIT - PART I

Riker leads an undercover away team searching for a missing Picard. He learns that Picard died in a bar fight and tracks the mercenaries responsible to Barradas III. In the ensuing phaser fight, Riker is captured by the mercenaries. The *Enterprise*, however, is unable to track the mercenary ship at warp speeds. Data determines that Calder II will be the next stop for the mercenaries who are plundering ancient Romulan ruins.

Baran, the leader of the mercenaries, decides to keep Riker as a hostage. Riker finds Picard among the crew of the ship, posing as an artefact smuggler. He convinced them that he could be valuable to them and joined their crew. As the episode ends, the mercenaries attack Calder II just as the *Enterprise* shows up.

TRIVIA QUESTIONS

1. Why can't the *Enterprise* track the mercenary ship at warp speed? **(3pts)**
2. What price does the Yridian ask in the bar for his information? **(3pts)**
3. Who is Riker's 'sister'? **(3pts)**
4. The outpost officer says no one is allowed to visit the ruins without authorization from whom? **(3pts)**
5. What did Picard say he tried to smuggle from the ruins on Calder II? **(4pts)**
6. Where was Riker once relieved of command according to Picard? **(4pts)**
7. How many subsystems could be the cause of the problem in the engine's intermix chamber? **(4pts)**
8. What was Barradas III once used for? **(4pts)**
9. Why would the Klingons be interested in the Yridian? **(4pts)**
10. Where does the Yridian want to go instead of being extradited to the Klingons? **(3pts)**

✪ SPECIAL ASSIGNMENT (15pts)

What is the lot number of the first artefact Picard analyzes?

MULTIPLE CHOICE QUESTIONS

1. What defensive capabilities does the Federation outpost have? **(3pts)**
   A. two phaser banks and ten cobalt fusion warheads with magnetic propulsion
   B. Merculite rockets and Artonian lasers
   C. a minimum of two phaser banks and possibly photon torpedoes
   D. multiple phaser banks and antimatter mines

2. What is the device on the side of Riker's neck called? **(2pts)**
   A. pain in the neck
   B. neural servo
   C. pain servo
   D. pain stik

3. Which three planets have Romulan ruins on them? **(5pts)**
   A. Calder II, Draken IV, and Yadalla Prime
   B. Vulcan, Draken IV, and Narenda III
   C. Calder II, Emila II, and Yadalla Prime
   D. Milika III, Draken IV, and Volchok Prime

4. What readings does Dr Crusher's tricorder get from the bar floor? **(3pts)**
   A. human cellular debris
   B. Starfleet fibre traces
   C. microcrystalline damage
   D. traces of Picard's DNA

5. What readings does Dr Crusher's tricorder get from the bar wall? **(2pts)**
   A. traces of Picard's DNA
   B. Starfleet fibre traces and human cellular debris
   C. microcrystalline damage
   D. tachyon residue

ANSWERS

TRIVIA ANSWERS

1. it is encased in an energy-absorbing material, rendering it invisible to sensors
2. five bars of gold-pressed latinum
3. Dr Crusher
4. Federation Science Council
5. Sakethan Glyph Stone
6. the Cardassian Incident at Minos Korva
7. any one of 30
8. as an outpost of the Debrune civilization almost 2,000 years ago
9. he has 12 outstanding arrest warrants for fraud and petty theft throughout the Klingon Empire
10. the Federation Rehabilitation Colony

SPECIAL ASSIGNMENT SOLUTION

Lot Number 478B
Congratulations! Starfleet Command is proud to award you the Starfleet Medal of Honour and 15 extra points.

MULTIPLE CHOICE ANSWERS

1. C. a minimum of two phaser banks and possibly photon torpedoes
2. B. neural servo
3. A. Calder II, Draken IV, and Yadalla Prime
4. C. microcrystalline damage
5. B. Starfleet fibre traces and human cellular debris

MISSION PERFORMANCE RATING:

45 – 65 points **Superior:** So you like to switch transponder codes, do you?

40 – 44 points **Above Average:** You're pretty handy with a magnaspanner.

30 – 39 points **Average:** Let me turn up the pain level on your neural servo.

20 – 29 points **Fair:** Baran's looking for some cannon fodder for the next raid!

0 – 19 points **Poor:** You're just a bunch of cellular debris and Starfleet fibres!

GAMBIT - PART II ⚛

Riker and Picard help the mercenaries attack the *Enterprise*. The pair, in concert with Data on the *Enterprise*, make it appear that the attack has damaged the Federation flagship.

Picard learns that a mercenary posing as a Romulan is actually a Vulcan. Tallera tells Picard that Baran's crew has been hired by an extremist Vulcan group to find the components of an ancient Vulcan weapon.

Meanwhile, the *Enterprise* detains a Klingon shuttle pilot who has one of the pieces Baran needs. Baran sends a raiding party aboard the *Enterprise*, led by Picard and Riker. Picard supposedly kills Riker and then returns to the mercenary ship. Picard starts a mutiny on the ship and Baran is killed. Picard takes over and the ship heads to Vulcan to deliver the cargo.

The mercenaries send an away team to Vulcan to deliver the merchandise and collect their fee. Tallera assembles the weapon and uses it to kill the others in the away team. Picard quickly determines how the weapon works and is able to render it inoperative.

TRIVIA QUESTIONS

1. Baran wants Picard to prepare a party of five for what? **(3pts)**
2. What excuse does Worf use to detain the Klingon shuttlecraft pilot? **(3pts)**
3. What is the name of the ancient Vulcan weapon? **(3pts)**
4. What is Picard's first official act as the new captain of the mercenary ship? **(3pts)**
5. Where are the two artifacts to be delivered? **(5pts)**
6. Which two Vulcan gods are described on the anterior side of the artefact? **(3pts)**
7. What sensible thing did Picard do? **(3pts)**
8. The captured mercenaries face charges from whom? **(4pts)**
9. What agency does Tallera tell Picard she belongs to? **(4pts)**
10. Data says Riker technically faces what? **(4pts)**

SPECIAL ASSIGNMENT (10pts)

Which file on the navigational computer contains the secret message sent to the *Enterprise*?

MULTIPLE CHOICE QUESTIONS

1. How did Riker track Picard to the caverns? **(3pts)**
   A. using Picard's com badge signal
   B. using Picard's neural implant
   C. using a bioscan from *Enterprise*'s lateral sensor array
   D. using his intuition and information from Tallera

2. How does Picard know the second artefact is real? **(5pts)**
   A. he translates the inscription
   B. the computer scan analysis rated it at a 98.4% match
   C. the artefact pieces fit together
   D. he recognizes the inscription pattern from the first artefact

3. What does the Klingon do with the drink Data gives him? **(3pts)**
   A. slowly pours it onto the floor
   B. rapidly drinks it and then smashes the glass against the wall
   C. quickly pours it onto Data's lap
   D. throws it in Data's face

4. Why is Baran supposed to meet with the Klingon vessel? **(2pts)**
   A. the Klingon will take the artefacts and deliver them to the Vulcans
   B. the Klingon is delivering another artefact to Baran
   C. the Klingon knows where the last artefact is
   D. the Klingon wishes to join the mercenary group

5. Data orders what released to simulate damage to the *Enterprise*? **(2pts)**
   A. attitude stabilizers
   B. a plasma stream
   C. inertial dampers
   D. saucer section

ANSWERS

TRIVIA ANSWERS

1. raiding the *Enterprise*
2. needs to perform a Health and Safety inspection
3. the Stone of Gol
4. he destroys Baran's neural servo control box
5. to the T'Karath Sanctuary on Vulcan
6. the god of war and the god of death
7. switched Baran's neural servo transponder codes with his own
8. Klingons, Ferengi, Cardassians, and at least seven other worlds
9. V'Shar – Vulcan Security
10. 12 counts of court-martial offences

SPECIAL ASSIGNMENT SOLUTION

File 137/Omega

Congratulations! Starfleet Command is proud to award you the Starfleet Medal of Honour and 10 extra points.

MULTIPLE CHOICE ANSWERS

1. B. using Picard's neural implant
2. D. he recognizes the inscription pattern from the first artefact
3. A. slowly pours it onto the floor
4. B. the Klingon is delivering another artefact to Baran
5. C. inertial dampers

MISSION PERFORMANCE RATING:

45 – 60 points **Superior:** The V'Shar have offered you a job!

40 – 44 points **Above Average:** So you pieced the weapon mystery together.

30 – 39 points **Average:** Your neural servo implant needs replacing.

20 – 29 points **Fair:** You're wanted in over 17 systems for whatchamacallit.

0 – 19 points **Poor:** Pick up the phaser while I hold the Stone of Gol.

PHANTASMS

STARDATE: 47225.7

Data begins to experience nightmares during his dream cycle and Troi figures prominently in them. Later, Data starts to have hallucinations while awake. In one such hallucination, he sees a mouth on Troi's shoulder and stabs it, injuring her.

Dr Crusher notices a rash where Data stabbed Troi. Further investigation reveals a creature feeding on Troi's cellular peptides. The creatures are found throughout the *Enterprise*, feeding on most of the crew. Although the creatures are just outside sensory range, Data seems to sense the creatures on an unconscious level.

Picard hopes that by exploring Data's dreams they might be able to learn more about the creatures. Geordi is able to hook Data into the holodeck so that his dreams will be recreated there. Data determines that an interphasic pulse will kill the creatures. He sends a pulse throughout the ship, ridding the *Enterprise* of the infestation.

TRIVIA QUESTIONS

1. What must Picard do in light of Data's behaviour in stabbing Troi? **(3pts)**
2. In Data's second dream where does he first appear? **(3pts)**
3. What do the workmen do to Data during his first dream? **(3pts)**
4. Where was the plasma conduit manufactured using a new interphasic fusing process? **(5pts)**
5. What will happen if the organisms aren't removed? **(4pts)**
6. What does Troi bring Data as turnabout? **(3pts)**
7. How do the organisms attach to the epidermal layers? **(4pts)**
8. What does Alexander play all night? **(3pts)**
9. What type of cake is Worf eating? **(3pts)**
10. What is Dr Crusher doing to Riker in Data's dreams? **(3pts)**

✪✪ SIGNIFICANT NUMBERS (2pts each)

Match the clues with the correct number. Some numbers may be used more than once.

Clues

1. Which starbase did the *Enterprise* obtain the new warp core from?
2. Which feline supplement does Spot prefer to eat?
3. Which starbase is hosting the Admiral's Banquet this year?
4. How many muscle spasms has Spot had according to Data?
5. How many admirals will be at the Admiral's Banquet?
6. Picard has avoided the Admiral's Banquet for the last how many years?
7. For how many minutes has Data been watching Spot sleep?

---

8. How many dreams has Data had since discovering his dream programme?
9. How many months ago did Data discover his dream programme?
10. What level diagnostic is Data running on the relays?
11. How many centimetres long was the knife Data used to cut the cake in his dreams?
12. How many minutes did it take Troi, Worf, and Geordi to wake Data?
13. How many minutes ago was Data supposed to have awakened?

Numbers

A. 15
B. 3
C. 6
D. 9
E. 219
F. 111
G. 25
H. 84
I. 5
J. 12
K. 35
L. 50

ANSWERS

TRIVIA ANSWERS

1. relieve him of command and confine him to his quarters
2. in Ten-Forward
3. they rip his arms, legs, and head off
4. Thanatos VII
5. their bodies will lose cellular cohesion and collapse into a few pounds of chemicals
6. a cake in the shape of Data
7. using osmotic tendrils
8. the jazz music programme Riker gave him
9. cellular peptide cake with mint frosting
10. sucking his brains out through a straw

SIGNIFICANT NUMBERS ANSWERS

1. H 84; 2. G 25; 3. E 219; 4. J 12; 5. L 50; 6. C 6; 7. A 15; 8. F 111; 9. D 9; 10. B 3; 11. G 25; 12. I 5; 13. K 35

MISSION PERFORMANCE RATING:

30 – 60 points **Superior:** You're Starfleet's top psychoanalyst!

25 – 29 points **Above Average:** Chef in training, huh? Great cake!

20 – 24 points **Average:** You *forgot* to feed Spot!

10 – 19 points **Fair:** Take this pickaxe and go work on the plasma conduit.

0 – 9 points **Poor:** They need another cellular peptide cake in Ten-Forward.

Lwaxana is preparing a telepathic race, known as the Cairn, for a meeting with Federation officials. Being an exclusively telepathic race, Lwaxana must teach them to communicate verbally. Lwaxana suddenly falls into a coma.

Troi and Maques feel that some psychic trauma from the past has resurfaced and caused Lwaxana's coma. Troi searches through her mother's journals for clues and with Picard's help she finds an unexplained gap in her mother's journals. Troi goes into her mother's mind and confronts Lwaxana. Eventually, she reveals that Troi had an older sister who died in an accident. Lwaxana blames herself and Troi helps her mother forgive herself. Lwaxana comes out of her coma and begins the healing process.

TRIVIA QUESTIONS

1. What does Hedril do in the arboretum just before Lwaxana goes into a coma? **(3pts)**
2. What are the two children in the arboretum near the pool of water doing? **(3pts)**
3. Who is Lwaxana preparing the Cairn to meet? **(3pts)**
4. What have the Cairn never used until now? **(3pts)**
5. What events mark the beginning and the end of the seven year gap in Lwaxana's journals? **(5pts)**
6. When did Lwaxana delete the files from her journal? **(4pts)**
7. Mr Homn saved a picture of whom? **(3pts)**
8. Where did Deanna and her family live on Betazed when she was a baby? **(4pts)**
9. What is special about the Jewel plant? **(3pts)**
10. Which poet does Deanna quote? **(4pts)**

MULTIPLE CHOICE QUESTIONS

1. How much of her mother's journal has Deanna read when Picard asks her? **(3pts)**
    A. all of it
    B. the first seven years
    C. the last five years
    D. the last thirty years

2. What was Deanna's sister chasing when she drowned? **(2pts)**
    A. family dog
    B. Tarkassian razorbeast
    C. stray dog
    D. Deanna

---

3. Where did the accident happen with Deanna's sister? **(3pts)**
    A. near a river during a flood
    B. at a pond while she was with Deanna
    C. beside some cliffs near the ocean
    D. at a lake while on a picnic with the entire family

4. Where does Deanna end up after stepping off into empty space at the end of the corridor? **(4pts)**
    A. Ten-Forward
    B. her quarters
    C. arboretum
    D. her childhood house

5. What greeting could Maques not remember when he first met Deanna? **(3pts)**
    A. 'Pleased to meet you.'
    B. 'I've heard a lot about you!'
    C. 'Hello, how are you?'
    D. 'Let's get married.'

ANSWERS

TRIVIA ANSWERS
1. she falls into the pool of water
2. playing ball
3. Federation Council
4. a spoken language
5. begins one year after Lwaxana's wedding and ends a couple of months after Deanna was born
6. almost 30 years ago
7. a picture of Kestra, Deanna, and their father
8. near Lake El'nar
9. plant secretes a resin which collects in the blossom and hardens into a rare and beautiful gem
10. John Milton

MULTIPLE CHOICE ANSWERS
1. C. the last five years
2. A. family dog
3. D. at a lake while on a picnic with the entire family
4. C. arboretum
5. A. 'Pleased to meet you.'

MISSION PERFORMANCE RATING:

45 – 50 points **Superior:** Your mind is spotless and your psyche strong!

40 – 44 points **Above Average:** No dark areas in your mind.

30 – 39 points **Average:** Your mind is a scary place to roam.

20 – 29 points **Fair:** Your psyche has collapsed into the basement of your mind.

0 – 19 points **Poor:** You've lost your mind and can't remember where it is.

The *Enterprise* goes to Kesprytt III to deal with a request for associate membership of the Federation. The planet is split into two spheres of influence, the democratic Kes and the xenophobic Prytt. As Picard and Dr Crusher prepare to beam down to meet with Kes officials, the transporter beam is redirected to a Prytt security cell.

Picard and Dr Crusher later discover that they have been given some form of neural implant. A Kes operative, however, helps Picard and Dr Crusher escape from the detention cell. As time goes by Picard and Dr Crusher realize that they can hear each other's thoughts via the neural implants. The next day Picard and Dr Crusher make it to the border and back to the *Enterprise*. Although their relationship has been enriched by this intimate form of communication, Picard and Beverly decide to remain friends only.

TRIVIA QUESTIONS

1. The Prytt suspect the Kes of preparing to use Federation technology to build what? **(3pts)**
2. Where on Dr Crusher's tricorder has something been added? **(4pts)**
3. What do the Prytt think the Kes and Federation are trying to establish? **(3pts)**
4. The Kes suspect the Prytt of preparing to use Federation aid to do what? **(4pts)**
5. What remark ended Dr Crusher's sole date with Tom? **(5pts)**
6. In which village are Picard and Dr Crusher supposed to meet with the Kes operatives? **(4pts)**
7. What is the name of the Kes facility in charge of the defensive shields? **(3pts)**
8. What are the implants connected directly to? **(3pts)**
9. What do the Prytt charge Picard and Dr Crusher with? **(3pts)**
10. The implanted devices will soon be calibrated to what? **(3pts)**

SPECIAL ASSIGNMENT (10pts)

Where is the modulation frequency found for setting up a multiphase pulse using a tricorder?

MULTIPLE CHOICE QUESTIONS

1. Which two ingredients for vegetable soup did Dr Crusher mention? **(4pts)**
    A. beef shank and carrots
    B. peas and carrots
    C. corn and potatoes
    D. peas and corn

2. Whom does Worf say is hailing the *Enterprise*? **(3pts)**
   - **A.** Prytt Security Ministry
   - **B.** Kes Ambassador
   - **C.** Prytt Prime Minister
   - **D.** Prytt Security Council

3. What has been added to Dr Crusher's tricorder? **(2pts)**
   - **A.** a map of the escape route
   - **B.** a multiphase pulse generator
   - **C.** a world map of Kesprytt III
   - **D.** an emergency transponder

4. How does Dr Crusher open their cell door? **(3pts)**
   - **A.** uses the tricorder to manually override the security lockout
   - **B.** feigns injury and the guard opens the cell door to check on her
   - **C.** uses the code that has been entered into her tricorder
   - **D.** shorts out Picard's neural implant with tricorder to bypass door's security lock

5. How much of the planet do the Kes occupy? **(3pts)**
   - **A.** 60% of the planet
   - **B.** 45% of the planet
   - **C.** nearly ½ of the planet
   - **D.** nearly ¾ of the planet

MISSION PERFORMANCE RATING:

45 – 60 points **Superior:** We'll go with your recommendation on the Kes.

40 – 44 points **Above Average:** You heard that, didn't you?

30 – 39 points **Average:** You've been accused of spying by both sides!

20 – 29 points **Fair:** You've been arrested by Prytt security forces.

0 – 19 points **Poor:** You were last seen running from Prytt security forces!

FORCE OF NATURE

STARDATE: 47310.2

The *Enterprise* searches for the missing Federation ship, the *Fleming*, in the Hekaras Corridor. The corridor provides safe passage through some unusual navigational hazards in the sector. The *Enterprise* is disabled by a device hidden in a debris field.

Shortly thereafter, a small ship approaches with two Hekaran scientists aboard. The scientists tell the crew that warp drive is damaging the subspace fabric of this area. They have mined the corridor to call attention to the problem.

Data's analysis of the scientists' research leads him to conclude that their theories may be correct but he cannot be certain. One of the scientists flies off and causes her ship to self-destruct. The explosion rips open a rift in subspace and proves her theories correct. The *Fleming* is sucked into the rift but the *Enterprise* is able to rescue the survivors. The Federation then decides to set a speed limit on warp drive after the incident.

TRIVIA QUESTIONS

1. Who evaluated Serova's preliminary research? **(3pts)**
2. What poses a navigational hazard to warp driven vessels in the Hekaras region? **(3pts)**
3. What does Serova do to her ship? **(3pts)**
4. What is the subspace rift generating? **(3pts)**
5. Data says that to prove Serova's theory, an area would have to be exposed to what? **(5pts)**
6. Why was Geordi taking care of Spot? **(3pts)**
7. What are the Hekaran mines disguised as? **(3pts)**
8. The *Intrepid*'s chief engineer tells Geordi he should try what? **(3pts)**
9. How did Geordi's sister train her cat to jump into her arms on command? **(4pts)**
10. What type of Ferengi ship is encountered in the corridor? **(5pts)**

✪✪ SIGNIFICANT NUMBERS (1pt each)

Match the clues with the correct number. Some numbers may be used more than once.

Clues

1. What percentage is the maximum saturation level for the nacelles?
2. For how many seconds does the *Enterprise* fire its warp engines at maximum intensity to create a warp pulse?
3. Worf reports damage to which decks after the *Fleming* initiates their warp drive within the rift?

---

4. The subspace rift increased by what percentage when the *Fleming* initiated their warp drive?
5. On which decks did the structural integrity fields fail when the *Enterprise* rode the distortion wave?
6. Hull stress is what percentage above tolerance when Worf says a structural breech is imminent?
7. What Warp is the speed limit set at?
8. How many light years away do the long range sensors locate the *Fleming*?
9. How many hours before the *Fleming*'s shields fail after being caught in the subspace rift?
10. How many metres in diameter is the small metallic object sensors detect in the debris field?
11. Which feline supplement does Data feed Spot?
12. How many light years in diameter is the subspace rift initially?
13. Which decks received minimal damage from the Ferengi weapons fire?
14. How many hours does Geordi say it will take to restore warp engines?
15. How many hours before Serova can have the warp engines back on-line?
16. What percentage did the chief engineer get the *Intrepid*'s power conversion level to?
17. How many days would it take to complete a level-1 search of the corridor?
18. Approximately how many light years long is the Hekaras Corridor?
19. What percentage did Geordi get the *Enterprise*'s power conversion level to?
20. How many days ago did the *Fleming* last contact Starfleet?

Numbers
A. 120
B. 36
C. 97.1
D. 5
E. 18.3
F. 3.5
G. 97.2
H. 2.3
I. 221
J. 4
K. 6, 14
L. 10
M. 2
N. 12
O. 0.3
P. 6.3
Q. 0.1
R. 10–16
S. 5, 7

ANSWERS

TRIVIA ANSWERS

1. Federation Science Council
2. unusually intense tetryon field
3. creates a warp core breech
4. high energy distortion waves
5. warp field energy one million times greater than that produced by a starship
6. he wanted to experience what it was like before getting a cat of his own
7. Federation signal buoys
8. cleaning the plasma grid once in a while
9. she walked around for two months with a piece of tuna in her blouse
10. Ferengi D'Kora class transport ship

SIGNIFICANT NUMBERS ANSWERS

1. E 18.3; 2. P 6.3; 3. K 6, 14; 4. H 2.3;
5. R 10–16; 6. A 120; 7. D 5; 8. O 0.3;
9. N 12; 10. F 3.5; 11. I 22I; 12. Q 0.1;
13. S 5, 7; 14. N 12; 15. L 10; 16. C 97.1;
17. M 2; 18. N 12; 19. G 97.2; 20. J 4

MISSION PERFORMANCE RATING:

30 – 55 points **Superior:** You got the power conversion level up to 97.4%.

25 – 29 points **Above Average:** You got us out of the rift! Good work.

20 – 24 points **Average:** This piece of tuna is for you. Now go train Spot.

10 – 19 points **Fair:** Go deactivate the verteron mines and take a shuttle.

0 – 9 points **Poor:** Geordi will be in charge of your training. He likes phasers.

INHERITANCE ⚙

The *Enterprise* assists scientists from Atrea III with a geological disaster on their planet. Because their planet's core is cooling, Geordi and Data suggest a plasma infusion to reliquefy it. One of the Atrean scientists admits to Data that she is the former wife of Dr Soong, his creator. They spend some time together getting to know one another better. Data notices several unusual things that lead him to deduce that his mother, Juliana, is not human.

While preparing the sites for the plasma infusion on the planet, an accident leaves Juliana unconscious and dismembered, confirming Data's suspicions. A message from Dr Soong explains that the real Juliana was dying and he created another android in her image. Dr Soong never told Juliana she was an artificial life form. Data decides it's best not to tell his mother, either. The *Enterprise* is successful in solving Atrea III's problem and Data says good-bye to his mother.

TRIVIA QUESTIONS

1. What convention did Data feel it was unnecessary to follow during his early years? **(3pts)**
2. Where is the music recital held? **(3pts)**
3. Why did Juliana and Soong marry secretly? **(3pts)**
4. What excuse did Juliana give for leaving Data behind on Omicron Theta? **(3pts)**
5. What does Geordi find while poking around in Juliana's head? **(3pts)**
6. Why do scans show Juliana as human? **(4pts)**
7. In what style is the second of Data's paintings that Juliana looks at done? **(5pts)**
8. What did Geordi reconfigure the phasers to create? **(3pts)**
9. Who can't confirm that Juliana and Soong were married on Mavala IV? **(5pts)**
10. What will be set up in the pockets within the magma layer? **(3pts)**

CHARACTER QUOTE
(2pts per word + 3pts for identifying the speaker.)

Unscramble the words below and then identify the character.

'_____ of the _____ _____ to _____ an _____
MSEO   ILNOSCTSO EBTJODEC VGHNAI MLATCOYIAANL

_____ _____ _____ _____ _____ any _____ on.'
RTOCRCE RIADODN UNIRGNN URDNAO HUWTOIT   HLSCTEO

SPECIAL ASSIGNMENT (10pts)

Which database does Data consult to check passenger manifests?

ANSWERS

TRIVIA ANSWERS

1. wearing clothes
2. Ten-Forward
3. her mother thought Soong was too old and eccentric
4. there was only room for two in the escape pod
5. an information module with a holographic interface
6. she has a feedback processor designed to send out a false biosignal
7. early French Impressionist
8. a highly focused particle beam
9. Registrar's office
10. plasma infusion units

CHARACTER QUOTE SOLUTION

'Some of the colonists objected to having an anatomically correct android running around without any clothes on.' – Juliana

SPECIAL ASSIGNMENT SOLUTION

Commercial Transport Database Archive
Congratulations! Starfleet Command is proud to award you the Starfleet Medal of Honour and 10 extra points.

MISSION PERFORMANCE RATING:

55 – 70 points **Superior:** Your modesty programme has failed.

50 – 54 points **Above Average:** What painting phase are you in?

40 – 49 points **Average:** You play the viola like a human.

30 – 39 points **Fair:** Data's going to rip his arm off and beat you with it!

0 – 29 points **Poor:** Hey, you're not only adopted, you're an android too!

Worf returns to the *Enterprise* on a shuttlecraft after attending a nearby bat'leth competition. Soon, he begins to experience subtle shifts in reality. Worf suddenly finds himself on the bridge but unable to raise the shields during a Cardassian attack. The *Enterprise*, with Riker as captain, is badly damaged and Geordi mortally wounded. Worf also discovers he is married to Troi. He tells her about the shifts and together they work with the crew to determine what is happening.

It seems Worf's shuttlecraft passed through a quantum fissure, causing him to jump between an infinite number of parallel universes. As the phenomenon increases, alternate *Enterprises* begin appearing. Data concludes that the rift in the space/time continuum can be closed by sending Worf back through the rift in his original shuttlecraft. As Worf makes his way towards the rift in the shuttlecraft, one of the *Enterprises* fires on him. They have come from a Borg ravaged universe and don't want to go back. Riker's ship returns fire to protect the shuttlecraft and destroys the other Borg-universe *Enterprise*. Worf makes it through the fissure and all is normal again.

TRIVIA QUESTIONS

1. Why can't Worf raise the shields? **(3pts)**
2. What trophy does Worf possess in the reality where he lost the competition? **(3pts)**
3. Where was the bat'leth competition held? **(3pts)**
4. How many hails does the *Enterprise* receive? **(4pts)**
5. At one point, Worf and Troi have a three-year-old boy named what? **(4pts)**
6. What does Data detect in Worf's cellular RNA? **(3pts)**
7. Which episode is alluded to in which Picard supposedly died? **(3pts)**
8. Based on the shuttle logs, what illegal move was used against Worf during the competition? **(5pts)**
9. Worf wants Troi to become his what? **(4pts)**
10. What song was very hard to translate into Klingon? **(3pts)**

✪ SPECIAL ASSIGNMENT (15pts)

Which four Federation sites were targeted for observation by the Cardassians via the Argus Array?

MULTIPLE CHOICE QUESTIONS

1. Troi tells Worf he probably wants to be alone on his birthday so he can do what? **(2pts)**
   - **A.** smash a glass table
   - **B.** kill something on the holodeck
   - **C.** sulk about how old he is getting
   - **D.** meditate or hit himself with a painstik

2. What has Data remodulated the shuttle's engines to emit? **(3pts)**
   - **A.** a quantum flux field
   - **B.** an inverse warp field
   - **C.** a tachyon pulse
   - **D.** a subspace warp stream

3. How long does Data say Worf and Troi have been married? **(5pts)**
   - **A.** three years, two months and 22 days
   - **B.** two years, one month and 12 days
   - **C.** two years, two months and six days
   - **D.** three years, one month and ten days

4. What birthday present did Worf receive from Alexander? **(3pts)**
   - **A.** a cast of his hands and feet
   - **B.** a new bat'leth
   - **C.** a cast of his forehead
   - **D.** a reality shifting device

5. What does Worf call a surprise birthday party? **(2pts)**
   - **A.** an unanticipated social meeting
   - **B.** an unforeseen social throng
   - **C.** an unexpected social gathering
   - **D.** an abrupt social gathering

ANSWERS

TRIVIA ANSWERS

1. it's a different panel configuration
2. ninth place
3. Forcas III
4. 285,000
5. Eric-Christopher
6. quantum flux
7. 'The Best of Both Worlds'
8. T'gha Manoeuvre
9. Soh-chIm
10. *For He's A Jolly Good Fellow*

SPECIAL ASSIGNMENT SOLUTION

Deep Space 5, Starbase 47, Iadara Colony, and Utopia Planitia Fleet Yards

Congratulations! Starfleet Command is proud to award you the Starfleet Medal of Honour and 15 extra points.

MULTIPLE CHOICE ANSWERS

1. D. meditate or hit himself with a painstik
2. B. an inverse warp field
3. B. two years, one month and 12 days
4. C. a cast of his forehead
5. C. an unexpected social gathering

MISSION PERFORMANCE RATING:

45 – 65 points   **Superior:** You must be close to that promotion to Admiral by now!

40 – 44 points   **Above Average:** You really are the Captain!

30 – 39 points   **Average:** In some other universe you could be a captain!

20 – 29 points   **Fair:** In some universe Wesley's a lieutenant; what are you?

0 – 19 points   **Poor:** Yah, yah, you're trapped in the wrong reality and . . .

THE PEGASUS

STARDATE: 47457.1

Admiral Pressman, former captain of the *Pegasus*, accompanies the *Enterprise* on a secret mission to find the missing Federation ship. Riker was serving under Pressman at the time the ship was lost. Picard asks Riker about what happened but the Commander is under orders from the Admiral not to talk about it.

The *Enterprise* arrives at the search site, an asteroid field, and finds a Romulan ship in the area supposedly doing research. The *Enterprise* begins searching and soon locates the *Pegasus* deep within one of the asteroids. Picard reluctantly takes the *Enterprise* into a fissure in the side of the asteroid. Pressman and Riker then beam over to the *Pegasus* to retrieve an experimental cloaking/phasing device.

The Romulans seal the entrance to the fissure, trapping the *Enterprise* inside the asteroid. Geordi is able to hook up the device to the *Enterprise* and the ship easily passes to the surface. As the cloaking/phasing device violates a treaty, Picard informs the Romulans of the incident and then places Pressman under arrest.

TRIVIA QUESTIONS

1. What would it take to destroy the asteroid containing the *Pegasus*? **(3pts)**
2. Where does Starfleet Intelligence have an operative? **(3pts)**
3. What has Picard arranged to have next month? **(3pts)**
4. What is special about the cloaking device removed from the *Pegasus*? **(3pts)**
5. When the *Pegasus* was lost, how long had Riker been out of the Academy? **(5pts)**
6. What are the Romulans supposedly doing in the asteroid system? **(3pts)**
7. What was the supposed cause of the *Pegasus'* destruction? **(3pts)**
8. How many of the *Pegasus'* crew supposedly made it to the escape pods? **(5pts)**
9. What starship does the *Enterprise* meet with? **(3pts)**
10. When was the *Pegasus* lost? **(4pts)**

✪✪ MATHEMATICALLY SPEAKING (15pts)

Add the following numbers together:

1. How many hours has the *Enterprise* been trapped when the cloaking device is ready to use? **(2pts)**
2. How many kilometres of rock did the *Enterprise* have to pass through to

---

exit the asteroid? **(2pts)**

3. Picard will abort the mission if the fissure narrows to less than how many metres wide? **(2pts)**
4. What percentage of the Pegasus is contained within the asteroid? **(2pts)**
5. Within how many kilometres does the *Enterprise* get to the asteroid when they return the next morning? **(2pts)**
6. What is the dosage (in cubic centimetres) of the pain relieving drug given to Riker? **(2pts)**

Total: _____

What is the significance of this number in relation to the episode? **(3pts)**

ANSWERS

TRIVIA ANSWERS

1. most of the *Enterprise's* photon torpedoes
2. in the Romulan High Command
3. a Commander Riker Day
4. it changes the structure of matter, allowing a ship to pass through normal matter
5. seven months
6. conducting a survey of gaseous anomalies
7. a warp core breech
8. nine in total (Riker, Pressman, and seven others)
9. *Crazy Horse*
10. 12 years ago

MATHEMATICALLY SPEAKING

1. 8
2. 3 (Worf said they passed through 2 kilometres and had 1 kilometre to the surface)
3. 500
4. 65
5. 15
6. 10
Total: 601
The *Pegasus* is located in asteroid Gamma 601.

MISSION PERFORMANCE RATING:

45 – 50 points **Superior:** The *Pegasus* is yours, Captain, if you can get it out!

40 – 44 points **Above Average:** Prelaw student, huh? You're gonna need it!

30 – 39 points **Average:** Get a shuttle and check out that fissure over there.

20 – 29 points **Fair:** Only half of your brain rematerialized outside the rock.

0 – 19 points **Poor:** You know what Starfleet does to mutineers? It isn't pretty!

The *Enterprise* responds to a distress call from Worf's stepbrother, Nikolai, on Boraal II. The planet's atmosphere is dissipating and all life will die on the planet in a short time. Worf beams down alone to search for his brother and finds that Nikolai has broken the Prime Directive.

Picard refuses to interfere with the situation on the planet. While Picard and the rest of the crew watch the final stages of the planet's destruction, Nikolai beams the villagers to the holodeck where he has created a programme of the caves on Boraal II. Picard, without any other options, utilizes the *Enterprise* crew to find a suitable planet for resettlement. Worf and Nikolai lead the villagers on a holodeck journey to a place that looks like their new home world. The Boraalans and Nikolai are then discreetly beamed down to the planet's surface.

TRIVIA QUESTIONS

1. What is Nikolai's mission on Boraal II? **(3pts)**
2. What did Vorin finally decide to do? **(3pts)**
3. What part of the *Enterprise* did Vorin wander into? **(3pts)**
4. Where does the holodeck first destabilize? **(3pts)**
5. What does Worf take as he prepares to leave Vacca VI? **(3pts)**
6. How long have the Boraalans maintained their chronicle? **(5pts)**
7. How much of the Boraalan chronicle was Vorin able to save? **(4pts)**
8. What is a good omen to travellers? **(3pts)**
9. Which holodeck has Nikolai beamed the Boraalans to? **(5pts)**
10. What is destroying the planet's atmosphere on Boraal II? **(3pts)**

CHARACTER QUOTE
(2pts per word + 4pts for identifying the speaker.)

Unscramble the words below and then identify the character.

'I _____ _____ to let _____ _____ ___ ___ _____
   NTAWS' IGNGO   ESHTE EOLPEP IDE SJTU AECUEBS

____ _____ _____ _____ _____ _____ to me.'
UYRO APNCITA DTTRSAE TUNOIQG ANRIDOFETE GDMOA

✪ SPECIAL ASSIGNMENT (15pts)

Which aft bridge station shorts out?

ANSWERS

TRIVIA ANSWERS

1. cultural observer
2. perform ritual suicide
3. Ten-Forward
4. a pool of water
5. one of the Boraalans' chronicle scrolls
6. 17 generations
7. only the last six generations
8. the Sign of La Forge
9. Holodeck 5
10. intense plasmodic reactions

CHARACTER QUOTE SOLUTION

'I wasn't going to let these people die just because your captain started quoting Federation dogma to me.' – Nikolai

SPECIAL ASSIGNMENT SOLUTION

Science Station II

Congratulations! Starfleet Command is proud to award you the Starfleet Medal of Honour and 15 extra points.

MISSION PERFORMANCE RATING:

60 – 80 points **Superior:** You're in charge of the Boraalan relocation project.

50 – 59 points **Above Average:** You are the new chronicler for the Boraalans.

40 – 49 points **Average:** You've been promoted to cultural observer on Kataan.

30 – 39 points **Fair:** It's the Sign of La Fair – a bad omen for getting promoted.

0 – 29 points **Poor:** Wesley will graduate before you reach lieutenant.

Dr Crusher attends the funeral of her grandmother, Felisa Howard, at Caldos Colony. Later, she goes to her grandmother's house and meets the groundskeeper who warns her not to stay or she'll end up like Felisa.

Dr Crusher reads her grandmother's journals and learns that Felisa was having an affair with a young man named Ronin. Later, Dr Crusher has several erotic encounters with the ghostly presence of Ronin. Ronin is an anaphasic parasite that has fed on the Howard women through the centuries due to their unique biochemistry. However, Ronin's bonding with the women also poisons them. Dr Crusher and the crew uncover the truth and put an end to Ronin's parasitic ways.

TRIVIA QUESTIONS

1. What is a caber toss? **(5pts)**
2. How old was Felisa when she died? **(3pts)**
3. Caldos is one of the Federation's first what? **(3pts)**
4. How far is Caldos from Earth? **(4pts)**
5. Why do anaphasic beings need an organic host? **(3pts)**
6. Troi asks Dr Crusher if she's going to what class? **(3pts)**
7. What year does Ronin say he was born? **(4pts)**
8. How old is Ronin according to Felisa's journals? **(3pts)**
9. When did Felisa and Ronin first meet? **(3pts)**
10. How long has the weather control system been working perfectly? **(4pts)**

✪✪ SPECIAL ASSIGNMENT (15pts)

When Dr Crusher and Troi are standing in the cemetery talking, what is the name on the gravestone visible in the background between them?

MULTIPLE CHOICE QUESTIONS

1. What does Dr Crusher tell Riker to close off after she destroys the candle? **(5pts)**
    A. the *Enterprise*'s plasma vents
    B. the primary plasma conduit
    C. the plasma conduits in the weather control system
    D. the plasma transponder on the surface

---

2. What do Geordi and Data want to do at Felisa's grave site? **(2pts)**
   - **A.** exhume her body
   - **B.** mourn her passing
   - **C.** analyze soil samples
   - **D.** wait for Ronin to show up

3. What does Dr Crusher use the computer to do while she is in her quarters? **(3pts)**
   - **A.** access a database on Caldos Colony
   - **B.** replicate a glass of tea
   - **C.** light the candle
   - **D.** secure the door

4. Why can't Data disengage the power transfer to the surface? **(3pts)**
   - **A.** Ned has dismantled the primary power conduit at the surface substation
   - **B.** Ronin is sleeping inside the transfer beam
   - **C.** a feedback loop has formed in the transfer beam
   - **D.** a power coupling failure has destabilized the remote disengage

5. What are Dr Crusher and Troi meeting in Ten-Forward to discuss? **(2pts)**
   - **A.** upcoming mental competency hearing for Lieutenant Barclay
   - **B.** personnel reports
   - **C.** last night's dates
   - **D.** plans for Worf's next birthday party

ANSWERS

TRIVIA ANSWERS

1. an ancient Scottish contest where a long heavy pole is tossed end over end as a show of strength
2. 100 years old
3. terraforming projects
4. 200 light years
5. to maintain molecular cohesion
6. Mok'bara
7. 1647
8. 34 years old
9. shortly after the death of Dr Crusher's great-grandmother
10. 22 years

SPECIAL ASSIGNMENT

McFly.

Congratulations! Starfleet Command is proud to award you the Starfleet Medal of Honour and 15 extra points.

MULTIPLE CHOICE

1. C. the plasma conduits in the weather control system
2. A. exhume her body
3. D. secure the door
4. C. a feedback loop has formed in the transfer beam
5. B. personnel reports

MISSION PERFORMANCE RATING:

45 – 65 points **Superior:** Starfleet Caber Toss Grand Champion!

40 – 44 points **Above Average:** So, you write ghost stories do you?

30 – 39 points **Average:** You are nothing but a ghost of an officer.

20 – 29 points **Fair:** Having a problem maintaining your molecular cohesion?

0 – 19 points **Poor:** Go help Ned the groundskeeper pull out the primary plasma conduit.

LOWER DECKS ⬥

Ensign Sito has been assigned to the *Enterprise* after graduating from the Academy (see 'The First Duty'). It becomes apparent to the junior officers that something is going on when the *Enterprise* moves near the Cardassian border and someone is beamed directly to sickbay.

Sito meets Picard who briefs her on the mission. A Federation operative, a Cardassian, has brought valuable information to the *Enterprise*. The operative needs a Bajoran 'prisoner' so he can pose as a bounty hunter in order to get back across the border. Afterwards, she is to return to Federation space via the shuttle escape pod. The *Enterprise* waits at the meeting point for Sito but she is long overdue. A Cardassian message is intercepted, reporting a Bajoran prisoner killed as she escaped.

TRIVIA QUESTIONS

1. How long has Sito served aboard the *Enterprise*? **(3pts)**
2. Taurik asked Lavelle if he ever considered learning what? **(3pts)**
3. What did Sito use the internal sensors for during her $1/2$ hour stint at ops? **(3pts)**
4. How many hours overdue is Sito according to Riker? **(4pts)**
5. Where does Data detect debris? **(4pts)**
6. Taurik says the odds of his winning the current poker hand are what? **(5pts)**
7. What are the Cardassian's injuries prior to surgery? **(4pts)**
8. What device is Taurik using that few crew members get a chance to use? **(3pts)**
9. Who maintains a constant chant for the benefit of the Bajoran people? **(3pts)**
10. For what position are Lavelle and Sito both being considered? **(3pts)**

SPECIAL ASSIGNMENT (10pts)

Which scientist's work is Taurik basing his computer simulations on?

MULTIPLE CHOICE QUESTIONS

1. What is said to be a treaty violation? **(2pts)**
   A. sending a shuttle into Cardassian territory
   B. launching a probe into Cardassian territory
   C. beaming a Cardassian out of Cardassian territory
   D. scanning a debris field inside Cardassian territory

2. What does Ogawa need to synthesize? **(3pts)**
   A. a gallon of Aldebaran whiskey
   B. a litre of chech'tluth
   C. at least one litre of Cardassian blood
   D. two litres of Cardassian plasma cell extract

3. Why is Sito stationed outside sickbay? **(2pts)**
   A. she is a security officer and Worf is punishing her
   B. she is a security officer and is ordered to allow only Picard into sickbay
   C. she is a medical tech and is triaging patients
   D. she is a security officer and is ordered to allow only senior officers into sickbay

4. What is the Bajoran equivalent of the human saying 'a fly on the wall'? **(3pts)**
   A. a spider under the table
   B. a tick on the arm
   C. a dog under the table
   D. an arachnid on the wall

5. What is Lavelle's hand during the junior officer's poker game? **(5pts)**
   A. three sixes
   B. two pairs – sevens and sixes
   C. two pairs – jacks and fours
   D. two pairs – tens and deuces

ANSWERS

TRIVIA ANSWERS

1. seven months
2. lip-reading
3. to find a lost puppy
4. 32 hours
5. 200,000 kilometres inside Cardassian space
6. less than 39:1
7. he's comatose and has a subdural haematoma
8. phaser rifle
9. the vedeks of the Janlin Order
10. the night duty officer for ops

SPECIAL ASSIGNMENT SOLUTION

Dr Nils Diaz at the Tallian Propulsion Laboratory

Congratulations! Starfleet Command is proud to award you the Starfleet Medal of Honour and 10 extra points.

MULTIPLE CHOICE ANSWERS

1. B. launching a probe into Cardassian territory
2. C. at least one litre of Cardassian blood
3. D. she is a security officer and is ordered to allow only senior officers into sickbay
4. A. a spider under the table
5. B. two pairs – sevens and sixes

MISSION PERFORMANCE RATING:

45 – 60 points **Superior:** That big promotion could happen anytime now!

40 – 44 points **Above Average:** Big poker player, huh?

30 – 39 points **Average:** The Cardassians want to talk to you!

20 – 29 points **Fair:** You fit in really well with the other *junior* officers.

0 – 19 points **Poor:** Sito's sick today, so you're replacing her on this mission.

Data is sent to retrieve some radioactive fragments from a crashed Federation probe on Barkon IV. However, Data is hit with a power surge while interacting with the probe's computer and his memory is lost. He wanders into a village carrying the radioactive fragments in a container.

Later, Data sells some of the fragments to the local blacksmith, who makes jewellery out of them. People in the village begin to come down with a mysterious disease: the result of radiation poisoning from the fragments. Data begins an investigation into the cause of the disease as his memory partially returns. He develops a cure and is able to add it to the village well. Just then, one of the villagers, who thinks that Data is the disease carrier, runs him through with a rod. Since he appears dead, the villagers bury Data.

Meanwhile, Troi studies for the bridge officer's test so she can attain the rank of full commander. She eventually passes the holodeck simulation part, but not without difficulty. She realizes that to pass she must make a life or death decision and order Geordi into a deadly situation in order to save the ship. Data is recovered and reactivated.

CROSSWORD PUZZLE CLUES

ACROSS

3. Data tells Garvin he came from the _____. (1pt)
5. One of the items Talur told Data to eat plenty of. (1pt)
6. Data's teeth according to Talur. (3pts)
7. Closest one to village is two days away. (2pts)
12. Ship the *Enterprise* met with to pick up supplies. (3pts)
13. Data thinks his name might be _____. (2pts)
17. Episode Troi alludes to. (3pts)
18. Type of supplies *Enterprise* picks up. (1pt)
19. Name Gia gives to Data. (2pts)
21. The blacksmith says the metal fragments are slightly _____. (2pts)
22. Blacksmith. (3pts)
23. Unit of length used by the Barkonians. (3pts)
24. Shape of candle on table at school. (2pts)
25. Unit of currency used by the Barkonians. (3pts)
26. Tears half Data's face off. (3pts)

DOWN

1. Catalyst that gets Troi to take the bridge officer's test. (1pt)
2. Nature of creatures supposedly living in the mountains. (1pt)
4. Data lifting the anvil. (1pt)
8. Name of mountains Talur mentions. (3pts)
9. Garvin is the town _____. (1pt)
10. Place where metal fragments were buried by villagers. (2pts)
11. Barkonian society. (3pts)
14. Some of the material in the probe's _____ is radioactive. (2pts)
15. The supplies are destined for the _____ Colony. (3pts)
16. Item responsible for Gia's illness. (1pt)
20. Talur thinks Data is an _____. (2pts)
25. Shish kebab. (1pt)

SPECIAL ASSIGNMENT (10pts)

During the holodeck simulation, Geordi says that they just lost contact with what part of the ship?

SPECIAL ASSIGNMENT SOLUTION

everything above
Deck 21 including
the bridge
Congratulations!
Starfleet Command
is proud to award
you the Starfleet
Medal of Honour
and 10 extra points.

MISSION PERFORMANCE RATING:

50 – 65 points Superior: You passed the bridge officer's test the first time!

44 – 49 points Above Average: You almost passed the bridge officer's test.

40 – 44 points Average: You've lost more than just your memory!

30 – 39 points Fair: Talur says that people like you are related to the Icemen.

0 – 29 points Poor: You're a Barkonian's worst nightmare!

The *Enterprise* encounters a new comet and begins scanning the interior of the object. Alien artefacts begin appearing all over the *Enterprise* as the sensor scan continues. Data is then taken over by multiple alien personalities. The comet is melted and an alien archive is uncovered. The archive is transforming the *Enterprise* into a representation of the culture that built it.

Through Data, several personalities warn Picard that Masaka is coming. Picard learns that only Korgano can speak to the dangerous Masaka. Soon Data takes on Masaka's persona. Picard plays the role of Korgano and is able to speak to Masaka lulling her into sleep. The *Enterprise* returns to normal.

TRIVIA QUESTIONS

1. What does Worf suggest could be used to destroy the alien archive? **(3pts)**
2. Where does Ihat come from? **(3pts)**
3. Where do the alien artefacts first manifest themselves? **(3pts)**
4. What intense effect does the Enterprise experience when first studying the comet? **(3pts)**
5. According to legend, what became of Masaka's father? **(3pts)**
6. What might suggest a database within the alien structure? **(5pts)**
7. From what system does Data say the comet originated? **(3pts)**
8. How long has the comet been travelling? **(4pts)**
9. What is the comet's outer shell composed of? **(4pts)**
10. What techniques is Worf supposed to teach? **(4pts)**

CHARACTER QUOTE
(2pts per word + 7pts for identifying the speaker.)

Unscramble the words below and then identify the character.

' _____ we'd _____ ____ out _____. The _____ _____
  YBMEA   TRBTE LTKA   EHRE   AVOSRTNBOIE GUENLO
has _____ ____ a _____.'
    NRDTEU TNOI AWMPS

SPECIAL ASSIGNMENT (10pts)

What does Data sculpt to depict an abstract concept?

ANSWERS

TRIVIA ANSWERS

1. a photon torpedo reconfigured for manual launch
2. Masaka City
3. Troi's quarters
4. sensor echo
5. Masaka chopped him up and used his bones to create the world
6. a repetitive node configuration
7. D'Arsay
8. 87 million years
9. gaseous hydrogen and helium surrounding an icy mantle
10. Mok'bara throwing techniques

CHARACTER QUOTE SOLUTION

'Maybe we'd better talk out here. The observation lounge has turned into a swamp'. – Riker

SPECIAL ASSIGNMENT SOLUTION

treble clef

Congratulations! Starfleet Command is proud to award you the Starfleet Medal of Honour and 10 extra points.

MISSION PERFORMANCE RATING:

55 – 70 points **Superior:** Thanks Korgano, we owe you one!

50 – 54 points **Above Average:** Already been to Masaka City, huh?

40 – 49 points **Average:** You look good in a mask.

30 – 39 points **Fair:** Masaka heard what you said and knows where you live!

0 – 29 points **Poor:** You're assigned to shuttle duty looking for rogue comets.

Troi and Worf investigate the suicide of Lieutenant Kwan, who jumped into the plasma stream feeding one of the engine nacelles. Troi experiences a flood of negative emotions at the location of the suicide. She returns with Worf later and experiences images of several people including a crew member named Pierce. Worf and Troi later question Pierce but he can offer little help.

Worf and Troi start an affair that evening. The next day Troi becomes wildly jealous of Worf paying attention to an ensign. Troi tracks the pair to the Ensign's quarters and grabs a phaser, blasting Worf in the chest and killing him. She hurries to the nacelle tube and prepares to commit suicide just as Kwan did. Worf grabs Troi at the last minute and she snaps out of a hallucination.

Troi and the crew piece together what happened in the nacelle control room. Apparently, while the *Enterprise* was still under construction, Pierce found his girlfriend with another man and killed them both. He threw the bodies into the plasma stream and then jumped into the stream himself. Because Pierce was partially telepathic, the plasma stream left an empathic signature in the nacelle area. Kwan and Troi were both overwhelmed by the psychic impressions.

TRIVIA QUESTIONS

1. Troi saw a tool crate labelled what? **(3pts)**
2. Why was Pierce partially telepathic? **(3pts)**
3. When did Kwan arrive at the fleet yards? **(3pts)**
4. The cargo bay will be off-limits to whom? **(3pts)**
5. Who transferred to the *Enterprise* over a year ago? **(5pts)**
6. Where is Lieutenant Zef stationed on the *Enterprise*? **(4pts)**
7. Whom does Troi say came on board the *Enterprise* six months ago? **(4pts)**
8. What type of drink does Riker order in Ten-Forward? **(4pts)**
9. Picard orders Data to release the exterior hull plate in preparation for what? **(3pts)**
10. What did Riker supervise only a few days ago with Kwan? **(3pts)**

✪ SPECIAL ASSIGNMENT (15pts)

Full name of person whose file was on-screen just before Finn's file came up.

MULTIPLE CHOICE QUESTIONS

1. Why did Kwan open the access panel to the main ODN line? **(5pts)**
   A. he heard a strange noise
   B. he was repairing a plasma conduit
   C. he was splicing an ODN junction box
   D. he was refitting a field coil

2. Pierce remembers installing what behind a wall in Engineering? **(3pts)**
   A. plasma vent
   B. ODN junction box
   C. EPS tap
   D. power conduit

3. How long will it take Dr Crusher to synthesize the telepathic inhibitor drug? **(3pts)**
   A. eight hours
   B. 16 hours
   C. 12 hours
   D. one day

4. Troi says everything in Kwan's personal logs indicate he was what? **(2pts)**
   A. suicidal
   B. maladjusted and optimistic
   C. well adjusted and optimistic
   D. depressed but not suicidal

5. How long did Calloway and Kwan know each other? **(2pts)**
   A. over two years
   B. two months
   C. one year and seven months
   D. one year

ANSWERS

TRIVIA ANSWERS

1. Utopia Planitia
2. his maternal grandmother was born on Betazed
3. six months after Finn disappeared
4. everyone except medical personnel
5. Ensign Salvatore
6. in Quantum Mechanics
7. Lieutenant Pierce
8. Til'amin froths
9. possible jettison of the core
10. a tube refit

SPECIAL ASSIGNMENT SOLUTION

Alfonse D. Pacelli

Congratulations! Starfleet Command is proud to award you the Starfleet Medal of Honour and 15 extra points.

MULTIPLE CHOICE ANSWERS

1. D. he was refitting a field coil
2. D. power conduit
3. B. 16 hours
4. C. well adjusted and optimistic
5. A. over two years

MISSION PERFORMANCE RATING:

45 – 65 points **Superior:** So you designed and built the *Enterprise*?

40 – 44 points **Above Average:** Dixon Hill could use a partner!

30 – 39 points **Average:** Still working at Utopia Planitia, huh?

20 – 29 points **Fair:** Don't worry, you're just having a psychic hallucination.

0 – 19 points **Poor:** At this rate you'll see the inside of a bulkhead.

During a test firing of some newly upgraded photon torpedoes, one of them goes astray without exploding. Picard and Data take a shuttle out in search of the torpedo.

Picard and Data return several days later to find the *Enterprise* listing to one side. After getting aboard ship they find that the crew has de-evolved into a mixture of strange creatures. Picard and Data re-establish power on the ship and stabilize some systems. They discover the cause of the de-evolution and Data synthesizes a cure. He releases it into the *Enterprise*'s ventilation system, returning everyone to normal.

TRIVIA QUESTIONS

1. Which two areas of the ship contain large concentrations of life forms? **(3pts)**
2. Status of the conn officer when Data and Picard go to the bridge? **(3pts)**
3. How many degrees has Troi's body temperature fallen according to Dr Crusher? **(3pts)**
4. How many life forms can Data detect on the *Enterprise*? **(3pts)**
5. Which two doctors does Dr Crusher call in? **(5pts)**
6. Troi orders a double what in Ten-Forward? **(3pts)**
7. How many male felines on the *Enterprise*? **(3pts)**
8. What is the first thing Barclay is convinced he has? **(4pts)**
9. What is the second condition Barclay thinks he has? **(4pts)**
10. What is Barclay diagnosed as having? **(4pts)**

WHO AM I? (25pts)

I'm speechless for I haven't a clue. Some would say I suffer from ichthyo-mania. My spine is host to many.

✪ SPECIAL ASSIGNMENT (15pts)

To what deck and section has Data traced Nurse Ogawa's com-badge?

ANSWERS

TRIVIA ANSWERS

1. arboretum and Aquatics Lab
2. dead, upper spinal column broken in three places
3. 8°
4. 1,011
5. Dr Selar and Dr Hacopian
6. Ongilin caviar
7. 12
8. Terellian Death Syndrome
9. Symbalene Blood Burn
10. a mild case of Urodelian flu

WHO AM I? SOLUTION

Riker

EXPLANATION:

I'm speechless for I haven't a clue. – Riker no longer understands spoken language after de-evolving.
Some would say I suffer from ichthyomania. – An excessive fascination with fish. Riker was trying to get at the fish in Picard's ready room.
My spine is host to many. – Riker rolled onto a Cyprion cactus and received a backful of cactus spines.

SPECIAL ASSIGNMENT SOLUTION

Deck 17, Section 21-Alpha
Congratulations! Starfleet Command is proud to award you the Starfleet Medal of Honour and 15 extra points.

MISSION PERFORMANCE RATING:

36 – 75 points **Superior:** You never de-evolved, you just got better and better!

30 – 35 points **Above Average:** Great Hallowe'en party! Nice costumes!

20 – 29 points **Average:** Go find Lieutenant Barclay/Spiderman in Engineering.

10 – 19 points **Fair:** You turned into a unicellular heterotroph with pseudopods.

0 – 9 points **Poor:** You de-evolved into primordial soup!

JOURNEY'S END

STARDATE: 47751.2

Wesley joins the *Enterprise* crew during a vacation break at the Academy. The *Enterprise* is headed for Dorvan V to evacuate the colonists there. The planet has recently been ceded to the Cardassians following the peace agreement. The colonists are descendants of the North American Indians.

Lakanta, one of the colonists, befriends Wesley. He explains to Wesley that he needs to seek a vision and leads him to their sacred ritual place. There, Wesley has a vision that he should seek his own path and resigns from the Academy.

The colonists are against leaving the planet. Meanwhile, a small contingent of Cardassians arrives on the surface. Picard is able to defuse the situation and reach a compromise with the colonists, allowing them to remain on the planet. Wesley learns that Lakanta is actually the Traveler and has come to show Wesley his true destiny: to stay on Dorvan V and continue his studies with the Traveler.

TRIVIA QUESTIONS

1. What do the colonists give up to stay on Dorvan V? **(3pts)**
2. How many other planets in the sector have the same conditions as Dorvan V? **(3pts)**
3. How long did it take the Federation to negotiate the treaty with the Cardassians? **(3pts)**
4. What does the Gul order his ship to do initially when his men are taken hostage? **(3pts)**
5. What did the Gul lose during the war with the Federation? **(4pts)**
6. What historical event does the council leader tell Picard about? **(5pts)**
7. Where will Wesley visit Dr Crusher every Sunday? **(4pts)**
8. Lakanta first saw Wesley during what? **(3pts)**
9. How long have the colonists been on Dorvan V? **(4pts)**
10. When did the colonists first leave Earth? **(3pts)**

MULTIPLE CHOICE QUESTIONS

1. Why have the Cardassians arrived on Dorvan V? **(2pts)**
    - **A.** to investigate rumours that the colonists don't want to leave
    - **B.** to do a preliminary survey of all buildings and equipment being left behind
    - **C.** to perform a mineralogical survey of the planet
    - **D.** to supervise the Federation withdrawal from the planet

---

2. What does Picard strongly urge Admiral Nechayev to do? **(3pts)**
    A. to taste the canapés
    B. to request an emergency session of the Federation Council
    C. to authorize defensive action taken against the Cardassians
    D. to participate in a vision quest

3. How long after the Indian revolt before the Spanish returned? **(5pts)**
    A. 10 years
    B. 15 years
    C. 20 years
    D. 22 years

4. What has Lakanta known for the past two years? **(3pts)**
    A. that he was actually the Traveler
    B. that the Federation and Cardassians would eventually produce a treaty
    C. that Wesley would resign from Starfleet
    D. that Wesley was coming to Dorvan V

5. Why did the colonists leave Earth? **(2pts)**
    A. they were forced to relocate
    B. they needed more space
    C. they wanted to preserve their cultural identity
    D. they wanted to find a sacred place to live

ANSWERS

TRIVIA ANSWERS
1. their Federation citizenship
2. three
3. three years
4. send an armed squad of troopers to rescue the two Cardassians and occupy the village
5. two of his three sons
6. Pueblo Revolt of 1680
7. Old Doctor's Home
8. a vision quest
9. 20 years
10. more than 200 years ago

MULTIPLE CHOICE
1. B. to do a preliminary survey of all buildings and equipment being left behind
2. B. to request an emergency session of the Federation Council
3. A. 10 years
4. D. that Wesley was coming to Dorvan V
5. C. they wanted to preserve their cultural identity

MISSION PERFORMANCE RATING:

45 – 50 points **Superior:** You're even more brilliant than Dr Vassbinder!

40 – 44 points **Above Average:** Your journey is only beginning.

30 – 39 points **Average:** Your ancestors were also average.

20 – 29 points **Fair:** Your journey has just ended. Report back to the Academy!

0 – 19 points **Poor:** The Cardassians took you hostage and we don't care!

FIRSTBORN

Worf decides to expose Alexander to some Klingon culture by taking him to a nearby festival. That night Worf and Alexander are attacked after the festival. Just then, K'mtar, a trusted friend of Worf's family, turns up and helps fend off the attackers. A knife carried by one of the attackers proves to be from the House of Duras. K'mtar tries to encourage Alexander to embrace his father's Klingon ways despite what his mother may have said.

Riker eventually tracks down the Duras sisters. They claim to know nothing of the attack. However, the knife carried by the assassins bears the mark of one of the sisters' sons, as yet unborn. K'mtar then reveals his true identity to Worf. He is actually Alexander and has travelled back in time to urge himself to choose the path of the warrior. Worf reassures him that whatever he chooses to do will be worthy and honourable.

TRIVIA QUESTIONS

1. Where were the Duras sisters last seen a few months ago? **(3pts)**
2. What does it mean to light a kor'tova candle? **(3pts)**
3. Where does Worf die according to K'mtar/Alexander? **(3pts)**
4. What does Riker offer in exchange for the stolen ore the Yridian has? **(5pts)**
5. What is the name of K'mtar's holodeck programme? **(3pts)**
6. Quark said Riker was the only man to do what? **(3pts)**
7. How many vouchers does Riker have from Quark? **(4pts)**
8. What was Alexander watching at night with some friends he made at the outpost? **(4pts)**
9. Whose head does a man offer to show Alexander and his friends for a price? **(3pts)**
10. What festival does Worf take Alexander to see? **(4pts)**

✪ SPECIAL ASSIGNMENT (15pts)

What year in the future did K'mtar/Alexander come from?

MULTIPLE CHOICE QUESTIONS

1. What does Picard suggest could be recalibrated over the four day layover? **(2pts)**
   - **A.** new conn display terminals
   - **B.** weapons targeting system
   - **C.** lateral sensor array
   - **D.** warp engines

2. Where does Riker beam the stolen ore from the freighter? **(3pts)**
   - **A.** directly off the *Enterprise*'s port bow
   - **B.** Cargo Bay 4
   - **C.** into the Klingon bird-of-prey's cargo hold
   - **D.** directly off the *Enterprise*'s starboard bow

3. How does K'mtar assess Alexander's fighting skills? **(2pts)**
   - **A.** he's years behind other Klingon boys his age
   - **B.** he's more cunning than other Klingon boys his age
   - **C.** he's years ahead of other Klingon boys his age
   - **D.** he's swifter than other Klingon boys his age

4. What are the most important weapons of a warrior according to K'mtar? **(5pts)**
   - **A.** swiftness, cunning, honour
   - **B.** skill, honour, powers of observation
   - **C.** skill, cunning, powers of observation
   - **D.** size, cunning, skill

5. Why didn't Quark have enough latinum to cover Riker's winnings? **(3pts)**
   - **A.** Quark's brother misplaced the key to the safe
   - **B.** another customer had just won a big jackpot and cleaned out the last of Quark's latinum
   - **C.** Quark was having a slow business week
   - **D.** Quark just loaned the last of his latinum to his sister

ANSWERS

TRIVIA ANSWERS

1. Deep Space 9
2. the Klingon boy is declaring his intention to become a warrior
3. on the floor of the Great Council Chamber in Alexander's arms
4. 1/2 gram of Anjoran biometic gel
5. K'mtar Alpha-One
6. win triple Dabo on one of his tables
7. enough for 12 bars of latinum
8. fire dancers
9. supposedly Molor's mummified head
10. Kot'baval Festival

SPECIAL ASSIGNMENT SOLUTION

2410 (based on Alexander saying he came from 40 years in the future and the current year is 2370)

Congratulations! Starfleet Command is proud to award you the Starfleet Medal of Honour and 15 extra points.

MULTIPLE CHOICE ANSWERS

1. B. weapons targeting system
2. D. directly off the *Enterprise's* starboard bow
3. A. he's years behind other Klingon boys his age
4. C. skill, cunning, powers of observation
5. A. Quark's brother misplaced the key to the safe

MISSION PERFORMANCE RATING:

45 – 65 points **Superior:** There is no regret in your heart, only honour!

40 – 44 points **Above Average:** You have become a fine warrior!

30 – 39 points **Average:** Go back to the future, we don't need your help.

20 – 29 points **Fair:** And just *how* do you expect to get back to the future?

0 – 19 points **Poor:** We'll let you keep Gorta company on Kalla III.

BLOODLINES △

The *Enterprise* encounters a probe from the Ferengi known as Bok (see 'The Battle'). Picard learns that he has a son that he did not know about. Bok threatens to kill Picard's son, Jason, in retribution for Picard killing Bok's son in battle many years ago.

The *Enterprise* speeds to Jason's home planet and beams the young man aboard. Although genetic testing confirms that Jason is Picard's son, the two have little else in common. Dr Crusher eventually discovers that Jason's DNA has been tampered with and that he is not really Picard's son.

Bok beams Jason off the *Enterprise* despite their safety precautions. Geordi and Data jury-rig the *Enterprise*'s system into a subspace transporter and beam Picard over to Bok's ship. Picard tells the Ferengi what's really going on and they detain Bok for the Ferengi authorities.

TRIVIA QUESTIONS

1. What has value on Camor V? **(3pts)**
2. Where on the *Enterprise* does Picard find Jason hanging around? **(3pts)**
3. What is the first artefact that Picard shows Jason? **(4pts)**
4. What rare artefact does Picard give Jason as a parting gift? **(4pts)**
5. What is Dr Crusher's diagnosis of Jason's problem? **(5pts)**
6. What is B'Zal? **(3pts)**
7. What does Jason say just gets in the way? **(3pts)**
8. How did Picard meet Miranda? **(3pts)**
9. Where was Miranda born? **(3pts)**
10. What does Riker say the Ferengi government is debating? **(4pts)**

✪✪ SIGNIFICANT NUMBERS (1pt each)

Match the clues with the correct number. Some numbers may be used more than once.

Clues
1. How many kilometres to starboard does the third probe materialize?
2. How many years ago does Bok say Picard killed his son?
3. How old was Jason when he and his mother came to Camor V?
4. Miranda took care of over how many children on Camor V?
5. Jason has been watching out for himself since he was how old?
6. How many times has Jason been arrested for petty theft?
7. How many times has Jason been arrested for disorderly conduct?
8. How many years old is Jason?
9. How many humans does Data detect with the sensors on Camor V?

10. How many female humans does Data detect with the sensors on Camor V?

11. How many infant male humans does Data detect with the sensors on Camor V?

12. How many elderly male humans does Data detect with the sensors on Camor V?

13. How many middle-aged male humans does Data detect with the sensors on Camor V?

14. How many kilometres below the surface of Camor V is the eighth human detected?

15. How many years ago did Jason and Miranda leave Earth?

Numbers

A. 15	F. 500
B. 8	G. 40
C. 3	H. 12
D. 23	I. 2
E. 1	J. 10

ANSWERS

TRIVIA ANSWERS

1. anything you can eat or sell (everything else is luxury)
2. Holodeck 4
3. Sylvan glyph stone
4. Gorlan prayer stick
5. Forrester Trent syndrome
6. a Ferengi code using alternating patterns of light and darkness
7. antigrav harness
8. through a friend during shore leave
9. New Gaul
10. an amendment to the Rules of Acquisition

SIGNIFICANT NUMBERS ANSWERS

1. F 900; 2. A 15; 3. J 10; 4. G 40; 5. A 15; 6. C 3; 7. I 2; 8. D 23; 9. B 8; 10. C 3; 11. E 1; 12. E 1; 13. I 2; 14. I 2; 15. H 12

MISSION PERFORMANCE RATING:

30 – 50 points **Superior:** Nice rescue, Captain!

25 – 29 points **Above Average:** I bet your son is on the honour roll!

20 – 24 points **Average:** You're not a bad climber.

10 – 19 points **Fair:** Oops! We still have a few bugs in the new transporter!

0 – 9 points **Poor:** You'd better take your fat Ferengi friends and leave!

EMERGENCE ⊿

The holodeck malfunctions while Picard and Data are using it. Later, the *Enterprise* independently jumps to warp speed to avoid an undetectable phenomenon. While looking into the malfunctions, Geordi and Data find circuit nodes all over the *Enterprise*. They appear to be growing in number and taking control of vital areas of the ship. It is speculated that an intelligent life form may be evolving from within the *Enterprise*.

Since the holodeck seems to be the nerve centre of the new intelligence, several crew members enter a holodeck programme to communicate with the life form. After several unsuccessful attempts at trying to regain control of the ship, the officers agree to assist the life forms.

A physical form begins to develop in one of the cargo bays and seems to need an infusion of vertions to grow. Geordi finds an outside source of vertion particles and the life form departs the *Enterprise*.

TRIVIA QUESTIONS

1. What does the *Enterprise* use to collect the vertion particles? **(3pts)**
2. How does Worf get the train back on schedule? **(3pts)**
3. Initially, what is the only way Geordi can take the *Enterprise* out of warp? **(3pts)**
4. What is Dikon Alpha? **(3pts)**
5. What is the new destination after the train starts to head for another white dwarf star? **(3pts)**
6. What is the name of the first white dwarf the *Enterprise* heads for? **(5pts)**
7. What Warp speed does the *Enterprise* 'decide' to suddenly go to? **(4pts)**
8. What dangerous condition was building up around the *Enterprise*? **(4pts)**
9. What is Data attempting to perform during the play on the holodeck? **(4pts)**
10. At its peak how many people travelled on the Orient Express each year? **(3pts)**

✪✪ DOUBLE SPECIAL ASSIGNMENT (15pts each)

Assignment I:
What number is behind the brick wall after it collapses?

Assignment II:
What are the last three digits of the taxi's licence plate?

MULTIPLE CHOICE QUESTIONS

1. What does the *Enterprise* start to lose as Data begins depolarizing the power grid? **(3pts)**
   A. warp power
   B. life support
   C. attitude control
   D. structural integrity

2. How does Data plan to disengage the nodes without harming them? **(5pts)**
   A. depolarize the power grid by using a low frequency diversion field
   B. depolarize the power grid by using a low frequency inversion field
   C. depolarize the power grid by using a high frequency inversion field
   D. repolarize the power grid by using a high frequency inversion field

3. Data says the train holodeck sequence contains what? **(2pts)**
   A. a mixture of odd and disturbing characters
   B. a mystery
   C. portions of seven distinct holodeck programmes
   D. the key to understanding the developing life form

4. What did Data say is improbable but possible? **(2pts)**
   A. that Troi survived a brick wall crashing down on her with only minor injuries
   B. that a random power fluctuation caused the *Enterprise* to jump into warp drive
   C. that a new life form would develop in the manner described
   D. that shovelling coal into a holodeck train boiler will increase warp power

5. What type of stars in the region does Riker say makes the area unsuitable for surveying? **(3pts)**
   A. mostly main sequence binaries
   B. mostly blue giants
   C. mostly neutron stars
   D. mostly red and brown dwarfs

ANSWERS

TRIVIA ANSWERS

1. a modified tractor beam
2. shovels coal into the train's boiler
3. perform an Emergency Core Shutdown
4. a class-9 pulsar
5. New Vertiform City
6. Tambor Beta VI
7. Warp 7.3
8. theta flux distortion
9. a Neoplatonic magical rite
10. over 10,000

DOUBLE SPECIAL ASSIGNMENT SOLUTION

Assignment I: 1136

Assignment II: 638 (Data's hand is covering the first two digits which appear to be 20)

Congratulations! Starfleet Command is proud to award you the Starfleet Medal of Honour and 15 or 30 extra points.

MULTIPLE CHOICE ANSWERS

1. D. structural integrity
2. B. depolarize the power grid by using a low frequency inversion field
3. C. portions of seven distinct holodeck programmes
4. B. that a random power fluctuation caused the *Enterprise* to jump into warp drive
5. A. mostly main sequence binaries

MISSION PERFORMANCE RATING:

45 – 80 points **Superior:** Wow, we'll have to classify *you* as a new life form!

40 – 44 points **Above Average:** You'll make a good conductor.

30 – 39 points **Average:** Go shovel some more coal into the boiler.

20 – 29 points **Fair:** Starfleet Command expects your resignation by 07:00 hours

0 – 19 points **Poor:** Stand over by that brick wall while I depolarize the grid!

PREEMPTIVE STRIKE

STARDATE: 47941.7

Ro Laren returns to the *Enterprise* after attending advanced training classes. Shortly thereafter, Picard is briefed by an admiral on recent peace accords that have left several Federation colonies in either Cardassian space or a demilitarized zone. Many of the colonists have chosen to stay behind and have formed a paramilitary group for protection known as the Maquis. The Admiral wants Ro to infiltrate the group and gather intelligence.

Ro accepts the mission and successfully infiltrates a cell of the Maquis. Picard hopes to lure a major Maquis force to attack a convoy of ships. A Federation attack force will hide in a nearby nebula to dispatch the Maquis.

Later, several Cardassians attack the colony and kill many civilians. This prompts Ro to decide that Starfleet has no right to fight the Maquis. As the Maquis ships approach the convoy, Ro warns them of the fleet hiding in the nebula. Ro then beams off her ship to join the Maquis.

TRIVIA QUESTIONS

1. Where did the convoy set out from? **(3pts)**
2. Why is Ro supposedly wanted by Starfleet? **(3pts)**
3. What did Starfleet catch the Cardassian government doing? **(3pts)**
4. What three things is the convoy supposedly carrying? **(5pts)**
5. During the aborted Maquis attack on the convoy, what is Ro's designation? **(3pts)**
6. What does Ro's ship shoot into the nebula? **(4pts)**
7. Where has Ro been for the last year? **(3pts)**
8. What are all along the demilitarized zone? **(4pts)**
9. What are extremely fattening? **(3pts)**
10. What type of weapon did the Maquis use on the Cardassian ship? **(4pts)**

CHARACTER QUOTE
(2pts per word + 3pts for identifying the speaker.)

Unscramble the words below and then identify the character.

'_____ an ____ _____ ____ me ____, _____ _____ ____
  EHWN   LDO TGRFHEI KLEI   ISDE MOENSOE WSLYAA PTSSE

_____ to _____ his _____.'
  RAODRFW   KTAE   LCPAE

SPECIAL ASSIGNMENT (10pts)

Where are Ro's new quarters located on the *Enterprise*?

ANSWERS

TRIVIA ANSWERS

1. Deep Space 9
2. she's responsible for the death of a Cardassian soldier
3. supplying weapons to their colonists in the demilitarized zone
4. isomiotic hypos, plasma flares, and quarantine pods
5. Alpha 7
6. a low intensity particle beam
7. Advanced Tactical Training
8. sensor buoys with proximity detectors
9. Bularian canapés
10. photon torpedoes and type-8 phasers

CHARACTER QUOTE SOLUTION

'When an old fighter like me dies, someone always steps forward to take his place.' — Macias

SPECIAL ASSIGNMENT SOLUTION

Deck 4, Section 8

Congratulations! Starfleet Command is proud to award you the Starfleet Medal of Honour and 10 extra points.

MISSION PERFORMANCE RATING:

55 – 70 points **Superior:** Graduated Advanced Tactical Training with honours!

50 – 54 points **Above Average:** Your fiery hasperat is legendary!

40 – 49 points **Average:** Maybe the Maquis are right, who's to say?

30 – 39 points **Fair:** You Cardassian collaborator, you'll hang for this!

0 – 29 points **Poor:** You better hide and hope Starfleet doesn't find you!

ALL GOOD THINGS . . .

STARDATE: 47988

Picard feels as if he is shifting back and forth through time. He seems to be jumping between a future where he is suffering from Irumodic syndrome, a degenerative neurological disorder, and the past when he first took command of the *Enterprise*.

In the future timeline, Geordi helps Picard to locate Data and together they try to determine what is happening. In both the past and present time-lines, Starfleet has dispatched the *Enterprise* to investigate the Devron system for some type of subspace anomaly. The Romulans are also massing ships along the Neutral Zone. The three hitch a ride to the Neutral Zone on Captain Beverly Picard's ship, the *Pasteur*. Worf grants Picard permission to travel into what is Klingon territory in the future.

Picard learns that Q is behind the time-shifting. The Q Continuum has reached a verdict and has decided to eradicate mankind, with Picard as the instrument of that destruction. Since no anomaly exists in the future timeline, Data suggests an inverse tachyon pulse might detect it. The *Pasteur* begins beaming a tachyon pulse while Picard implements the same thing in the other two timelines. Unknown to Picard at this point, the convergence of the three pulses actually creates an anti-time rift in the space/time continuum. The rift becomes larger the further back in time it goes until it threatens the early formation of life on Earth.

The *Pasteur* is suddenly attacked by several Klingon ships. A refitted *Enterprise* arrives just in time with Admiral Riker. Riker beams off the *Pasteur*'s crew from the badly damaged ship and plots a course to return to Federation space. Meanwhile, Picard is transported to Earth's distant past by Q and figures out the paradox.

Picard is returned to the future and persuades Riker to return to the Devron system. Picard, leaping back and forth through time, gets the other two *Enterprises* to assist in closing the rift. All three *Enterprises* are eventually lost trying to seal the anti-time rift but their efforts save humanity. Picard is returned to his present-day *Enterprise*.

TRIVIA QUESTIONS

1. Why isn't there a Neutral Zone in the future? **(3pts)**
2. What do Federation starships routinely use in the future? **(2pts)**
3. What does Picard have to programme into the replicator system on the *Enterprise*? **(2pts)**
4. What does Data reconfigure the *Pasteur*'s main deflector to emit? **(3pts)**
5. Why is Geordi having pain in his eyes? **(3pts)**
6. What holodeck programme did Worf always find to be a stimulating experience? **(5pts)**

---

7. What has Leah been made director of? **(2pts)**
8. Where are Geordi and Leah living? **(3pts)**
9. What did Picard think about Geordi's last novel? **(4pts)**
10. Who once lived in the house Data is staying in at the university? **(3pts)**
11. Worf is Governor of what small Klingon colony? **(5pts)**
12. What speeds are starships capable of in the future? **(4pts)**
13. How large is the anomaly in the present? **(5pts)**
14. How large is the anomaly in the recent past? **(4pts)**
15. Why can't the *Enterprise* cloak for the next seven hours? **(5pts)**

✪ SPECIAL ASSIGNMENT (15pts)

When Picard talks with Riker at the Farpoint Station over subspace, who is standing behind and to the left of Riker? *HINT: this footage is reused from an earlier episode.*

MULTIPLE CHOICE QUESTIONS

1. Data's housekeeper thinks he looks like a bloody what? **(2pts)**
   A. polecat
   B. badger
   C. skunk
   D. anteater

2. Where does Q appear to Picard as an old man? **(3pts)**
   A. in Admiral Riker's ready room
   B. in the post-atomic horror courtroom
   C. next to the primordial ooze pond
   D. in the *Pasteur*'s ready room

3. Data didn't realize that Picard was so well versed in the intricacies of what? **(2pts)**
   A. temporal theories
   B. Starfleet etiquette
   C. Jaradan protocol
   D. time travel

4. How does Data describe the anomaly after the tachyon pulse is initiated? **(5pts)**
   A. a multiphasic spatial convergence in the Q continuum
   B. an inverted temporal convergence in the space/time continuum
   C. a multiphasic temporal convergence in the space/time continuum
   D. a multiphasic temporal divergence in the spatial continuum

5. How far back in time does Q take Picard where the anomaly fills the whole quadrant? **(3pts)**
   - **A.** 35 billion years
   - **B.** 3.5 billion years
   - **C.** 35 million years
   - **D.** 3.5 million years

ANSWERS

TRIVIA ANSWERS

1. the Klingons have overrun the Romulan Empire
2. cloaking devices
3. Earl Grey tea
4. an inverse tachyon beam
5. the DNA in his optic nerves is regenerating
6. Black Sea at Night
7. Daystrom Institute
8. Rigel III
9. his protagonist was too flamboyant
10. Sir Isaac Newton
11. H'atoria
12. Warp 13
13. 200 million kilometres in diameter
14. 400 billion kilometres in diameter
15. the cloak isn't functioning due to a hit on the starboard plasma coil

SPECIAL ASSIGNMENT SOLUTION

Captain Paul Ricer in 'Arsenal of Freedom'
Congratulations! Starfleet Command is proud to award you the Starfleet Medal of Honour and 15 extra points.

MULTIPLE CHOICE ANSWERS

1. C. skunk; 2. D. in the *Pasteur's* ready room; 3. A. temporal theories; 4. C. a multiphasic temporal convergence in the space/time continuum; 5. B. 3.5 billion years

---

MISSION PERFORMANCE RATING:

60 – 80 points **Superior:** How does it feel to be an Admiral?

50 – 59 points **Above Average:** Where to now, Captain?

40 – 49 points **Average:** Are you dizzy from all that time travelling?

30 – 39 points **Fair:** Start again at Farpoint Station and try to do better!

0 – 29 points **Poor:** Go back to your primordial ooze pond.

STAR TREK:
GENERATIONS

STARDATE: 48650.1 ▰▰▰▰▰▰▰▰▰

ENTERPRISE-B TRIVIA (4pts each)

1. What vintage of Dom Perignon was used to christen the *Enterprise-B*?
2. How does Captain Harriman refer to Kirk, Scotty, and Chekov?
3. Who is the helmsman on the *Enterprise-B*?
4. What is Sulu's first name?
5. What type of refugees are on the *Lakul*?
6. When will the tractor beam be installed on the *Enterprise-B*?
7. When was the last time Kirk met Demora?
8. How does the *Enterprise-B* simulate a photon torpedo blast?
9. Where are the deflector relays located on the *Enterprise-B*?
10. Where does the *Enterprise-B* suffer a hull breach?

---

78 YEARS LATER TRIVIA

1. What rank is Worf promoted to?
2. What is the name of the observatory that was attacked?
3. Which three races use type-3 disruptors?
4. What is Soran's first name?
5. The drink Data samples in Ten-Forward and hates is from where?
6. Who does Soran recognize in Ten-Forward?
7. What compound is a nuclear inhibitor?
8. How long ago did Geordi tell the joke that Data is only now understanding with the emotion chip?
9. How is the hidden observatory door sealed?
10. Where was Picard going next month and with whom?
11. How did René and Robert die?
12. At what battle did one of Picard's ancestors fight?
13. What did one of Picard's ancestors win?
14. The implosion of the star has generated what?
15. What race is Guinan?
16. How often does the energy ribbon pass through the galaxy?
17. Which starship was forced to make a course correction due to the destruction of the first star?
18. What is located on Veridian IV?
19. How old is Soran?
20. What is the population of Veridian IV?
21. How powerful is Soran's force field on Veridian III?
22. What is the *Enterprise*'s shield modulation?
23. What type of ship are the Duras sisters using?

SPECIAL SECTION

SPECIAL SECTION

ANSWERS

24. What is defective on the bird-of-prey?
25. A member of which pacifist race is seen in the corridor as the star drive is evacuated?
26. What is Kirk doing in the Nexus when Picard finds him?
27. What is the name of Kirk's dog?
28. What type of eggs does Kirk cook for Antonia?
29. Where does Kirk's uncle have a farm?
30. How many different emotional states has Data experienced since implanting the emotion chip?

ENTERPRISE-B TRIVIA ANSWERS

1. 2265; 2. 'A group of living legends'; 3. Demora; 4. Hikaru; 5. El-Aurian; 6. not until Tuesday; 7. 12 years ago; 8. a resonance burst from the main deflector dish; 9. Deck 15, Section 21 Alpha; 10. Decks 13, 14, 15 and Sections 20–28

78 YEARS LATER TRIVIA ANSWERS

1. Lieutenant Commander; 2. Amargosa; 3. Romulans, Klingons, and Breen; 4. Tolian; 5. Forcas III; 6. Guinan; 7. trilithium; 8. seven years ago during the Farpoint mission; 9. magnetically; 10. to San Francisco with his brother and his family; 11. they burned to death in a fire; 12. the Battle of Trafalgar; 13. Nobel Prize for chemistry; 14. a level-12 shockwave that will destroy everything in the entire system; 15. El-Aurian; 16. every 39.1 years; 17. *USS Bozeman*; 18. a preindustrial humanoid civilization; 19. over 300 years old; 20. 230 million people; 21. 50 gigawatts; 22. 257.4; 23. a class D-12 Klingon bird-of-prey; 24. plasma coils; 25. Mizarian; 26. he's using an axe to split firewood; 27. Butler; 28. Ktarian eggs; 29. Idaho; 30. 261

MISSION PERFORMANCE RATING:

131 – 160 points	**Superior:** You can return to the Nexus! (SEE BELOW)
101 – 130 points	**Above Average:** You figured out how to get to the Nexus safely!
51 – 100 points	**Average:** Might be enough to get you promoted to Commander.
26 – 50 points	**Fair:** Just booked you passage on the *Lakul*, have a good trip!
0 – 25 points	**Poor:** You never saw the movie, huh?

If you have received a SUPERIOR Mission Performance Rating –

Congratulations!
Starfleet Command is proud to award you
the Kragite Order of Heroism and 100 extra points.

STAR TREK: ♦ FIRST CONTACT

TRIVIA (4pts each)

1. Lieutenant Barclay is using the spiraled copper tubing to replace what on Cochrane's ship?
2. How many people died during World War III according to Riker?
3. What is the name of the Borg/crewman Picard had to kill on the holodeck?
4. What type of comet did the first sensor sweep of the Neutral Zone reveal?
5. How many decks does Picard say the *Enterprise-E* has?
6. What are standard temperature and humidity levels on a Borg ship?
7. What is the *Enterprise*'s deflector dish charged with?
8. What is the casing of Cochrane's ship constructed of?
9. Why didn't the Vulcan ship detect the *Enterprise* in orbit around Earth?
10. What does Dr Crusher use to create a diversion in sickbay while escaping from the Borg?
11. How did Worf fix the puncture in his spacesuit?
12. Who did Admiral Hayes receive a disturbing report from?
13. What are the Borg trying to transform the *Enterprise*'s deflector dish into?
14. What did Data use to isolate the main computer from the Borg?
15. Which starship does Picard say is adrift but salvageable?
16. How long was Data tempted by the Borg Queen's offer?
17. What is the name of Cochrane's ship?
18. Name the three departments on Deck 11 mentioned by Lieutenant Hawk.
19. What book did Lilly never read?
20. Who does Geordi place in command of Engineering before beaming down to Earth?
21. Where did Geordi go to high school?
22. Where is Admiral Hayes mobilizing a fleet to confront the Borg?
23. What type of mission are the Vulcans on?
24. Name three features on the moon mentioned by Riker.
25. What is the date of first contact?
26. How large is the Federation?
27. When Data touches the surface of Cochrane's ship he detects temperature variations in what?
28. What is the correct chapter from the holographic novel that Picard is looking for?
29. What type of particles do the Borg use to create the temporal vortex?
30. What does Data experience when the Borg Queen blows on his grafted skin?
31. How large is the cockpit on Cochrane's ship?

SPECIAL SECTION

32. True cybernetic life forms can't survive without what?

33. What is the destination of the escape pods leaving the *Enterprise*?

34. How many particles of dust did the first sensor sweep of the Neutral Zone reveal?

35. What is a required course at the Academy according to Geordi?

36. What is the name of the holographic woman who kisses Picard?

37. What is Dr Crusher's diagnosis of Lilly's condition in the missile silo?

38. Picard asks the holographic bartender where whom is?

39. How many people are living on the moon in the 24th century?

40. What is the name of the crewman who escorts Dr Crusher and her group off Deck 16 to Deck 14?

ANSWERS

1. the damaged warp plasma conduit; 2. 600 million; 3. Ensign Lynch; 4. class-2; 5. 24 decks; 6. 39.1°C, 92% humidity; 7. antiprotons; 8. titanium; 9. the moon's gravitational field obscured the warp signature; 10. EMH programme; 11. he used the tubing from the severed Borg's arm as a tourniquet; 12. Deep Space 5; 13. an interplexing beacon; 14. a fractal encryption code; 15. *USS Defiant*; 16. 0.68 seconds; 17. *Phoenix*; 18. Hydroponics, Stellar Cartography, and Deflector Control; 19. *Moby Dick*; 20. Porter; 21. Zefram Cochrane High School; 22. Typhon Sector; 23. survey mission; 24. Tycho City, New Berlin, and Lake Armstrong; 25. 5 April 2063; 26. over 150 planets spread across 8,000 light years; 27. fuel manifold; 28. Chapter 13; 29. chronometric; 30. goose bumps; 31. 4 metres; 32. their organic components; 33. Gravett Island; 34. 20 particles per cubic metre; 35. basic warp design; 36. Ruby; 37. severe theta-radiation poisoning; 38. Nicky the Nose; 39. 50 million; 40. Lopez

MISSION PERFORMANCE RATING:

150 – 180 points	**Superior:** You're Starfleet's time travel expert! (SEE BELOW)
120 – 149 points	**Above Average:** Certified Borg hunter.
70 – 119 points	**Average:** The Borg Queen wants you to be her equal.
40 – 69 points	**Fair:** You act like you've just been assimilated.
0 – 39 points	**Poor:** Transferred to zero-G combat duty; use Worf's suit!

If you have received a SUPERIOR Mission Performance Rating –

Congratulations!
Starfleet Command is proud to award you
the Star Cross and 100 extra points.

DIFFICULT WORD LIST FOR CROSSWORD PUZZLES

Argyle

Balduk
Barron
Benzan
Brentalia

Callosum
Cochrane
Cytherians

Debin
Dorak
Draco

Fento

Gilvos

Hali

Imzadi

Jayden

Kohlan

Lagana
Lemma

Madena
Martinez
Milan
Morath

Norep

Rozhenko

Selton
Skoran
Straleb

Taranko
Thaduin
Thallium
Tricellite
Tricordrazine

Vellorian

Xaenes

Yanar

Zephram

STARFLEET RECORDS

Points awarded, commendations received, and promotions

SEASON ONE	Score		Score
Encounter at Farpoint – Part 1		Encounter at Farpoint – Part II	
The Naked Now		Code of Honor	
Haven		Where No One Has Gone Before	
The Last Outpost		Lonely Among Us	
Justice		The Battle	
Hide and Q		Too Short a Season	
The Big Good-bye		Datalore	
Angel One		11001001	
Home Soil		When the Bough Breaks	
Coming of Age		Heart of Glory	
The Arsenal of Freedom		Skin of Evil	
Symbiosis		We'll Always Have Paris	
Conspiracy		The Neutral Zone	

SEASON TWO	Score		Score
The Child		Where Silence Has Lease	
Elementary, Dear Data		The Outrageous Okona	
The Schizoid Man		Loud as a Whisper	
Unnatural Selection		A Matter of Honor	
The Measure of a Man		The Dauphin	
Contagion		The Royale	
Times Squared		The Icarus Factor	
Pen Pals		Q Who	
Samaritan Snare		Up the Long Ladder	
Manhunt		The Emissary	
Peak Performance		Shades of Gray	

SEASON THREE	Score		Score
The Ensigns of Command		Evolution	
The Survivors		Who Watches the Watchers	
The Bonding		Booby Trap	
The Enemy		The Price	
The Vengeance Factor		The Defector	
The Hunted		The High Ground	
Déjà Q		A Matter of Perspective	
Yesterday's Enterprise		The Offspring	
Sins of the Father		Allegiance	
Captain's Holiday		Tin Man	
Hollow Pursuits		The Most Toys	
Sarek		Ménage à Troi	
Transfigurations		The Best of Both Worlds	

SEASON FOUR	Score		Score
The Best of Both Worlds – Part II		Suddenly Human	
Brothers		Family	
Remember Me		Legacy	
Reunion		Future Imperfect	
Final Mission		The Loss	
Data's Day		The Wounded	
Devil's Due		Clues	
First Contact		Galaxy's Child	
Night Terrors		Identity Crisis	
The Nth Degree		Qpid	
The Drumhead		Half a Life	
The Host		The Mind's Eye	
In Theory		Redemption	

SEASON FIVE	Score		Score
Redemption II		Darmok	
Ensign Ro		Silicon Avatar	
Disaster		The Game	
Unification I		Unification II	
A Matter of Time		New Ground	
Hero Worship		Violations	
The Masterpiece Society		Conundrum	
Power Play		Ethics	
The Outcast		Cause and Effect	
The First Duty		Cost of Living	
The Perfect Mate		Imaginary Friend	
I Borg		The Next Phase	
The Inner Light		Time's Arrow	

SEASON SIX	Score		Score
Times's Arrow – Part II		Realm of Fear	
Man of the People		Relics	
Schisms		True Q	
Rascals		A Fistful of Datas	
The Quality of Life		Chain of Command – Part I	
Chain of Command – Part 2		Ship in a Bottle	
Aquiel		Face of The Enemy	
Tapestry		Birthright – Part I	
Birthright – Part II		Starship Mine	
Lessons		The Chase	
Frame of Mind		Suspicions	
Rightful Heir		Second Chances	
Timescape		Descent	

SEASON SEVEN	Score		Score
Descent – Part II		Liaisons	
Interface		Gambit – Part I	
Gambit – Part II		Phantasms	
Dark Page		Attached	
Force of Nature		Inheritance	
Parallels		The Pegasus	
Homeward		Sub Rosa	
Lower Decks		Thine Own Self	
Masks		Eye of the Beholder	
Genesis		Journey's End	
Firstborn		Bloodlines	
Emergence		Preemptive Strike	
All Good Things …			

SPECIAL SECTIONS	Score		Score
Character Trivia		Actors and Such …	
Repel the Borg Invasion		Phraseology	
Darmokisms		Technical Matters	
Star Trek: Generations		Star Trek: First Contact	

STARFLEET COMMENDATIONS:	Score

STARFLEET PROMOTIONS:	Date
Admiral	
Vice Admiral	
Captain	
Commander	
Lieutenant Commander	
Lieutenant	
Lieutenant, Junior Grade	
Ensign	